Parties

timeout.com

Time Out Guides Limited
Universal House
251 Tottenham Court Road
London W1T 7AB
Tel + 44 (0)20 7813 3000
Fax + 44 (0)20 7813 6001
Email guides@timeout.com
www.timeout.com

Editorial
Editor Emma Howarth
Deputy Editor Jan Fuscoe
Copy Editors Edoardo Albert, Ros Sales
Listings Editor Cathy Limb
Researchers Alex Brown, Alice Malivoire, Charlotte Middlehurst, Kohinoor Sahota, Meryl O'Rourke
Proofreader Kieron Corless
Indexer Ismay Atkins

Managing Director Peter Fiennes
Financial Director Gareth Garner
Editorial Director Sarah Guy
Series Editor Cath Phillips
Editorial Manager Holly Pick
Assistant Management Accountant Ija Krasnikova

Design
Art Director Scott Moore
Art Editor Pinelope Kourmouzoglou
Senior Designer Henry Elphick
Graphic Designers Gemma Doyle, Kei Ishimaru
Advertising Designer Jodi Sher

Picture Desk
Picture Editor Jael Marschner
Deputy Picture Editor Katie Morris
Picture Researcher Gemma Walters
Picture Desk Assistant Marzena Zoladz

Advertising
Commercial Director Mark Phillips
Sales Manager Alison Wallen
Advertising Sales Ben Holt, Alex Matthews, Jason Trotman
Advertising Assistant Kate Staddon
Copy Controller Alison Bourke

Marketing
Marketing Manager Yvonne Poon
Sales & Marketing Director, North America Lisa Levinson
Marketing Designers Anthony Huggins, Nicola Wilson

Production
Group Production Director Mark Lamond
Production Manager Brendan McKeown
Production Controller Damian Bennett
Production Coordinator Julie Pallot

Time Out Group
Chairman Tony Elliott
Group General Manager/Director Nichola Coulthard
Time Out Communications Ltd MD David Pepper
Time Out International Ltd MD Cathy Runciman
Group IT Director Simon Chappell
Circulation Director Polly Knewstub
Head of Marketing Catherine Demajo

Contributors
Venue reviews in this guide were written by Joe Barry, Nuala Calvi, Jonathan Derbyshire, Alexi Duggins, Clare Forster, Jan Fuscoe, Charlie Godfrey-Faussett, Ronnie Haydon, Emma Howarth, Kate Hutchinson, Ben Isaacs, Amanda Nottage, Phillip Othen, Candice Pires, Gemma Pritchard, Lucy Smallwood, Eleni Stefanou, Maisie Tomlinson, Patrick Welch, Rachel Williams. **Food & Drink** Nina Caplan, Jan Fuscoe, Emma Howarth (*Numbers game* Nina Caplan; *The perfect cheeseboard, Unusual food ideas* Emma Howarth). **Music & Entertainment** Simone Baird, Cyrus Shahrad (*How to get the best out of performers, Tips for DIY DJs* Simone Baird; *Unusual entertainment* Nuala Calvi). **Party Shops & Decorations** Kate Riordan, Lucy Smallwood, Rachel Williams. **Organisation & Planning** Gemma Pritchard. **Weddings** Emma Howarth, Amanda Isaacs (*Ceremony basics, Gift lists, World wide wed* Emma Howarth; *We're going to the town hall and we're...* Jan Fuscoe). **Interviews** Nuala Calvi.

The Editor would like to thank Deborah Armstrong, Simone Baird, Sarah Ellison, Sarah Guy, Pinelope Kourmouzoglou, Jenni Muir, Cath Phillips, Elizabeth Winding, David Wolanski, the DJs and party professionals who agreed to give us playlists and insider tips, and the *Time Out* contributors whose work and recommendations provided valuable insights for this book.

All photography by Heloise Bergman, except: page 18 (top right) Alys Tomlinson; pages 18, 24, 29, 128, 129, 130, 144, 160, 184, 185, 226, 231 Ming-Tang Evans; pages 23, 30, 32, 236 Nerida Howard; pages 133, 183, 229 Rob Greig; pages 178, 179, 189 Britta Jaschinski; page 194 Clare Richardson; page 207 James McCauley; page 243 Amanda Clay, www.clayphotography.co.uk.
The following images were provided by the featured establishments/artists: pages 35, 131, 136, 143, 146, 148, 149, 156, 159, 172, 173, 194, 192, 195, 196, 197, 201, 203, 204, 205, 206, 208, 209, 210, 211, 216, 220, 223, 235, 240.

Cover image © Rob Greig.
Helium balloons and piñata from a selection at Circus; www.circuscircus.co.uk. Christmas crackers from a selection at the Christmas Shop; www.thechristmasshop.co.uk. Cupcake from a selection at Crumbs & Doilies; www.crumbsanddoilies.co.uk. Canapés from Lettice Party; www.letticeparty.com. Mask and oversized bow tie from a selection at Angels Fancy Dress; www.fancydress.com. Glasses from a selection at Heals; www.heals.co.uk. Wedding cake from Patisserie Valerie; www.patisserie-valerie.co.uk, call 7935 6240 for locations. Butterflies from a selection at VV Rouleaux; www.vvrouleaux.com. Flowers from a selection at Angel Flowers; www.angel-flowers.co.uk, 7704 6312. Present boxes from a selection at Paperchase; call 7467 6218 for stockists. Lantern from a selection at Cox & Cox; www.coxandcox.co.uk. Bunting from a selection at Zigzag Bunting; www.zigzagbunting.com. Gold party poppers and party blower from a selection at Party Party; www.ppshop.co.uk. Glitterball from a selection at DZD; www.dzd.co.uk.

Printer St Ives (Web) Ltd, Storeys Bar Road, Eastern Industrial Estate, Peterborough, PE1 5YS
Time Out Group uses paper products that are environmentally friendly, from well managed forests and mills that use certified (PEFC) Chain of Custody pulp in their production.

ISBN 978-1-905042-33-3

Distribution by Seymour Ltd +44 (0)20 7429 4000
For further distribution details, see www.timeout.com

About the guide

DETAILS

Venues

We've tried to make this guide as useful and informative as possible, listing addresses, telephone numbers, websites, transport, availability for hire, capacities and, where possible, a hire charge and/or minimum spend. However, as party hire arrangements are generally negotiable, you should always confirm any details before committing yourself. For example, we might list the capacity of a private room as 60, but with a bit of table tweaking an amenable venue owner may well be happy to fit in a few more. Similarly, prices are almost always open to negotiation, depending on the day, time of year and/or type of event you're planning. Where a venue was unable to confirm a starting price we have specified that you will have to call for details.

Below each review you'll find a list of services provided, including catering, disabled access, music equipment and outside space. Once again, always confirm any essentials with the venue before hiring as such facilities can often be subject to change.

Essentials

For services recommended in this section, we list starting prices and/or minimum spends where possible. We also mention whether delivery is available (note: while many caterers don't offer drop-off delivery, they do provide on-site catering). For shops and online services, we list opening hours only. Not every service listed is based in London, but all will happily deliver or travel to the capital.

Weddings

Venues follow the same listings format as those in the rest of the guide, with the addition of information on civil ceremony licences. We list starting prices for photographers and opening hours only for shops.

TELEPHONE NUMBERS

All London telephone numbers listed in this guide assume that you are calling from within the capital. If you're ringing from outside the city, you will need to use the area code (020) before the phone number we've listed. If you're calling from abroad, dial your international access code, then 44 for the UK; follow that with 20 for London, then the eight-digit number.

CREDIT CARDS

If credit cards are *not* accepted, we've said so in our listings; otherwise, establishments should accept major credit cards (MasterCard, Visa and, usually, American Express).

INDEXES

You'll find useful indexes at the back of the guide (starting on p245) listing all the venues featured by their maximum capacity and by type (gallery, bar, restaurant, museum and so on). There is also an A-Z index of all the listed venues, shops and services.

WHAT DO YOU THINK?

Have we missed out a fantastic party venue, shop or service? We welcome suggestions for anywhere you think we should include in future editions of the guide, and take note of your criticism of our choices. You can email us at guides@timeout.com with your comments.

ADVERTISERS

No payment or PR invitation of any kind has secured inclusion in this guide, or influenced its content. No establishment appears because it has advertised in any of our publications. The editors select the venues and activities listed, and reviews were compiled before any advertising space was sold. The opinions given in this book are those of Time Out writers, and are entirely independent.

Contents

Introduction

Think of the best party you've ever been to. The chances are that it wasn't the result of a hollered 'all back to mine' at 2am one Sunday morning. Lifting a party into the 'fabulous' category always requires some forward planning. And this is where *Time Out Parties* comes in.

Looking for a show-stopping venue? Why not set your summer soirée around an ice-cool outdoor pool? Or how about a speakeasy-style engagement do in a mirror-clad converted public loo? Perhaps you're on the hunt for a fabulous steelband? An ornate Bedouin tent? Or a team of oyster-shuckers to inject some energy into cocktail hour? Maybe you just want to find somewhere cheap, cheerful and available tomorrow for a last-minute birthday bash? Whatever you're looking for, this guide is for you.

This is a guide for fancy-dress fans and barbecue lovers, dinner-party cheats and bedroom DJs. It's for parents at their wits' ends with competitive bouncy castles, and office managers who'd rather fake their own death than organise another Christmas bash. It's for surprise-party planners, foodies and musos, the super-organised and the terminally chaotic. It's for anyone who recently popped the question. And anyone who just said 'yes'. Above all, this is a guide that aims to take the stress out of party planning – so you can concentrate on being the life and the soul. Read on for ideas, inspiration and insider tips on everything from lighting to cocktails, decorations to playlists. Plan an event that'll secure your place in party history and guarantee you return invitations for life. What are you waiting for… get the party started.

Tailor-made madness

Rachel Williams investigates the party trend where nothing is quite what it seems. Illustration by **Peter Strucic**.

Blame it on the *Mighty Boosh*. Or fancy dress-themed festivals. Or even a hedonistic last fling before the credit crunch really kicks in. But there has never been a bigger appetite for spectacular bespoke parties. And where once party organisers were synonymous with bland sponsored events, novelty ice fountains and second-rate magicians, the party boom means there are now myriad inventive party specialists ready to cater to every possible whim.

Whimsy is the mantra of party promoter Bex Cameron, who puts on 'sabotage' parties in and around east London. The premise is thus: you hire Cameron and her team – the Reprobates – to hijack a pre-planned celebration by kidnapping you and your guests and taking you on a completely different night out to the one everyone thought was intended.

'I just think people are looking for something a bit different now, a bit edgy,' says Cameron. 'We're all bored of the traditional pub/club night out these days; it offers no surprises.'

The kidnapping itself is rescued from any potential terror by the theatrics the team use to accompany it. The Reprobates dress up as French mime artists and Left Bank sophisticates who sing and mime bizarre jokes as they escort guests into their van. At the team's most recent sabotage, an unsuspecting birthday boy ended up in a fully equipped dungeon, where he found his mates clad in risqué costumes dancing to an electro new wave soundtrack. A bit of a departure from the Slug & Lettuce, then.

The concept is fantastically original, but what makes the Reprobates' sabotage parties special is the execution. The team can provide fabulous costume and interior designers, cutting-edge DJs, catering and bar staff – all tailored to the theme and priced according to requirements.

The biggest thrill, though, is the continued deliberate sabotage throughout the night; think inappropriate tunes and planted comedy guests. At a recent 'conspiracy theory' themed party, 'French Resistance' cell members left coded notes and planted escape plans while guests were dressed up in provocative costumes referencing characters from *Lost* and *JFK*. In the loos, guests stumbled upon Elvis giving impromptu performances from one of the cubicles, complete with glammed-up backing singers.

For sheer descent into *Through the Looking Glass* madness, sabotage parties really can't be topped. As Cameron puts it: 'Most of us are quite jaded partygoers now; we've done it all and nothing lives up to our expectations. Our parties work by deliberately confusing expectations; we mislead you into having a good time!' The element of surprise and wonder gives sabotage parties an electric vibe; throw one and watch your mates party like it's 1989 all over again.

Of course there's always the risk of a sabotage backfiring. And if you can't afford to pay for the whole thing yourself, you may find potential cohorts reluctant to sub a party they feel they won't get the credit for. It's worth noting, though, that Cameron is very happy to make the production on her events as lavish or low-key as budgets require. She has tons of potential ideas ready to go too – a Truman Capote-style 'Black and White Ball' perhaps? The Reprobates also have plans to branch out into creating debauched but glamorous film- and book-themed daytime parties in unusual locations around London.

What Cameron and her team lack in size and experience, they more than make up for

capital's most unusual venues.

'What you get when you put on a bespoke party is a sense of magic that comes from creating your own space. You can create something truly unique,' says Heathcote.

What makes a Heathcote Bailey production really stand out is the dedicated attention to detail. At the wedding of co-founder Bailey, guests were housed in a village of white Saharan tents, and in the morning cockney newspaper boys strode through the encampment whistling and handing out newspapers filled with stories about the couple.

Although they have a reputation for working with the west London glitterati, putting on events for Jade Jagger and Mark Ronson, among others, Heathcote Bailey is enthusiastic about taking on any brief. With headquarters in a west London art gallery and a background in putting on events for clients such as MTV, HB has the capital's party scene sewn up.

Bespoke party pioneer Deborah Armstrong, who runs ultra-cool events company Strong & Co, has been putting together weird and wonderful parties for aeons. She is responsible for creating many of the surreal and theatrical landscapes you may have stumbled upon at

in imagination; we recommend them for hedonistic birthday parties rather than high-end corporate dos. Sabotage is spot-on for anyone looking for an unforgettable celebration on a budget. Think impromptu madness: sick rather than slick.

The sabotage trend owes much to the festival, underground and bespoke party scenes. West London party promoter Heathcote Bailey is one company that offers a similarly imaginative approach to events. Former promoters of club night ETA, directors Hugo Heathcote and Eazy Bailey were quick to realise that they could bring their talent for creating outlandish warehouse parties to putting on unique bespoke events. They use their club-promoting expertise to ensure quality sound systems, edgy DJs, stunning visuals and access to some of the festivals over the years. In 2008, Armstrong produced the much-lauded Shangri La area at Glastonbury, where guests hovered above the party, mojitos in hand, as a stream of performers and robot horses frolicked below.

While Armstrong's roots are firmly planted in the underground and festival world, she and her team are equally adept at creating carnivalesque events for corporate clients. A recent party Armstrong organised for Channel 4 had a brilliantly anarchic feel, with Derren Brown supping whisky in an antler-clad drawing room and Gok Wan throwing shapes in one of three raucous discos.

Lavish is another company that specialises in the madcap and the theatrical. Director Ami Jade Cadillac used to be a circus performer before she moved into show-producing for festivals. Lavish has been involved with the Latitude festival since it started; the team design the concept areas and set up the avant-garde art area with its dyed pink sheep.

Lavish has also made a name putting on high-octane corporate dos. The team's strength lies in a real affinity with artists and performers – even the most anodyne corporate event becomes an adults' adventure playground.

While the services of these imaginative event organisers inevitably come at a price, the results really speak for themselves. Armstrong is constantly fielding requests from potential new clients, despite her sole source of advertising being word-of-mouth recommendation. And party guests sabotaged by the Reprobates are always desperate to get the team in to hijack the next bash they have planned. Most importantly, you really can't put a price on becoming part of party folklore: 'Do you remember that party where…'.

Heathcote Bailey
07939 573198/www.heathcotebailey.co.uk.
Cost from £10,000.
For more information, *see p203.*

Lavish
0845 128 4199/www.lavish-design.com.
Cost from £12,000.

The Reprobates
07834 923462/7267 4260/www.thereprobates.co.uk.
Cost from £2,000.

Strong and Co
07980 827772/www.strongandco.net.
Cost from £15,000.
For more information, *see p206.*

DIY SABOTAGE PARTIES

With a bit of imagination and half-decent organisation skills, you could even organise your own DIY sabotage. Invite your mates round for low-key birthday drinks then pile them into a minibus and take them to the seaside. Meet up for a swanky afternoon tea that morphs into a twisted disco the second the clock strikes 6pm. The possibilities are endless. Just make sure you follow a few simple rules:

• **Time** Make sure everyone knows what time things kick off. If you're hiring transport, you don't want latecomers or they'll miss it.
• **Dress** Give folk a deliberately misleading dress code. Tell them to dress for cocktails, then take them to a rave or bring a fancy dress box along so you can dress everyone up as part of the sabotage fun.
• **Venue** Choose very carefully. If you want a mosh-pit, don't hire a swanky bar. Make sure management know the scoop.
• **Money** If money is involved – casino, dogs, clubbing – ensure folk bring enough spons with them or it could be more expensive for you than you planned.
• **Alcohol** Watch the drinking if you're planning on incorporating any, even vaguely, dangerous sports – rally-driving, clay-pigeon shooting – or even just going for a swim.
• **Food** See above and, if you're planning on having any kind of bun-fight, see 'dress' and 'venue' above too.
• **Weather** If your sabotage is weather-dependent, make sure you have a Plan B, even if it's just the nearest boozer.
• **Friends** Some will be up for it, others may never speak to you again. Make sure you've worked out which are which before you start.
• **Secret** Sounds obvious, but don't blab to anyone likely to let the secret slip.
• **Time**, again. Don't reserve your sabotage for parties – you can do it any time. 'Why don't you pop over and we'll have a quiet night in (just the 50 of us).'

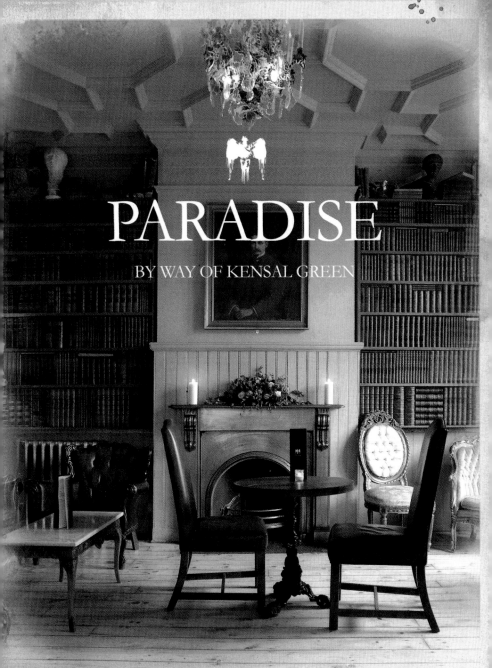

PARADISE

BY WAY OF KENSAL GREEN

To reserve an exclusive area or a private room for drinks, canapés or private dining please contact Melissa 020 8969 0098

19 Kilburn Lane, Kensal Green, London W10 4AE

WWW.THEPARADISE.CO.UK

A WILD PLACE TO SHOP AND EAT®

EVENTS AT RAINFOREST CAFE

If you are looking for a uniquely themed
Central London venue look no further!

- Press/Product Launches •
- Christmas Parties •
- Media Events •
- • Private Dining
- • Corporate Parties
- • Photo Shoots

With our fantastic food and fully licensed bar,
Rainforest Cafe is guaranteed to ensure
your event is one to remember.

Please call the Events Team
on **020 7437 1799**
email sales@therainforestcafe.co.uk

20 Shaftesbury Avenue,
Piccadilly Circus, London W1D 7EU
www.therainforestcafe.co.uk

Any excuse for a party

We reckon there's a reason to have a party at least once a fortnight.
Dates for religious holidays vary; please refer to Christian, Hindu, Islamic,
Jewish and Sikh calendars.

January

1 Jan	New Year's Day
8 Jan	Elvis's birthday
21 Jan	National Hugging Day
25 Jan	Robert Burns Night (Burns Night)
Jan/Feb	Chinese New Year

February

1st Sun	British Yorkshire Pudding Day
14 Feb	Valentine's Day
27 Feb	National Doodle Day
29 Feb	Leap Day
Feb/Mar	Shrove (Pancake) Tuesday
Feb/Mar	Oscar Night

March

1 Mar	St David's Day
17 Mar	St Patrick's Day; elastic bands were patented
20/21 Mar	Vernal Equinox
mid Mar	Mothering Sunday
27 Mar	Shoelaces were invented, 1790
29 Mar	The first London marathon, 1981
late Mar	British Summer time begins
Mar/Apr	The Boat Race (Oxford versus Cambridge Universities)
Mar/Apr	Good Friday
Mar/Apr	Easter Sunday

April

1 Apr	April Fool's Day
13/14 Apr	Vaisakhi (Sikh New Year)
15 Apr	The bottle opener was invented, 1793
23 Apr	St George's Day
27 Apr	International Day of the Dog
late Apr	Flora London Marathon

May

1st wk May	Chimney Sweeps' Festival
early May	Bank (May Day) Holiday
mid May	Eurovision Song Contest
25 May	Africa Day
late May	National Barbecue Week
late May	Spring Bank Holiday

June

4 June	Death of Giovanni Casanova, 1798
mid June	London Naked Bike Ride
mid June	Fathers' Day
20/21 June	Summer Solstice/Longest Day
28 June	First dog show held, 1859; champagne invented, 1682

July

5 July	The bikini made its debut, 1946
14 July	Emmeline Pankhurst Day
15 July	St Swithin's Day
21 July	First man landed on the Moon, 1969
23 July	Haile Selassie I's birthday
30 July	England won the football World Cup, 1966

August

9 Aug	Jesse Owens won 4th Olympic gold, 1936; Britain opened first nudist beach (Brighton), 1979
late Aug	Notting Hill Carnival
late Aug	Summer Bank Holiday
Aug/Sept	Ramadan (first day)

September

13 Sept	Cornflakes invented, 1915
21/22 Sept	Autumnal Equinox
30 Sept	Tony Blackburn joined Radio 1, 1967
Sept/Oct	Eid Al-Fitr (end of Ramadan)
Sept/Oct	Yom Kippur (Day of Atonement)

October

early Oct	Pearly Kings & Queens Harvest Festival
3 Oct	The aerosol is patented, 1941
31 Oct	Halloween
Oct/Nov	Diwali

November

1 Nov	All Saints' Day
5 Nov	Bonfire (Guy Fawkes) Night
19 Nov	Table tennis invented, 1889
30 Nov	St Andrew's Day
Nov/Dec	Eid Al-Adha (Festival of Sacrifice)
Nov/Dec	Hanukkah

December

early Dec	Great Christmas Pudding Race
9 Dec	Mr (frozen food) Birdseye born, 1956
20/21 Dec	Winter Solstice/Shortest Day
23 Dec	First British beauty show held, 1905, Newcastle-on-Tyne
25 Dec	Christmas Day
26 Dec	Boxing Day
31 Dec	New Year's Eve

Venues

Birthdays

This is the one party you're guaranteed to get to be a part of – once a year at least – so pledge to make the most of it. Debauched 21sts, flamboyant 30ths and swanky 60ths are all well and good, but why leave out the in-betweens? Here's to stupendous 29ths, OTT 43rds and truly riotous 87ths. Organising a fuss-free bash really couldn't be easier either. Browse the below for a suitable venue (we think somewhere with a ready-to-go bar, staff on hand and a decent sound system should see you right), gather together a hotchpotch of friends, crack open the champagne and watch the gifts roll in. It's also worth taking a look at the other venues listed in this guide too.

VENUES

CENTRAL

Bea's of Bloomsbury
44 Theobald's Road, WC1X 8NW (7242 8330/www.beasofbloomsbury.com). Holborn tube. **Available for hire** 6-10pm Mon-Sat; 10.30am-10pm Sun. **Capacity** 18 seated/ 30 standing. **Minimum spend** £15/person. Shop/café
This fabulous cake shop (the heavenly cupcakes and birthday cakes are much admired by London's foodie contingent) is happy to open its doors for the occasional private party and makes a beautiful spot for a low-key celebration. There's space for around 18 for a sit-down tea party or around 30 for a cocktails-and-canapés type event. There's a tiny bit of outside space and the catering couldn't be easier to arrange, with an array of sweet and savoury (excellent quiches, for example) specialities at your disposal. Bea's is also available for private cooking lessons. *Catering: in-house. Music: MP3 port. Outside space: very small area (for hire).*

Bourne & Hollingsworth
28 Rathbone Place, W1T 1JF (7636 8228/ www.bourneandhollingsworth.com). Goodge Street or Tottenham Court Road tube. **Available for hire** 5pm-midnight Mon-Thur, Sun; 5pm-12.30am Sat. **Capacity** Venue 90 standing. **Minimum spend** £1,500. Bar For review, see p30.
Catering: in-house; kitchen facilities. Music: DJ equipment; MP3 port. Projector.

Bea's of Bloomsbury

Carpenter's Arms

68-70 Whitfield Street, W1T 4EY (7580 3186). Goodge Street tube. **Available for hire** *Venue* noon-midnight Sat, Sun. *Private rooms* 3: noon-midnight Mon-Wed, Sat, Sun. **Capacity** *Venue* 200 standing. *Private rooms* 4-100 standing. **Minimum spend** *Venue* £2,500. *Private rooms* from £200. Gastropub

This boho boozer smack bang in the middle of Noho's meeja enclave has three areas for hire. Downstairs there's a back room with retro '70s flowery wallpaper and long soft-furnished benching that gives it a kitschy working men's club feel, as well as a more intimate front-of-bar space. It's upstairs that the venue comes into its own, however, with a second bar leading on to one of Fitzrovia's prettier outdoor drinking spots. The wooden-decked smoking area has four tables set amid wicker fences, birdcages strewn with blue fairy lights and a back wall decorated with avian prints and the kind of oriental-patterned china plates that leave you feeling like you've stumbled across a Malaysian bird market rather than a boozer on Whitfield Street.

Catering: in-house. Disabled: toilet. Licence extension possible. Music: DJ equipment; MP3 port. Outside space: patio, terrace (upstairs bar has access; for hire).

Courthouse Hotel Bar

19-21 Great Marlborough Street, W1F 7HL (7297 5555/www.courthouse-hotel.com). Oxford Circus tube. **Available for hire**

9am-11.30pm daily. **Capacity** *Roof terrace* 120 standing. *Private rooms* 4: 60-200 standing. *Cinema* 94 seated. **Hire charge** *Roof terrace* £1,500. *Private rooms* £500-£800. *Cinema* £225/hr. **Minimum spend** *Roof terrace* £3,500. Hotel bar
For review, *see p24.*
Catering: in-house. Disabled: lift; toilet. Licence extension possible. Projector (cinema). Outside space: roof terrace (for hire).

Green Man
36 Riding House Street, W1W 7ES (7580 9087). Goodge Street or Oxford Circus tube. **Available for hire** noon-11pm Mon-Thur; Sat, Sun. **Capacity** *Private room* 70 standing. **Minimum spend** £250 Mon-Wed; £350 Thur, Sat; free Sun. Pub
Fully spruced up and relaunched, the Green Man's USP is its love of cider – there are eight fine brews to choose from; five on tap. Add decent grub, matey staff and an upstairs room with funky, mismatching retro furniture and you've got yourself a nifty little space for a post-work or intimate birthday/Christmas bash. There are no bar facilities in the function room but there's a jukebox, retro arcades games, decks, an MP3 port and a projector. The whole place has a cosy, pleasingly hectic vibe that'd suit any low-key gathering of friends down to the ground. Any overspill can be taken up by the pub or outside, where you'll even find a few pavement tables.
Catering: in-house. Music: DJ equipment; jukebox; MP3 port. Projector. Outside space: pavement tables.

Lucky Voice
52 Poland Street, W1F 7NH (7439 3660/ www.luckyvoice.co.uk). Oxford Circus tube. **Available for hire** 5.30pm-1am Mon-Thur; 3pm-1am Fri, Sat; 3.30-10.30pm Sun. **Capacity** *Venue* 130 seated/standing. *Private rooms* 9: 4-12 seated/standing. **Hire charge** *Venue* call for details. *Private rooms* from £5/hr per person. Karaoke bar
Comedy wigs and song sheets at the ready – what could be finer than gathering together 12 of your closest friends and forcing them to listen to your rendition of Geri Halliwell's 'It's Raining Men' at close proximity? Nothing, that's what. Lucky Voice's high-tech karaoke rooms (touch-screen track listings; press a button and drinks appear like magic) have been known to generate near-hysterical levels of enthusiasm among individuals

Lucky Voice

School
Disco

EVERY SATURDAY
THE PALACE MUSIC HALL
52 WANDSWORTH HIGH STREET, SW18

SCHOOLDISCO.COM ● TEL:0871 872 1234

Albert & Pearl

who'd usually rather chop off their arm with a blunt junior hacksaw than sing in public. The potent cocktails certainly help, but we think it all comes down to the intimate vibe, enticing song list and optional blow-up guitars. Perfect for birthdays, hen nights or office nights out with a difference.
Catering: in-house. Licence extension possible.

Party Bus

0845 838 5400/www.partybus.co.uk.
Capacity 55-70 (minimum 20 Mon-Fri).
Cost £29.95/person. Bus

A tack-fest of the highest order and predictably popular with hens, stags and excitable students on an irony binge, Party Buses can be hired in their entirety (you'll need at least 55 people on a Saturday) for birthdays and other parties, or you and your mates can simply join one of their regular tours. There's plenty of scope for entertaining banter and a higher than average level of comedy value, but it can all get a bit soul-destroying when you rock up at one of their partner venues (we're talking the Zoos, Sways and Strawberry Moons of this world) for drinks. Great for a no-trainers, no-sportswear trip back in time to the suburban clubs of your youth though. Enjoy!

Soho Revue Bar

11 Walkers Court, W1F 0ED (7734 0377/ www.sohorevuebar.com). Piccadilly Circus tube. **Available for hire** noon-3am Mon-Sat; noon-midnight Sun. **Capacity** 285 standing.
Hire charge call for details. Bar

This former strip joint – the legendary Raymond Revue Bar – is now a sexy, glamorous venue perfect for any classy birthday bash, corporate gig or even music video – Nick Cave made his latest here, complete with pole-dancers, Peaches Geldof and Will Self. The space boasts a Swarovski crystal bar (complete with famous chandelier), red leather banquettes that lead down to a sprung dancefloor, state-of-the-art music equipment and some serious entertainment options – anything from magicians to DJs to the services of singer Miss Holly Penfield, accompanied by Carl Joseph on the baby grand, can be arranged. Indeed, only the cost will hold you back.

NOTE

WEEKEND HIRE
While weekends are the busiest time for West End venues (and you're unlikely to get a bargain hire price), you may find that bars and pubs in the City (especially those that would have been closed otherwise) can offer cheap – or even free – hire for parties. Places to approach include Lewis + Clarke (www.lewisandclarke.com) – they have seven venues within the Square Mile – and Hatton Wall's lovely Deux Beers (www.deuxbeers.co.uk).

Catering: in-house. Disabled: toilet. Licence extension possible. Music: DJ equipment; MP3 port. Projector.

NORTH

Albert & Pearl

181 Upper Street, N1 1RQ (7352 9993/ www.albertandpearl.com). Highbury & Islington tube/rail. **Available for hire** 4.30pm-midnight Mon, Tue; 4.30pm-1am Wed, Thur; noon-2am Fri, Sat; noon-midnight Sun. **Capacity** *Private rooms* 3: 40-50 standing. **Minimum spend** £500. Bar
Where once stood Upper Street stalwart the Medicine bar, you'll now find beautifully decked out Albert & Pearl. The bar's theme is the 1920s and it's packed with chandeliers, *objets d'art*, drapes and super-flattering lighting concepts. Various spaces are available for private hire, including the glamorous Parlour room, where drinks are served from your own well-stocked cabinet, and the hip Bar room with its stonkingly good sound system. For a less private option, but one worth considering if you really hate cutting yourself off from the general throng or you're not too sure about your guests party credentials, book the Gramaphone Suite, a large area at the back of the ground floor that allows you to piggyback off the buzz in the rest of the bar.
Catering: in-house. Music: DJ equipment; MP3 port.

Barrio North

45 Essex Road, N1 2SF (7688 2882/ www.barrionorth.com). Angel tube. **Available for hire** noon-midnight Mon-Thur; noon-2am Fri, Sat; 3pm-midnight Sun. **Capacity** *Venue* 175 standing. *Private areas* 4: 8-70 standing. **Minimum spend** *Venue* £2,000. *Private areas* free-£500. DJ bar
For review, *see p24.*
Catering: in-house. Music: DJ equipment; MP3 port.

Camden Arms

1 Randolph Street NW1 0SS (7267 9829/ www.thecamdenarms.com). Camden Town tube. **Available for hire** *Private room* noon-11pm Mon, Tue, Sun; noon-11.30pm Wed, Thur; noon-midnight Fri, Sat. *Garden* noon-10.30pm daily. **Capacity** *Private room* 120 standing. *Garden* 35 seated/70 standing.
Hire charge *Private room* £150; reduced if spend is £500-£1,500. *Garden* call for prices. Gastropub
As far as pubtopias go, this place is almost faultless. It's always busy but rarely heaving, the gastro grub is tasty and well priced and the decor is smart yet uncontrived. Up the gilded staircase are two huge airy rooms, with space enough for all kinds of party intrigue. The accommodating staff help create a sense of occasion by dressing the room and can provide decks, karaoke, screening facilities, a stage and fantastic finger food. For a recent christening party there were

flowers, fairy cakes and coloured tablecloths to match the flowery sofas. For a birthday evening do, the team can deck the place out with balloon bouquets and put fairy lights around the monochrome rock 'n' roll photographs on the wall (taken by veteran photographer Pat Pope). A separate bar is well stocked with reasonably priced beer and a cocktail menu upon request. *Catering: in-house. Licence extension possible. Music: MP3 port. Outside space: garden (for hire)*

Harrison

28 Harrison Street, WC1H 8JF (7278 3966/ www.harrisonbar.co.uk). King's Cross tube/ rail. **Available for hire** noon-11.30pm Sat. **Capacity** *Venue* 100 standing. **Minimum spend** £300. Bar

Saturday nights are made for partying which makes it all the more pleasing when you track down a bar that's happy to offer exclusive hire on the night itself. Harrison is such a gem and fits up to 100 party people (70 is the most comfortable number to aim for) for intimate birthday bashes or festive shindigs. You can bring your own DJ to bust out the tunes as decks are supplied (alternatively just plug in an iPod), and a selection of buffet canapés will provide spot-on booze-soaking sustenance. The vibe is warm and inviting, and if you ask very nicely, they might even let you boogie until midnight. Wayward liggers and out-of-town guests might be pleased to know that there are hotel rooms here too. *Catering: in-house. Licence extension possible. Music: DJ equipment; MP3 port.*

Monkey Chews

3 Queens Crescent, NW5 4EP (7267 6406/www.monkeychews.com). Chalk Farm tube. **Available for hire** 5-11pm

Solid, spacious and substantial rather than flashy: **St Aloysius Social Club**. *See p26.*

BOOTHS, SNUGS AND COOL AREAS

Barrio North

Barrio North

The best seat in the house at this funky Essex Road DJ bar has to be the fairy-lit caravan on the mezzanine at the back – the perfect semi-private vantage point from which to kick back with a bottle of Brahma and a platter of nachos and watch the night unfold. It'll be a good one. Though innocently quiet early in the week, Barrio really goes off from Thursday night onwards. We're talking dancing in the aisles, clinking tequila glasses and much fun all round. The perfect party spot.
Best for Dancing, drinking and debauchery.
Must do Stock the caravan with ice buckets full of beer.
Inside tip Be prepared to wait a while for cocktails when it's busy.
For listings, see p21.

Courthouse Hotel Bar

For a soirée with a difference book a private space at the Courthouse Hotel's bar. The hotel itself is situated in an old Grade II-listed Magistrates' Court, which explains the three original holding cells that operate as private rooms. Book one and you'll be in good company – the likes of Mick Jagger, Keith Richards, Oscar Wilde and even John Lennon have passed through during various rock 'n' roll trials. The cells only fit up to eight people so be selective; don't invite any dead wood.

Best for Novelty appeal.
Must do Read up on the old court's history.
Inside tip Fitting eight in is a bit of a squeeze so smaller gatherings are better.
For listings, see p17.

Crazy Bear

This supremely glamorous bar and restaurant succeeds where so many others fail by ensuring its staff are impeccably polite, charming and helpful. On top of that, you'll find fine cocktails, upmarket dim sum and the coolest decor this side of Oxford Street. The glam, red-padded alcove booths can be booked for parties of eight or more and make a fabulous setting for an intimate soirée with a few close friends.
Best for Small celebrations and catch-ups.
Must do Turn straight to the cocktail menu.
Inside tip Gain entry to the baffling mirrored toilets by pushing a hidden door in the wall.
For full review & listings, see p88.

Exit

Large areas for up to 40 people can be reserved at this cosy Brick Lane bar. The vibe is classic shabby chic and the set-up is simple and works – a long narrow room with some leather seating and a bar up one side, and floor space for a bit of dancing at the back. They have a new menu of Moroccan-inspired

food, which if you ask nicely, can be catered for groups. An impressive cocktail list and trendy but friendly crowd make it a tried and trusted Brick Lane destination.
Best for Small birthday gatherings.
Must do Top and tail the night with a Brick Lane curry and club.
Inside tip Try to nab the front of the bar where the windows open onto the street.
For listings, see p27.

Hide

A sunken lounge with low lighting, sumptuous leather seating, beautiful wallpaper, and a chandelier made of old, crystal decanter tops sits behind the main bar area for your free, private delectation here. The intimate space feels exclusive (even though it is attached to the main bar) and staff are fantastically helpful. They certainly take their drinks seriously – bespoke cocktails can be arranged for events. The bar also hosts cocktail-making classes, which are proving especially popular with discerning hen parties at weekends.
Best for Classy soirées where the drinks really matter.
Must do Check the music they have planned for the night suits your crowd.
Inside tip Check out the library of old, leather-bound cocktail books and request an unusual tipple.
For listings, see p37.

Westbourne House

Part cosy gastropub, part swanky cocktail bar, this venue feels slightly schizophrenic – but it works. This may well be down to the charm of the Italian bar staff, who revel in the theatre of cocktail-making – there's an extensive and original list that's crying out for a sampling session. There are three private spaces connected to the main bar, good news for the lazy entertainer as an eclectic dance soundtrack and cast of beautiful people come ready provided. The management is happy to arrange bespoke cocktail menus and canapés should you desire them.
Best for Effortless party organising – all you have to do is turn up.
Must do Book early, especially for weekends.
Inside tip Stock the fridge with Lucozade and paracetamol – it's going to be a heavy night.
For listings, see p41.

Mon-Thur; 5pm-1am Fri, Sat; noon-11pm Sun. **Capacity** *Private room* 60 standing/30 seated. **Hire charge** £75. **Minimum spend** £500. Restaurant/bar
For review, *see p31.*
Big screen. Catering: in-house. Music: DJ equipment. Outdoor area: terrace.

Old Queen's Head

44 Essex Road, N1 8LN (7354 9993/ www.theoldqueenshead.com). Angel tube.
Available for hire *Private areas* noon-midnight Mon-Wed, Sun; noon-1am Thur. *Small areas* 11am-2am Fri, Sat. **Capacity** *Private areas* 12: 10-100 seated/20-200 standing. **Hire charge** *Small areas* £50. *Other areas & garden* call for prices. **Minimum spend** *Living room* £1,000. Pub/club/music venue
This TARDIS-like pub may have a tabloid whiff about it – thanks to Peaches 'n' Pixie's occasional attendance – but don't let that put you off. If you've got the budget, this is a fabulous space to host a party. The living room space upstairs has a huge parquet dancefloor and a proper DJ booth for serious party action, while the battered chesterfields, antique furnishings and well-stocked bar keep the wallflowers and people-watchers happy. Just make sure you have a promoter-sized coterie of friends to fill the place; or better still be a promoter who can do the professional sound system justice. There are also a number of lovely private areas that can be booked by groups of friends at weekends (in the pub and upstairs).
Catering: in-house. Licence extension possible. Music: DJ equipment; MP3 port. Outside space: garden (for hire).

Roebuck

15 Pond Street NW3 2PN (7435 7354). Belsize Park tube/Hampstead Heath rail.
Available for hire noon-11pm Mon-Thur; noon-12.30am Fri, Sat; noon-10.30pm Sun. **Capacity** 100 standing. **Hire charge** £100, plus £100 for barman. Bar
In contrast to the chi-chi vibe upstairs, this downstairs bar for hire has a slightly dingy feel, with low ceilings, grey wallpaper and school toilet-style tiled floors. By night, however, these flaws pale into insignificance when friendly barmen tending the well-stocked bar and a warm glow emanating from the golden-hued antique lamps. There are plenty of battered sofas to loll around on, a dartboard and screening facilities too. A good bet for low-key, private birthday drinks, you can bring a DJ (decks are not provided) and there's a bit of space for a jig around too.
Catering: in-house. Licence extension possible. Music: MP3 port.

St Aloysius Social Club

*20 Phoenix Road, NW1 1TA (7284 1087).
King's Cross tube/rail.* **Available for hire**
7pm-1am daily. **Capacity** *Venue* 150 seated/
200 standing. **Hire charge** from £140.
Minimum spend £800. **No credit cards**.
Social club

The St Aloysius Social Club has something of a
1980s northern town feel about it, from the
pool and trestle tables to the shimmering,
multicoloured, spangly drapes at the far end (you
know, the type that hide the speedboat in
Bullseye). That said, it is a mighty large space,
child-friendly and handily located near to King's
Cross station. The management will pretty much
leave you to your own devices and if imagination
fails you on the entertainment front, you can
always step up to the oche for a game of darts.
The sheer size of the room is probably this social
club's best feature, making it suitable for all sorts
of events and functions. It has played host to
various cabaret, comedy and quirky music nights
over recent years.
Catering: in-house; kitchen facilities.

EAST

Dalston Jazz Bar

*4 Bradbury Street, N16 8JN (7254 9728).
Dalston Kingsland rail.* **Available for hire**
Venue 5pm-3am Mon-Thur, Sun; 5pm-5am Fri,
Sat. **Capacity** 200 standing. **Hire charge** free
if full capacity Mon-Thur, Sun; from £4,000
Fri, Sat. **No credit cards**. Bar

Local polysexual over-21s flock to this cluttered
slice of '60s Americana for its late, late kick
out time, cheap and cheerful cocktails, and
fantastically eclectic DJ soundtrack. If you hire
the whole venue – bang on for pointy-shoed guys
and dolls – champagne and cake is included and
you can get discounted nosh from the local
Turkish and Caribbean restaurants. Any bands
you choose must be in keeping with DJB's groovy,
cosmopolitan style but the venue can provide jazz
and cabaret acts for a hassle-free do too. Our
advice? Take advantage of its pedestrian pace
on Sundays and invade.
Music: DJ equipment.

Dollar Grills & Martinis

*2 Exmouth Market, EC1R 4PX (7278 0077/
www.dollargrills.com). Farringdon tube/rail.*
Available for hire 6pm-1am Mon-Sat; 6pm-
midnight Sun. **Capacity** *Private areas* 10-40
standing. **Minimum spend** free; call for
details. Bar
For review, *see p30.*
Catering: in-house.

dreambagsjaguarshoes

*34-36 Kingsland Road, E2 8DA (7729
5830/www.dreambagsjaguarshoes.com).
Old Street tube/rail.* **Available for hire** noon-
midnight Mon; noon-1am Tue-Fri; 5pm-1am
Sat; noon-12.30am Sun. **Capacity** *Private
room* 100 standing. **Minimum spend** £500.
Bar/gallery

This too-cool-for-school bar is a fine place to
experience the East End's edgy yet elegant alt
scene. Graphic-design wallpaper plays host to art
exhibitions, paper owls hang from above the bar
and dark brown, slouchy couches form intimate
spaces around the tables. The metallic bar is long
enough to accommodate a dozen arms and can
be utilised to cool down after manic partying. The
basement – of similar style but with brick walls
and a low ceiling – can be hired out from Monday
to Wednesday and fits up to 100 guests. Make
sure they're fans of electro and alt-rock as hosts
don't have a say in the choice of music.
Catering: in-house. Music: MP3 port.

Drunken Monkey

*222 Shoreditch High Street, E1 6PJ
(7392 9606/www.thedrunkenmonkey.co.uk).
Liverpool Street tube/rail.* **Available for hire**
noon-midnight daily. **Capacity** *Venue* 250
standing. *Private rooms* 2: 28-35 standing/
12-15 seated. **Minimum spend** *Venue*
£2,000-£7,000. *Private rooms* free.
Bar/restaurant

For review, *see p29.*
*Services: Big screen. Catering: in-house.
Music: DJ equipment*

Exit

*174 Brick Lane, E1 6RU (7377 2088).
Aldgate East tube/Liverpool Street tube/
rail.* **Available for hire** 4pm-1am Tue-Thur;
4pm-2am Fri; 10am-2am Sat; 9am-2am
Sun. **Capacity** *Private areas* 40. **Minimum
spend** call for details. Bar
For review, *see p24.*
Catering: in-house.

FleaPit

*49 Columbia Road, E2 7RG (7033 9986/
www.thefleapit.com). Old Street tube/rail/
26, 48, 55 bus.* **Available for hire** noon-
12.30am daily. **Capacity** *Venue* 100.
The pit 60. **Hire charge** *Venue* from £450.
The pit from £250. Bar/gallery

The FleaPit boasts a bar area filled with retro
sofas, many tables, lamps for low-key lighting and
big slouchy armchairs. There's organic Freedom
beer on tap and cups of tea for the 'totallers
(served in mismatching vintage cups). The 'Pit
Freedom gallery has screening and projection

VENUES

THE OLD
QUEENS
HEAD

To reserve an exclusive area or a private room for drinks,
canapés or private dining please contact Melissa 020 7354 9993

44 ESSEX ROAD, ISLINGTON, N1 8LN
WWW.THEOLDQUEENSHEAD.COM

facilities, and could be used for anything from a book launch to a screening to an intimate club night or birthday party. The venue has a full entertainment licence and, if you want, you can even bring your own food in (to the gallery area, but note however that there are no kitchen facilities). Hirers have access to the bar/lounge area and – for a bigger do – you can take over the whole gaff. Just check the events calendar online and get booking.
Disabled: toilet. Licence extension possible. Music: MP3 port. Projector.

Gramaphone
60-62 Commercial Street, E1 6LT (7377 5332/www.thegramaphone.co.uk). Aldgate East tube. **Available for hire** noon-2.30am Mon-Fri; 9am-2.30am Sat; noon-midnight Sun. **Capacity** *Private room* 200 standing. **Hire charge** £150-£300. Bar/club
For review, *see p30.*
Catering: in-house. Licence extension possible. Music: DJ equipment.

Karaoke Box Smithfield
12 Smithfield Street, EC1A 9LA (7329 9991/ www.karaokebox.co.uk). Farringdon tube/rail. **Available for hire** noon-1am Mon-Wed; noon-3am Thur-Sat. **Capacity** 4-25 seated/ standing. **Hire charge** from £20/hr.
Karaoke bar
For a gregarious night on the tiles, Karaoke Box will get your party started in style – tackily drunken style but style nonetheless. Simply book yourself a room (they fit between four and 25 guests) for anything from half an hour to the entire night (prices start at £20 an hour for a room for four) and prepare for painful caterwauling, bad Eminem impressions and fights over who gets to sing the female vocals on 'Summer Nights'. Entry is free, except after 6pm Thursday to Saturday when there is a £3 charge per person. At Karaoke Box Smithfield, there is now a VIP Room for up to 14 guests too. The room has a projector screen, sofa, Wii, disco lights and the possibility of hiring your own bartender and DJ. Soho's Karaoke Box is on Frith Street (No.18, 7494 3878).
Catering: in-house. Projector (VIP room).

Medcalf
38-40 Exmouth Market, EC1R 4QE (7833 3533/www.medcalfbar.co.uk). Angel tube/ Farringdon tube/rail. **Available for hire** noon-11pm daily. **Capacity** *Private room* 18 seated/50 standing. **Hire charge** £200.
Restaurant/bar
Situated on lovely Exmouth Market, Medcalf is an exercise in classy good taste in the modern manner: fuss-free decor (floorboards, rickety furniture, stylised bare bulbs), fab food (pints of prawns, British cheeses), great cocktails and a well-sourced wine list. To the side of the long, thin main bar is a small function space with massive windows and an edgy Shoreditch feel. There's space for 18 for private dining (three-course menus from £26.50) or 50 for a drinks party (management are happy to supply buffets or canapés). The small size makes it the perfect venue for a low-key birthday bash – just plug in your iPod and you're done.
Catering: in-house. Disabled: toilet. Licence extension possible. Music: MP3 port. Outside space: terrace.

Old Cholmeley Boys' Club
68 Boleyn Road, N16 8JG (07963 778636). Highbury & Islington tube/rail/Dalston Kingsland rail. **Available for hire** 9am-3am daily. **Capacity** 150 standing. **Hire charge** from £200. **No credit cards.** Club
For an off-kilter, leftfield party venue, the Old Cholmeley Boys' Club is a quality choice. Tucked away in Dalston, with few neighbours to speak of, it's a little-known space that'd make a great spot for a bespoke birthday do. Thanks to flexible management, it has hosted yoga nights, life drawing classes and even a pedal-for-power rave (complete with exercise bikes providing the electricity) in recent months. There's room for up to 150 partygoers and the hotch-potch sofas, pianos and large mirrors give it an attractively eclectic aesthetic (you can bring your own decorations for themed parties). There is a balcony area (great for lording it over your guests), a terrace and a decent in-house sound system too. Food and drink are supplied by the party host and kitchen facilities are available.
Catering: kitchen facilities. Music: DJ equipment; MP3 port. Outside space: terrace (for hire). Projector.

Public Life
82A Commercial Street, E1 6LY (7375 1631/ www.publiclife.org.uk). Aldgate East tube/ Liverpool Street tube/rail. **Available for hire** 11am-1am Mon-Sat; 11am-midnight Sun. **Capacity** *Venue* 40 seated/60 standing. **Hire charge** £150. Bar
Raucous, non-stop party people, who don't mind getting a little shoulder-to-shoulder in their quest for dance nirvana, will find their spiritual home in this underground, 150-year-old east London venue. Once a public toilet – you can still find original tiles on the walls – its shoebox-small size and hip location add an exclusive edge to a birthday bash and minimise awkwardness in mixed groups as they hustle together on the

DRUNKEN MONKEY

Teetering precariously but, so far, surely on the suits and haircuts divide, the Drunken Monkey brings a little bit of Shoreditch cool to the City fringes. Red lanterns adorn the long, atmospheric bar and heavy wooden tables line the mirrored walls, creating an up for it, funky vibe. There are numerous party hire options available, including a private, quieter dining area at the back of the bar, smaller, intimate 'concubine rooms' or even the entire venue. Music is loud and housey, the dim sum menus provide perfect party sustenance and the cocktails are pleasingly potent. Most refreshingly, there's zero snooty pretence and everyone's made to feel welcome by the stellar staff, who will obligingly accommodate all your party requests.

For listings, see p27.

PLACES TO BRING YOUR OWN DJS

VENUES

Bourne & Hollingsworth

With flowered wallpaper and lacy tablecloths, the decor at this venue might remind you of your great granny's parlour – but that's where the similarity ends. Every night of the week it fills with groovers who love the intimate setting – it fits 90 so is ideal for full venue hire. Available any night apart from Fridays, you and your pals can enjoy excellent cocktails and the cosy retro atmosphere for just a £1,500 minimum spend. You can also bring your own food or take advantage of the in-house kitchen. There is a good quality sound system and DJ decks, as well as a screen and a projector.
Best for Cool crowds looking for a central but tucked-away space.
Must do A '20s theme to match the decor.
Inside tip The cocktails are fabulous so make sure they're on your party menu.
For listings, see p16.

Dollar Grills & Martinis

Dollar's red-lit and seductive basement bar makes a fine place for an intimate shindig. At weekends it quickly gets packed with frocked-up girls downing cosmos but during the week it's available for hire, as are various areas of the venue or the entire place. We're told that if you're interested in hiring the venue on what is normally a quiet night (Sunday through

Tuesday) the minimum spend is minimal too. Canapés can be provided for a bar reservation, and there are decks (CD and vinyl) so you can bring in your own DJs to supply the soundtrack. Martinis are the thing here and there are 20 cocktails to choose from.
Best for Mid-week parties with style.
Must do Down a Porn Star martini: Cariel vanilla vodka and passion fruit purée.
Inside tip The basement bar suits winter parties best and can seem rather dark on a summery night.
For listings, see p26.

Gramaphone

The basement of this bar/club is a blank canvas that lends itself nicely to events where dancing is a priority. Decks are set up so you can bring your own DJs and, for live entertainment, the hire fee includes a full PA and engineer, so you just need to supply the band. Popular with band and club promoters, it's also perfect for big birthday bashes. The low ceiling is draped with fabric, the wooden floor and furniture are battered and the lighting is dim, giving it a nicely worn-in feel that you won't be afraid to party in. What's more, you have your own bar with staff serving until 2.30am. Upstairs remains open to the public – trusted promoters can hire the whole venue.

Best for Parties with an up-for-it crowd.
Must do Ditch the heels, don your trainers and party like it's 1999.
Inside tip The owners are open to any music except R&B and grime.
For listings, see p28.

Idlewild

Though occasionally blighted by flaky bar staff, this stylish gastropub makes an impact with its four private (ish – they are connected to the main bar) areas. Packed with eclectic furnishings (sofas, cool lights, glass tables), each makes a great spot for lounging about and listening to the DJs. If you're keen to choose the tunes yourself, head up the magnificent staircase (lined with a smart collection of framed insects) to the grand, petrol blue cocktail lounge which is also available for hire. Here, revival cocktails and natty touches like blue decanter glasses and floor-to-ceiling draped windows will wow even the most jaded gastropub-goer. A canapé menu is available and a fierce sound system should satisfy any bedroom DJ's creative urges.
Best for Big celebrations with plenty of glamour.
Must do Put the mini steak and chips on your canapé menu.
Inside tip Book well in advance.
For listings, see p41.

Monkey Chews

In keeping with the ramshackle, riotous feel of the rest of this pub, this upstairs drinking den is the perfect setting for a debauched night out. Down one end is a well-stocked bar, backlit with pink fairy lights. Opposite is a stage and separate DJ booth framed by torn out sleazy magazine pages. In between, the stripped wooden flooring, antique fan chandelier and velvet banquette seating is fabulously louche, without even trying. But you don't have to be a libertine to put on a party here; they also cater for bridge-and-tunnel tastes – karaoke, Sky sports and film screenings are all possible, and catering can be provided. If you're after an atmospheric party, this place is well worth seeking out.
Best for Edgy dos where the music is the focus.
Must do Get stuck in to some of the canapés.
Inside tip Don't spread the word too wide.
For listings, see p23.

dancefloor. Dance is indeed the order of the day here, with regular nights Lost Souls Techno Club and Kubicle attracting a wealth of wide-eyed minimal and electro-techno fans. Whatever you have planned for the place, there's little that's bog standard about this bar.
Catering: in-house. Disabled: ramp, lift, toilets. Music: CD decks, DJ equipment, MP3 port. Outside area: street-level 'roof' terrace.

Red Lion

41 Hoxton Street, N1 6NH (7729 7920/ www.redlionhoxton.com). Old Street tube/rail. **Available for hire** noon-11pm daily. **Capacity** Private room 50 standing. **Hire charge** free.
Pub/bar
It's easy to underestimate this seemingly rather banal Hoxton bar. The cheap disco ball, fake insect adornments and grapefruit lights may have 'predictable kitsch' written all over them, but the contrast between its endearing grandfather-style decor and a hip Shoreditch crowd will guarantee your birthday bash goes down in you and your friends' memories. A decent roof garden, with picnic tables and a defunct jacuzzi, offers a breezy escape from the first-floor function room, which is occupied by glossy black chairs and a small marble table. The room can be hired out on weekdays and holds a maximum of 50 guests.
Licence extension possible. Music: MP3 port. Outside space: roof garden.

Rhythm Factory

16-18 Whitechapel Road, E1 1EW (7247 9386/www.rhythmfactory.co.uk). Aldgate East tube. **Available for hire** 11am-6am Mon-Sat. **Capacity** 500 standing. **Hire charge** £350-£600. Club/bar
Come sundown, this unimposing bar and Thai restaurant transforms into a renowned East End institution, flinging open its doors to a three-room space that thrives on beat-ridden raves and live music. The lurid blue main room's gargantuan stage – two 10kW sound systems and spotlights are crying out for ten-piece bands or dance troupes – and large bar stretching across the back wall combine to make this the perfect spot for the bash to end all bashes. Battered sofas abound, allowing easy collapse after the more strenuous dance-floor exertions, and a third room can be opened up (with a further bar and decks) to allow your party musical diversity. The main room isn't the airiest of environments for eating, but two different oriental finger buffet menus are available at £6 or £8 per person. Tip: look out for celebrity gatecrashers; Pete Doherty shambles around the place occasionally.
Catering: in-house. Music: DJ equipment. Outside space: terrace.

VENUES

Rosemary Branch

2 Shepperton Road N1 3DT (7704 2730/ www.rosemarybranch.co.uk). Old Street tube/ rail, then 21, 76, 141 bus. **Available for hire** noon-11pm Mon-Thur; noon-midnight Fri, Sat; noon-10.30pm Sun. **Capacity** *Venue* 200 standing. *Private room* 80 standing; *theatre* 90 seated. **Hire charge** *Venue* from £5,000. *Private room* £200-£500; *theatre* £1,200 per wk/£200 per night. Pub/theatre

Untainted by gentrification, Rosemary Branch is home to an eccentric crowd of locals and warm bar staff. Famed for the quirky theatre upstairs, it also has a beautifully redecorated function room with startling pink-flowered wallpaper, stripped floors and an ornate bar. It's fully equipped for parties, with a banging sound system, film-screening facilities and decks upon request. This makes a great space for a birthday or engagement party; for theatrical types it could serve as a plush green room/wrap party space. Those stuck for ideas might want to theme a party according to the theatre's current performance. Or, if you're feeling ambitious, put on a show of your own; the theatre hire price includes promotion, technical support, lighting and use of the battered grand piano. The open-minded staff will help dress the function room and arrange refreshments and canapés (prices available upon request).

Catering: in-house. Disabled: toilet. Licence extension possible. Music: DJ equipment. Outside space: garden.

Royal Inn on the Park

111 Lauriston Road, E9 7HJ (8985 3321). Mile End tube, then 277 bus. **Available for hire** 11am-11pm Mon-Thur, Sun; 11am-1am Fri, Sat. **Capacity** *Private room* 50 seated/ 120 standing. *Garden* 100 standing. **Hire charge** *Private room* £150/4 hours & £75 each subsequent hour (£50 bar staff charge). *Garden* call for prices. Pub/restaurant

Royal Inn on the Park's upstairs function room boasts a raggedly regal feel. It's probably not large enough for a royal entourage but is certainly spacious enough for either a banquet under the chandeliers (linked by faded red drapery) or a rockin' dance party next to the decks, which perch on old dressing tables. Dark velvet curtains, fireplaces and gilded picture frames and mirrors emphasise the grungy glam ambience, while the leafy environs of Victoria Park are on the doorstep. Top tip: if you order a buffet that costs over £500, you get a whole poached salmon thrown in for free. The attractive and sizeable garden space is also available for hire.

Catering: in-house. Disabled: ramp (venue), toilets. Music: DJ equipment to hire, MP3 port. Outside space: garden (for hire).

Scolt Head

107A Culford Road, N1 4HT (7254 3965/ www.thescolthead.com). Dalston Kingsland rail. **Available for hire** noon-midnight Mon-Sat; noon-11.30pm Sun. **Capacity** *Private room* 120 standing/60 seated. **Hire charge** £100. Bar

A sports-themed bash suits this pool bar-style back room best, be that a huddle around the large projection screen to watch the Wimbledon final or just a few beers with the local footie team to commiserate following yet another doomed season. There's a homely, coastal living room vibe thanks to a hotch potch of retro, modern and beachy decor and lots of low-slung lighting. Pool tables offer impromptu entertainment for competitive guests, while a jukebox is on hand, ready to blast through your favourite rock classics. The pub also caters for weddings, with a sit-down meal around a long table, champagne-and-canapés and/or hearty traditional meals served with real ales (prices from £10 a head) among the options.

Catering: in-house. Disabled: toilet. Music: DJ equipment; MP3 port.

The Space

269 Westferry Road, E14 3RS (7515 5577/ www.space.org.uk). Mudchute DLR. **Available for hire** 10 am-midnight Mon-Wed; 10am-2am Thur-Sat; 10am-10.30pm Sun. **Capacity** 90 seated/120 standing. **Hire charge** from £400. Arts space

The Space and its funky, locally adored bar/restaurant, Hubbub, combine to make a 32–carat party diamond in the rough of the Isle of Dogs. Formerly a church, now a 'multi-arts venue' the Space has bucketloads of atmosphere and offers plenty of potential for imaginative celebratory fun. Think raucous themed birthday parties, gigs or funky corporate dos. The in-house catering team offer fabulous finger and fork buffets (marinated chicken skewers, mediterranean vegetables, caesar salad), barbecues and plated menus at prices that'll make you wonder why you didn't head east sooner. Any staff you might need for your event can also be provided.

Catering: in-house. Disabled: ramps, lift, toilet. Licence extension possible. Music: CD player, MP3 port, PA system. Outside space: garden. Projector.

Visions Video Bar

588 Kingsland Road, E8 4AH (7275 7520). Dalston Kingsland rail. **Available for hire** noon-2am Mon-Thur, Sun; noon-5am Sat, Sun. **Capacity** 300 standing. **Hire charge** £150-£550. **No credit cards.** Bar

Cat's Back. *See p34*.

This long-running Dalston basement has a makeshift youth centre feel but is in demand for local wedding receptions and family occasions on account of its budget-friendly pricing. You can hear the thudding basslines from up the high street as cutting-edge club nights sick of Shoreditch pretension emigrate here for the quality PA system and an unkempt Hackney luxe vibe. Door staff, a car park, two bars and a DJ booth ensure the smooth running of youthful celebrations, but stacks of basic tables and chairs allow a banquet-style set-up too. Food isn't in-house, but there are facilities for heating up food, should you order your catering from elsewhere. Brand new toilets are a bonus too.
Catering: in-house. Music: DJ equipment; MP3 port.

Wenlock Arms

26 Wenlock Road, N1 7TA (7608 3406/ www.wenlock-arms.co.uk). Old Street tube/ rail. **Available for hire** *noon-1am daily. Private room* 30 standing. **Hire charge** £10; free to CAMRA members. **No credit cards. Pub**
A world away from the trendy pubs and bars of Hoxton, this is a proper old-school local boozer. Massively popular with Campaign for Real Ale drinkers on account of its revered taps, the function room is also free to the society's members. For the rest of us, hire of the ramshackle upstairs room costs just £10 'for the price of the cleaner' (or free if you leave the place as you find it). And it's worth every penny – although unremarkable from the outside and rough around the edges inside, this place oozes East End charm. The function room doesn't have its own bar but the pub stays open late, you can bring your own music and the ladies in the kitchen can provide catering – chicken drumsticks and sandwiches are on the menu. Perfect for a fuss-free birthday gathering.
Catering: in-house; kitchen facilities.

SOUTH

Cat's Back

86-88 Point Pleasant, SW18 1NN (8877 0818). East Putney tube. **Available for hire** *9am-midnight Mon-Thur, Sun; 9am-2am Fri, Sat. Garden 9am-10pm daily.* **Capacity** *Private rooms* 2: 20-35 seated/30-70 standing. *Garden* 100 seated/150 standing. **Hire charge** £150-£300 (room only).
Bar/restaurant
This quirky pub has a cult following due to its charming higgledy-piggledy decor (vaguely Americana in flavour) and friendly vibe. Although it is mainly regulars who decide to hold functions

here, staff make a point of being friendly and helpful to newbies too. Upstairs there is a canteenish restaurant, complete with its own bar, a sophisticated-looking DJ booth and space for a dancefloor. On the floor above, there's a function room with a large dining table, deep red walls and an aura faintly reminiscent of Miss Haversham's parlour. All very cosy, laid-back and perfect for an eccentric, pretension-free birthday party. Food is simple, old-fashioned English fare and the garden is available for hire.
Catering: in-house. Music: DJ equipment. Outside space: garden (for hire).

Concrete

The Hayward, Southbank Centre, Belvedere Road, SE1 8XX (7928 4123/www.concrete-daynight.co.uk). Waterloo tube/rail. **Available for hire** *6pm-1am Mon, Sun; 11pm-1am Tue-Sat.* **Capacity** 30 seated/80 standing. **Minimum spend** £1,000. **Bar/café**
There were whoops of joy when this bar/café replaced Starbucks on the South Bank. With its tongue-in-cheek name (set, as it is, in the vast Brutalist environs of the Southbank Centre), exposed piping, original factory lights and industrial-style seating, Concrete manages to be both cosy and fun. By day it operates as a café, serving healthy snacks, salads and the like, but by night it transforms into a popular bar. The space, which fits 30 for a seated dinner and around 80 standing, would be great for a special birthday celebration. The location, right next to the Hayward, will definitely make an impact on out-of-town guests. Hell, even a London crowd won't fail to be impressed with the great service, atmospheric lighting and edgy feel.
Catering: in-house. Disabled: toilet. Music: DJ equipment; MP3 port. Outside space: patio.

Dog House

293 Kennington Road, SE11 6BY (7820 9310). Kennington tube. **Available for hire** *noon-midnight Mon-Thur, Sun; noon-1.30am Fri, Sat.* **Capacity** *Private room* 35 seated/ 70 standing. **Hire charge** free. **Pub**
If you're looking for a low-key party venue with a dress code of jeans rather than cricket-club tie, then the Dog House's shabby charm might be just the ticket. Set above the well-worn and well-loved pub below. with its carpet-clad bar and rollies-and-a-pint clientele, the function room here echoes the same sentiment. Surprisingly clean and bright, you'll find an abundance of leather sofas that can be pushed back for up to 70 people to let their hair down to whatever DJ you choose to bring in. Banners and balloons are welcomed and for £50 you can have your own barman – great for avoiding any stair dramatics

with guests bringing up trays of drinks from the bar below. Food can be organised with the chef and starts at around £7 a head.
Catering: in-house. Licence extension possible. Music: DJ equipment (hire charge), MP3 port.

Dusk
339 Battersea Park Road, SW11 4LS (7622 2112/www.duskbar.co.uk). Battersea Park rail. **Available for hire** 6pm-midnight Tue-Wed; 6pm-1am Thur; 6pm-2am Fri, Sat; call for details Mon, Sun. **Capacity** *Venue* 300 standing. *Private areas* 4: 50-150 standing. **Hire charge** *Venue* from £400. *Private areas* free (cancellation charge). **Minimum spend** *Venue* £1,000. **Bar**
As comfortable with a bonkers birthday bash as with a more sedate (at first) wedding reception, Dusk bar may be off what many consider the beaten track, but its award-winning cocktails make it worth finding. Choose from one of four different areas – the Montgomery lounge, the VIP area, the cocktail tables or the private Playroom (with space for 150) – or, on quieter days, go for exclusive hire of the whole bar. Party guests will be welcomed by contemporary-meets-colonial styling that transforms into a luxurious candlelit haven at night. Well loved by hip locals, and known for its high-level of eye candy, a celebration at Dusk is likely to be anything but forgettable.
Catering: in-house. Licence extension possible. Music: DJ equipment.

Florence
131-133 Dulwich Road, SE24 0NG (7326 4987/www.florencehernehill.com). Herne Hill rail. **Available for hire** noon-midnight Mon-Thur; noon-1am Fri; 11am-1am Sat; 11am-midnight Sun. **Capacity** *Private room* 25 seated/40 standing. **Hire charge** free. **Gastropub**
A large mash tun and copper kettle stand proudly behind glass in the centre of this relaxed gastropub that stands opposite Brockwell Lido. These large vessels are central to the brewing process that takes place on the site (over 1,000 pints are brewed here each week). The Florence Brewery makes two beers – a blond ale called Weasel, and Bonobo, a darker, fruitier brew – and any party assembling here ought to make tasting them a priority (should these not satisfy, there's an unusually large range of bottled beers too, as well as an adventurous wine list). There are no wholly private spaces and there's not much scope for ordering food off the menu, so this probably isn't somewhere you'd want to hold a very formal occasion, but for a relaxed birthday celebration, or just a large gathering of friends,

David Quantick
WRITER, BROADCASTER AND AUTHOR

My favourite thing about birthdays is finding out what your friends think you're like from the bizarre presents you get. A panama hat? A teddy bear dressed as a pilot? A Libertines CD? These gifts are for a fat old maniac. Oh, I see.
The worst thing about getting older is the fear of descending into a malodorous self-abusing orangutan. Actually, it's getting dead that worries me.
The best parties start at about 8pm, then some people come along from the pub at 11pm, and then the DJ shuts up about 4am, and everyone sits around smoking cigars and talking nonsense until dawn.
Outfits are best avoided. Fancy dress makes you hot and cross. I used to dress as a monk as it was cool and 'roomy'.
Drinks should be in the right order. Beer or wine first, then spirits. Never start with a martini. Make sure you never serve jelly.
If I was in charge of the guest list I wouldn't invite that weird bloke who came last year and wouldn't talk to anyone but me.
Etiquette dictates one should talk to other people. Mingle! Mingle! My party piece is putting on iPod playlists that everyone hates. It's not deliberate; I just have terrible taste.
My ultimate party venue is the HMS *President* (www.hmspresident.com) on the Thames. It has a stage for bands (we had the Prellies, who do a pre-1963 Beatles set), a big bar and a barbecue on the stern deck. Arr!
I'll always dance to the Pet Shop Boys.
The best party I ever attended was my sister's sixth birthday, until my mum decided I was being disruptive and made me stand in the front garden, looking in. For three hours.
David Quantick is the author of Grumpy Old Men and co-writer of Harry Hill's TV Burp.

VENUES

ALL STAR LANES

The Bayswater branch of the hugely successful Bloomsbury stalwart offers a similarly upmarket take on wholesome '50s Americana, with eight bowling lanes surrounded by plush leather booths and a chequerboard diner straight out of *Happy Days*. Partygoers hoping to occupy more than one lane will need to book well in advance. The diner offers lane-side fodder a cut above the average and is priced accordingly – steaks range from £14.50 to £22 and there are all manner of belly- and budget-busting seafood platters on offer. There's also a milk bar for shakes and sundaes and one serving beer (in bottles or buckets) and a superb range of cocktails. A private room featuring two lanes, a personal cocktail bar and a DJ-friendly sound system is the ultimate choice for party potential (again, book well in advance). East Enders needn't feel left out – there's a new branch opening on Brick Lane in November 2008. *For listings, see p39.*

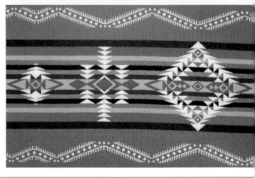

it's perfect. The conservatory seats around 30, but be warned that in summer people will be wandering through to get to the garden.
Catering: in-house. Outside space: garden.

Franklins
157 Lordship Lane, SE22 8HX (8299 9598/ www.franklinsrestaurant.com). East Dulwich rail. **Available for hire** 10am-1am daily. **Capacity** *Venue* 100 seated. *Private room* 30 seated. **Minimum spend** call for details. Restaurant/bar
This early gastronomic pioneer on East Dulwich's main drag has long enjoyed an excellent culinary reputation. And chef Tim Sheehan's imaginative variations on the staples of Modern British cuisine are the reason you'd choose this cosy restaurant as a venue for an upscale birthday or anniversary celebration, or even a small wedding party. There are two options: either hire the slightly gloomy basement, and dine with up to 25 friends while the usual business of the restaurant carries on upstairs, or else have the whole place to yourself with exclusive hire. The airy main space offers an elegant backdrop for a sit-down dinner, while the battered leather sofas and mismatched tables in the bar area provide a more relaxed setting for pre-prandial drinks.
Catering: in-house. Disabled: toilet. Licence extension possible.

Hide
39-45 Bermondsey Street, SE1 3XF (7403 6655/www.thehidebar.com). London Bridge tube/rail. **Available for hire** 10am-11pm Mon; 10am-midnight Tue; 10am-1am Wed, Thur; 10am-2am Fri; 5pm-2am Sat. **Capacity** *Venue* 100 standing. *Private room* 50 standing. **Minimum spend** *Venue* £5,000. *Private room* free. Gastrobar
For review, *see p25*.
Catering: in-house. Disabled: toilet. Music: MP3 port (venue).

Inc Bar
7A College Approach, SE10 9HY (8305 3091/www.incbar.com). Cutty Sark DLR. **Available for hire** 6pm-2am Mon-Thur, Sun; 7pm-3am Fri, Sat. **Capacity** *Venue* 300 standing. *Private room* 60 standing. **Minimum spend** *Venue* £5,000. *Private room* £1,200. Bar
With its interior decor originally by Laurence Llewellyn-Bowen, Inc Bar certainly makes a loud style statement. Of course, whether you find this showy and naff, or really swish is a matter of taste. You can hire the smaller, private bar at the back, which borrows features from its dome-ceilinged, fossil-bar big brother, and comes with

VENUES

a cosy little nook that's perfect for get-a-room impersonations of 16-year-olds. In the main bar, you can reserve the balcony without charge – a great vantage for eating, drinking and watching the young and funky denizens of Greenwich strutting their stuff. Best for singing and snogging, this is definitely good for birthday or Christmas party shenanigans.
Big screen (venue). Catering: in-house. Music: DJ equipment.

Lost Society
697 Wandsworth Road, SW8 3JF (7652 6526/www.lostsociety.co.uk). Clapham Common tube/Wandsworth Road rail.
Available for hire noon-midnight Mon-Wed; noon-1am Thur; noon-2am Fri, Sat.
Capacity *Venue* 280 standing. *Private area* 30-40 standing. *Top floor* 100 standing.
Minimum spend *Venue* £2-3,000 Mon-Thur, Sun; £15,000 Fri, Sat. *Private area* £150 refundable deposit. *Top floor* from £500. Bar
Some people have birthday parties. Others have Birthday Parties, and those people come here to throw them. Lost Society is not short of glamour if you want to celebrate your 30th as though you're worth a million dollars. Take your pick from the dramatic art deco cocktail bar with its glistening chandeliers, barely-lit clandestine corners and discreet bartenders, to the secret, wrought-iron garden or the more contemporary loft-styled dancefloor upstairs for your night of flighty high jinks. With a reputation for a Good Night Out, the bar's understandably popular, but you can still book an area with no charge for up to 40 people. During the week, you can also have exclusive hire of the top floor or even the entire place.

Catering: in-house. Licence extension possible. Music: DJ equipment; MP3 port. Outside space: garden.

The Rye
31 Peckham Rye, SE15 3NX (7639 5397). East Dulwich or Peckham Rye rail.
Available for hire noon-11pm Mon-Thur, Sun; noon-12.30am Fri, Sat. **Capacity** *Venue* 40 seated/120 standing. *Private areas* 2: 24-36 seated/50-60 standing.
Hire charge *Venue* £800. **Minimum spend** *Venue* £1,000. *Private areas* £600.
Pub/restaurant
The attractive wood-panelled main bar of the Rye, a refurbished corner boozer isn't available for hire, unfortunately. But the space that is available to revellers here is nonetheless unusual and really rather ideal for a relaxed summertime celebration. The secret is the Rye's backyard, between the bar and the garden, that has been covered and hung with drapes Bedouin-style. Scattered electric lamps and candles make it particularly atmospheric at night, and there are heaters in case there's a nip in the air. And if you bring an iPod, you can have your own music piped out to you. It's also child- and dog-friendly. There are several catering options: you can either choose food from the normal dining room menu (in which Thai and Malay dishes figure prominently) or else have a barbecue (summer only). And they'll also do canapés.
Catering: in-house. Disabled: ramp on request, toilets. Licence extension possible. Music: DJ for hire with equipment, MP3 port. Outside space: covered garden (for hire).

Tooting Tram and Social
46-48 Mitcham Road, SW17 9NA (8767 0278/www.antic-ltd.com). Tooting Broadway tube. **Available for hire** 5pm-midnight Tue-Thur; 4pm-2am Fri; noon-2am Sat; noon-midnight Sun. **Capacity** *Mezzanine area* 60 seated/standing. *Bar areas* 2-60 seated/standing. **Hire charge/minimum spend** free. Bar
Situated on the same strip as McDonald's is this grandiose former tram-shed for locals craving a dramatic yet intimate party setting. Eccentric design flourishes, from the fairy light-filled birdcages dangling from the towering ceiling to the stuffed deer heads and quaint white sideboards, add trashy Parisian character. The downstairs bar has areas that can be reserved, but the back area of the mezzanine level, which looks out over acres of chandeliers, is best for sophisticated birthday celebrations and seasonal post-work revelry. Split into three areas, you can book the entire floor or reserve

VENUES

cosier spots for small groups. Balham Bowls Club (another Antic outlet) can supply contemporary meze dishes at an additional cost. *Catering: in-house. Disabled: toilet.*

WEST

All Star Lanes
6 Porchester Gardens W2 4DB (7313 8361/ www.allstarlanes.co.uk). Bayswater tube. **Available for hire** 7am-11.30pm Mon-Thur, Sun; 7am-midnight Fri, Sat. **Capacity** *Venue* 350 seated/standing. *Private room* 80 seated/standing. **Hire charge** *Private room* £300/hr (reduced rates at weekend). *Venue* call for details. Bowling alley
For review, *see p36.*
Big sceen. Catering: in-house. Music: DJ equipment (Mon-Thur); MP3 port.

Amuse Bouche
51 Parsons Green Lane, SW6 4JA (7371 8517/www.abcb.co.uk). Parsons Green tube. **Available for hire** 4-11pm Mon; 4pm-midnight Tue-Thur; 4pm-12.30am Fri, Sat; 4-10.30pm Sun. **Capacity** *Private room* 38 seated/70 standing. *Seated terrace* 20 seated/40 standing. **Hire charge** £100. **Minimum spend** £1,000. Champagne bar
Stylish and laid-back, Amuse Bouche's Parsons Green champagne bar (the smaller sister of the Soho venue; *see p86*) is fantastically versatile. The main bar area, perfect for a glass of (very reasonably priced) champagne leads to a medina-inspired sitting area and cosy courtyard, perfect for a summery post-Wimbledon drinks party. The upstairs function room is shabby chic at its best. Generally used for birthday dinner parties, there is a sound system and space for a dancefloor. Food is catered for by the bar, BYO is permitted (plus corkage) and an inviting roaring fire is an option for chilly winter nights. There is a fee of £100 for hiring out either of the areas and a minimum spend of around £1,000.
Catering: in-house. Licence extension possible. Outside space: terrace (for hire).

Crazy Homies
125 Westbourne Park Road, W2 5QL (7727 6771/www.crazyhomieslondon.co.uk). Royal Oak or Westbourne Park tube. **Available for hire** 7pm-midnight daily. **Capacity** *Private room* 45 standing/seated. **Minimum spend** £1,750 (50% deposit). Bar/restaurant
Native Mexicanos may tease that this bar has all the authenticity of a Taco Bell, but we beg to disagree. In our opinion, the quesadillas here as good (even better) than any real Mexican taqueria

we've eaten in (a bespoke canapé menu is available on request) – and the Mexican themed park decor adds a pizzazz to any event. The downstairs bar is a riot of colour and kitsch, strewn with piñatas, Dia de los Muertos memorabilia and cleverly customised stools made from old... oil drums. As you'd expect, there's a huge choice of tequila shots including chocolate-, cinnamon- or caramel-flavoured, but the house speciality is the piquant chilli margarita. The original (but no longer working) vinyl jukebox in the corner is a novelty, but we recommend you engage the services of DJ Wheelie Bag (*see p159*) who has a residency here once a month; the eccentric old gent plays ska tunes from a portable set of decks on a shopping cart and hands out bingo cards so your guests can win prizes during his set.
Catering: in-house. Licence extension possible. Music: MP3 port.

Establishment
45-47 Parsons Green Lane, SW6 4HH (7384 2418/www.theestablishment.com). Parsons Green tube. **Available for hire** noon-midnight daily. **Capacity** *Private room* 24 seated/60 standing. **Minimum spend** £1,500.
Bar/restaurant
This grown-up bar and restaurant has a 1970s style aesthetic and a light and airy function room that makes a pleasant, albeit rather sedate, space for a birthday dinner. There's no dancefloor so you'll have to save your moves for the inevitable 'all back to mine' afterparty and unfortunately the lovely alfresco area isn't available for private hire. But there are fabulous cocktails – mixed to perfection by attentive bar staff – and decent gastro grub to compensate. Wednesday's jazz band makes a great background for impromptu mid-week drinks.
Catering: in-house. Outside space: courtyard.

Geales
2 Farmer Street, W8 7SN (7727 7528/ www.geales.com). Notting Hill Gate tube. **Available for hire** 6-11pm Mon; noon-11pm Tue-Sun. **Capacity** 12 seated/20 standing. **Hire charge** £100. Restaurant
Recently refurbished, Geales now has a first-floor function room that can be hired for dinners or cocktail parties. The decor is similar to the main dining room with light streaming through the windows, and a big sociable table seating up to 12 people. The hire charge of £100 can be negotiated, depending on the amount you're planning to spend on food and drink. There's certainly plenty of fine food to choose from – think prawn cocktail, fresh fish (caught daily in Cornwall) and chips, followed by treacle tart.

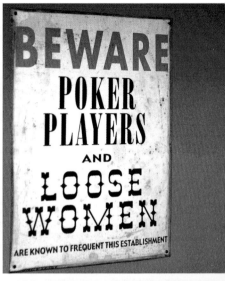

Ginglik

There's also a champagne bar where you can indulge in a few Duchy of Cornwall oysters and a glass of champers (dandelion and burdock for the children) before the proceedings begin. *Catering: in-house.*

Ginglik

1 Shepherd's Bush Green, W12 8PH (8749 2310/www.ginglik.co.uk). Shepherd's Bush tube. **Available for hire** 7pm-1am Mon-Thur; 7pm-3am Fri, Sat; 7pm-12.30am Sun. **Capacity** *Venue* 70 seated/200 standing. *Private room* 40 seated/60 standing **Hire charge** *Venue* from £150. *Private room* from £100 (includes 1 year full membership – normally worth £80). Club
Housed in converted public toilets outside Shepherd's Bush tube, Ginglik has a loyal local clientele, but after six years in business, the place could do with a lick of paint (particularly in the musty-smelling ladies' loos). The low-ceilinged red party room is cordoned off from the rest of the club by a curtain and feels a bit like a Somerset youth club. But its low-lit lamps, strategically placed mirrors and contemporary artwork lift it above the ordinary. There's always a convivial ambience in the rest of the place, but with no separate bar or entrance it's best to book it on a night when you like the rest of the entertainment on offer (or book the entire venue). Note: Ginglik operates a 'pay as you go' membership (as well as the full membership offered as part of the hire package) system making it a great spot for late drinks. *Big screen. Catering: in-house, preferred caterer list. Licence extension possible. Music: DJ equipment (venue), MP3 port.*

Idlewild

55 Shirland Road, W9 2JD (7266 9198/www.ruby.uk.com/idlewild). Warwick Avenue tube. **Available for hire** 4-11.30pm Mon-Thur; 4pm-midnight Fri; 11am-midnight Sat; 11am-11pm Sun. **Capacity** 80 standing. **Minimum spend** £1,500-£3,000. Gastropub
For review, *see p31.*
Catering: in-house. Music: DJ equipment (upstairs bar); MP3 port.

Troubadour

263-267 Old Brompton Road, SW5 9JA (7370 1434/www.troubadour.co.uk). West Brompton tube/rail. **Available for hire** *Club* 10am-midnight Mon, Sun; 10am-2am Thur, Sat. *Gallery* 10am-midnight daily. **Capacity** *Club* 120 standing/60 seated. *Gallery* 72 standing/32 seated. **Hire charge** *Club* £250-£600. *Gallery* £200. **Minimum spend** *Club* £1,000-£1,800. Café/bar

New Folkista promoters or partygoers seeking a place with bohemian charm need look no further; the Troubadour is the real deal. This is one of Earl's Court's original folk coffee shops, with an unrivalled rock pedigree, having played host to Bob Dylan and Jimi Hendrix back in the '60s. Nowadays the paintwork may be peeling, but your partygoers won't notice as they'll be so taken with the eccentric bric-a-brac, rock photography and convivial atmosphere. The club is designed for live music; they have a fantastic PA, stage and lighting. If you have more bourgeois tastes, the high-ceilinged art gallery space is also available for private dining while the charming Shackleton room in the café can also be reserved for special occasions. There's a charming secret garden upstairs too. Take advantage of the fantastic catering and book in-house finger food; even louche rock stars have stomachs. *Catering: in-house. Music: DJ equipment.*

Westbourne House

65 Westbourne House W2 4UJ (7229 2233/www.westbournehouse.net). Bayswater or Royal Oak tube. **Available for hire** 11am-11.30pm Mon-Thur; 11am-midnight Fri, Sat; 11am-11pm Sun. *Private areas* 3: 25-40 standing. **Hire charge** £100 Mon-Thur, Sun. £200 Fri, Sat. Bar
For review, *see p25.*
Catering: in-house.

White Horse

1-3 Parsons Green, SW6 4UL (7736 2115/www.whitehorseSW6.com). Parsons Green tube. **Available for hire** 8am-midnight daily. **Capacity** *Private room* 64 seated/100 standing. **Minimum spend** £1,000. Pub
Despite the laid-back and predominantly pubby atmosphere of the White Horse – known to most as the 'Sloaney Pony' – a very versatile function room is to be found upstairs. It can be hired for a variety of occasions – from corporate wine tasting events to a sit-down birthday dinner for around 60 – and makes a spacious if not wildly exciting spot. There is an annexe that is often used as a dancefloor and live bands can be accommodated. There is a bar and BYO is also available, although rather hefty corkage fees apply. A good selection of food is offered by the pub, from canapés – a favourite is rare roast beef and miniature Yorkshire puddings – to buffets and three-course meals. Prices for the room vary according to the nature of the event and there's a great outdoor area for people-watching, smoking and those laid-back summer drinking sessions (barbecues are a regular feature throughout the summer). *Catering: in-house. Music: MP3 port. Outside space: beer garden.*

VENUES

Anniversaries

Whether you've been married for decades or just spent a first joyous year living in sin, there's no better excuse for an annual celebration than true love. In this chapter, you'll find cosy restaurants just right for that celebration for two, pretty dining rooms for hearty family feasts and a host of cool, quirky and romantic venues ideal for raising a toast to civil partnerships, wedded bliss, long-term liaisons and new engagements. Many of the venues listed in the rest of the guide could also fit the bill for your party, so do take a look before making your mind up.

VENUES

CENTRAL

Adam Street

9 Adam Street, WC2N 6AA (7379 8000/ www.adamstreet.co.uk). Charing Cross tube/rail. **Available for hire** 9am-3am Mon-Sat. **Capacity** *Venue* 350 standing. *Restaurant* 80 seated. *Private rooms* 3: 12-60 seated/80-100 standing. **Hire charge** *Private rooms* £150-£450. *Venue* call for details. Members' club

The pleasing creakiness of this 18th-century Robert Adam house is offset by the sophisticated private members' club that occupies its vaults. Adam Street has been operating as a meeting place for creative types since 2001 and has gained a reputation as one of the area's best party spots. The Snug, a square dining room decked out with antique satirical art, is a fine spot for an intimate anniversary celebration (it fits up to 12 for dinner) or a swanky family gathering. For a larger bash, the basement Rehearsal room features bare brickwork, mirror panelling and a sprung dancefloor. Special lighting effects, DJs, magicians, ice luges, entertainers and casinos can all also be arranged. The restaurant's Modern British cuisine is much praised, and eats can be provided for all occasions, from a £17.50/head finger buffet to a gastronomic blowout.
Big screen. Catering: in-house. Music: DJ equipment; MP3 port.

Engineer. *See p49.*

Bentley's Oyster Bar & Grill

11-15 Swallow Street, W1B 4DG (7734 4756/www.bentleys.org). Piccadilly Circus tube. **Available for hire** *Crustacea room* noon-3pm, 6-10.45pm Mon-Sat; 11.30am-3.30pm, 6-10pm Sun. *Jameson room* noon-3pm, 6pm-3am Mon-Sat; 11.30am-3.30pm, 6pm-3am Sun. **Capacity** *Crustacea room* 14 seated. *Jameson room* 60 seated/100 standing. **Minimum spend** *Crustacea room* £840. *Jameson room* £1,800.

Restaurant/bar

This oyster bar and restaurant, famously rescued by Richard Corrigan, may look a tad trad for a party, but the lovely old Victorian building lends itself to a special gathering. The softly lit basement space – the Jameson room – has its own entrance, cloakroom, toilets (complete with Kenneth Turner toiletries), bar, plasma screen and collection area with sofas and is perfect for swanky anniversary bashes, birthdays and receptions (guests can be seated at six round tables). Upstairs, the Crustacea room, dominated by a striking John Wonnacott portrait, is an elegant, panelled dining space that fits up to 14. The food is terrific and ranges from a hot-and-cold canapé menu (quails' eggs, king prawns, spiced skate) to a choice of six three-course set meals for private dining. Parties with stamina will be pleased Bentley's has a licence until 3am. *Big screen (Jameson room). Catering: in-house. Disabled: toilet. Licence extension*

Converted convenience: **Cellar Door**.

possible (3am, Jameson room). Music:
equipment available to hire; MP3 port.
Outside space: terrace.

Cellar Door

Zero Aldwych, WC2R OHT (7240 8848).
Covent Garden or Temple tube. **Available
for hire** 4pm-1am daily. **Capacity** Venue
60 standing. **Minimum spend** £500.
Bar
With a wink to its former life as a West End public
convenience, this bar oozes risqué sex appeal.
Besides the provocative lipstick red walls, there
are buttock-shaped banquettes, kiss me/lick
me bar stools and racy toilets designed with
exhibitionists in mind (they appear transparent
but become opaque when locked). Clever design
makes the space feel intimate rather than
claustrophobic and the compact proportions
mean that your party – a fabulously louche
anniversary or engagement do, perhaps? – will
feel instantly buzzy. An SMS jukebox adds
novelty appeal (pick a tune without leaving your
seat) while the 'snortie' snuff range, including
chocolate, apricot and red bull flavours, is an
inspired innovation for addicts missing their
nicotine fix. Fantastic cocktails complete the
picture – the management can design bespoke
cocktail menus and imaginative canapés to
match any occasion.
Big screen. Catering: in-house. Licence
extension possible. Music: DJ equipment;
MP3 port.

China Tang

The Dorchester, Park Lane W1K 1QA (7629
9988/www.thedorchester.com). Marble Arch
tube/rail. **Available for hire** 11.30am-midnight
daily. **Capacity** Venue 120 seated/300
standing. Private rooms 3: 16-18 seated/20-
30 standing. **Minimum spend** Venue call for
details. Private rooms £1,000. Restaurant
The decor at this film star hang out is lavishly
modelled on 1930s Shanghai, with a vivacious
atmosphere faithful to the vision of its ebullient
designer/owner David Tang. Gorgeous art deco
features and motifs abound, and the romance of
the low lighting, polished mirrors, rosewood
panelling and white and chrome accents is offset
by quirky chinoiserie and art – even the loos are
a notch above with piped poetry. Three intimate
private rooms are screened off from the main
restaurant and can either be separated for cosy
dim sum or interconnected for one long spread.
Alternatively, the entire restaurant, with its
convivial round tables, can be hired for a sit-down
banquet with silver chopsticks. The highly reputed
Cantonese cuisine takes a traditional, purist
stance, but be prepared for a dent in your wallet.
Big screen. Catering: in-house. Disabled:
lift, toilet. Licence extension possible.
Music: CD/DVD player; equipment to hire;
MP3 port on request. Wi-Fi.

Cinnamon Club

The Old Westminster Library, 30-32 Great
Smith Street, SW1P 3BU (7222 2555/

DINNER À DEUX

For intimate anniversaries, Valentine's Day and proposals of the marrying kind.

Andrew Edmunds
46 Lexington Street, W1F 0LW (7437 5708). Oxford Circus or Piccadilly Circus tube. **Open** 12.30-3.30pm, 6-10.45pm Mon-Sat; 1-3.30pm, 6-10.30pm Sun.
This much-lauded cosy Soho restaurant offers a spot-on candlelit backdrop to romance. The classic Modern European dishes are satisfying without being overly adventurous: lots of flavoursome meat and fish mains. Champagne is £6.50 a glass.

Aurora
49 Lexington Street, W1F 9AP (7494 0514). Oxford Circus or Piccadilly Circus tube. **Open** 12.30-10pm Mon, Tue; 12.30-10.30pm Wed-Sat.
Small but perfectly formed, Aurora is delightfully intimate. And few things beat a table in the garden on a summer evening here. Make sure you're on the later sitting, so you can linger over dessert.

Le Comptoir Gascon
61-63 Charterhouse Street, EC1M 6HJ (7608 0851/www.comptoirgascon.com). Farringdon tube/rail. **Open** noon-2pm, 7-10pm Tue-Thur; noon-2pm, 7-11pm Fri, Sat.
This super-romantic French bistro focuses on cooking from the south-western provinces – much of it unashamedly, but deliciously, carnivorous. The blackboard-scrawled specials might include roast suckling pig or quail salad. Prices are reasonable too.

Green Room
182 Broadhurst Gardens, NW6 3AY (7372 8188). West Hampstead tube/rail. **Open** 6.30-11.30pm Tue-Fri; 6.30-midnight Sat; 12.30am-3pm; 6.30-10pm Sun.
This Hampstead bistro's pretty chandelier-lit dining room is perfect for more intimate soirées. An inviting Modern European menu sticks to the classics, cooked with real flair.

Le Mercury
140A Upper Street, N1 1QY (7354 4088/ www.lemercury.co.uk). Angel tube/Highbury & Islington tube/rail. **Open** noon-1am Mon-Sat; noon-11.30pm Sun.
Romantic and thrifty? The perfect combo. For Gallic charm at bargain prices, head here for well-executed starters at £3.95 and mains

– ranging from sea bass to rib-eye steak – at £6.45. There are plenty of tables for two, plus flickering candles set in vintage wine bottles.

Mosimann's
For the ultimate in flash romance book the Montblanc room for two at Mosimann's – quite possibly the world's smallest private dining room. It's decked out in luxurious black and gold, while a personal waiter ups the glamour factor no end.
For listings, see p47.

La Poule au Pot
231 Ebury Street, SW1W 8UT (7730 7763). Sloane Square tube. **Open** 12.30-2.30pm, 6.45-11pm Mon-Fri; 12.30-4pm, 6.45-11pm Sat; 12.30-4pm, 6.45-10pm Sun.
La Poule au Pot is a classic romantic hotspot. Things don't change much here, including the rustic French menu: expect robust dishes such as coq au vin and good house wines.

Saigon Saigon
313-317 King Street, W6 9NH (www.saigon-saigon.co.uk/0870 220 1398). Ravenscourt Park or Stamford Brook tube. **Open** 6-10pm Mon; noon-3pm, 6-11pm Tue-Thur; noon-3pm, 6-11.30pm Fri, Sat; 12.30-3.30pm, 6-10pm Sun.
This classy Vietnamese restaurant evokes the glamour of a bygone age with its bamboo screens and photos of '40s Saigon. Dishes such as chargrilled quail won't fail to impress.

Les Trois Garçons
1 Club Row, E1 6JX (7613 1924/www. loungelover.co.uk). Liverpool Street tube/rail/ 8, 388 bus. **Open** 7pm-midnight Mon-Sat.
A celebration of maximalism, Trois Garçons is generously gilded and crammed with bizarre *objets trouvés*. The food is equally artistically presented and cooking is spot on.

Upstairs
89B Acre Lane, entrance on Branksome Road, SW2 5TN (7733 8855). Brixton tube. **Open** 6.30-9.30pm Tue-Thur; 6.30-10.30pm Fri, Sat.
This discreet little gem requires diners to ring a bell to gain admittance. The Lilliputian dining room is lovely and the prix fixe menu has a strong seasonal focus.

VENUES

www.cinnamonclub.com). St James's Park or Westminster tube. **Available for hire** noon-midnight Mon-Sat. **Capacity** *Venue* 130 seated/320 standing. *Private rooms* 2: 30-60 seated/45-60 standing. **Minimum spend** *Venue* £25,000. *Private rooms* £1,500. Restaurant/bar
Set in the Grade II-listed Old Westminster library, the Cinnamon Club is cool, calm and classy. Its SW1 location makes it a popular venue for corporate events, but its sophisticated vibe suits more intimate celebrations too (it even has a licence for civil marriage ceremonies). As well as the large main restaurant, there's a private dining room, mezzanine and two bars – all are available for hire. Regardless of the type of bash you intend to throw, it would be a crime to miss out on the venue's inspired Indian cuisine. Indulge with an anniversary or birthday dinner in the beautiful private dining room. The mezzanine makes the most of the buzz in the restaurant below and can be arranged into two smaller areas if you fancy a drinks reception followed by a sit-down dinner. *Disabled: lift; toilet. Catering: in-house. Licence extension possible. Music: DJ equipment; MP3 port on request.*

Covent Garden Hotel

10 Monmouth Street, WC2H 9HB (7806 1000/ www.firmdale.com). Covent Garden tube. **Available for hire** 6am-midnight daily. **Capacity** *Private rooms* 3: 16-30 seated/15-50 standing. *Cinema* 53 seated. **Hire charge** *Private rooms* £100/hr + VAT, £500/day + VAT. *Cinema* £180/hr + VAT (minimum 2hr hire). Hotel
This Kit Kemp-designed hotel has lost none of its edge since being converted from a pharmacy ten years ago. Every bit the conventional Edwardian town house from outside, the interior is a witty mix of the traditional and the flamboyant, from the curlicued wallpaper to the floral upholstery. A decorative refurb due for completion in October 2008 promises to remain faithful to the hotel's existing style. Along with fabulous spaces for private dining and cocktail receptions, the venue boasts a private screening room perfect for showing a favourite film or wedding video as part of a swanky anniversary party. And if you can bear to part company with the cinema's snug leather seating, you'll find dinner menus showcasing classic Modern British and European dishes. *Big screen (extra £200 charge). Catering: in-house (no catering in cinema). Disabled: lift, toilet. Music: MP3 port.*

Mildreds

45 Lexington Street, W1F 9AN (7439 2392/ www.mildreds.co.uk). Oxford Circus or Piccadilly

Circus tube. **Available for hire** 7-11pm daily. **Capacity** *Private room* 24 seated (minimum 10). **Minimum spend** £250. Restaurant
Small, intimate dining venues are reasonably easy to locate, especially in bustling Soho, but it's always good to stumble across a place that offers something a little different. Seating between ten and 24 people in an attractive upstairs room, Mildred's private room provides an excellent vegetarian menu with a dedicated waiter to pander to your every whim and fancy (well, perhaps not all of them). The venue is predictably popular with local businesses and attracts its fair share of birthday and hen parties happy to plug in an iPod shuffle and watch the world go by outside. We think the interesting, offbeat erotic artwork and inspired, health-conscious menus make it a prime spot for gathering your nearest and dearest to raise a toast to a special anniversary. *Catering: in-house. Music: MP3 port.*

Mosimann's

11B West Halkin Street, SW1X 8JL (7592 1625/www.mosimann.com). Knightsbridge tube. **Available for hire** noon-midnight Mon-Sat; by arrangement Sun. **Capacity** *Venue* 120 seated/150 standing. *Private rooms* 7: 2-50 seated. **Hire charge** *Venue* £25,000. *Private rooms* £175-£700. Members' club
Tucked away in the affluent excesses of Knightsbridge, Mosimann's is a converted church and family-run restaurant, bar and members' club. While the main area is very impressive, with a plunging chandelier and high ceilings, it is the seven (yes, seven) private rooms that really take the breath away. Each is sponsored by a different company (in a manner that manages to be appealing rather than excessively branded) and the varying set menus and decor reflect this. The Bentley room has gorgeous black and white photographs of the classic car, for example, while the romantic Mont Blanc room seats just two (*see p45* **Dinner à deux**). Several rooms are licensed for weddings, with the Parmigiani (maker of specialist Swiss watches) holding 50 for the ultimate exclusive day. Best of all each room comes with a buzzer so you can dictate when the food and drinks arrive. *Catering: in-house. Licence extension possible. Outside space: terrace (Parmigiani room has access).*

Zuma

5 Raphael Street, SW7 1DL (7584 1010/ www.zumarestaurant.com). Knightsbridge tube. **Available for hire** noon-2.15pm, 6-11pm Mon-Thur; noon-2.45pm, 6-11pm Fri; 12.30-3.15pm, 6-11pm Sat; 12.30-3.15pm, 6-10pm

Covent Garden Hotel. *See p47.*

Sun. **Capacity** *Private rooms* 2: 10-14 seated. **Minimum spend** £1,000. Restaurant
For review, *see p53.*
Catering: in-house. No amplified music.

NORTH

Engineer
65 Gloucester Avenue NW1 8JH (7722 0950/ www.the-engineer.com). Chalk Farm tube/31, 168 bus. **Available for hire** 9am-midnight Mon-Sat; 6-11.30pm Sun. **Capacity** *Private rooms* 2: 20-32 seated (minimum 12-25). **Minimum spend** £30/person (£150 refundable deposit).
Gastropub
The Engineer remains unseduced by the garish wallpaper and faux aristo ornaments that have become de rigeur in newer gastro ventures. Instead its elegant function rooms emanate a well-turned out charm, with crisp white linen, huge floor-to-ceiling Georgian windows and, most importantly, fantastic food and service. The waiters are used to catering to large parties and have mastered the art of being attentive yet unobtrusive. The set menu changes regularly but features inventive mains such as miso-marinated cod or grilled pork chop with celeriac, alongside mouthwatering desserts. The serene white and wood-panelled main function room is the perfect space for an anniversary celebration, client-winning business lunch or perhaps even well-heeled football dinner (the large wall-mounted flatscreen shows Sky Sports). The terracotta-coloured mirror room next door is better suited to an intimate birthday gathering or reunion.
Big screen. Catering: in-house. Disabled: toilet. Outside space: garden.

Marquess Tavern
32 Canonbury Street, N1 2TB (7354 2975/ www.marquesstavern.co.uk). Highbury & Islington tube/rail. **Available for hire** 5-11pm daily. **Capacity** *Venue* 250 standing. *Restaurant* 40 seated/70 standing. **Minimum spend** *Venue* £2,500. *Restaurant* £1,500.
Gastropub
Attentive service and top-notch food are a given at this relaxed Islington gastropub. The light-filled, wood-panelled restaurant area at the back can be reserved for large groups and would make a fine spot for a low-key anniversary meal with friends or family. It's not a totally private space but the friendly clientele here are part of the draw, as is the fantastic malt whisky selection and adventurous selection of Belgian beers. Menus are packed with hearty British meat and fish mains that guarantee wide-reaching appeal – the substantial, hangover-defying Sunday roasts are

well renowned in these parts too. Alternatively, hire out the whole shebang – a reasonable minimum spend makes it perfect for a big bash.
Catering: in-house. Licence extension possible. Music: MP3 port.

Prince
59 Kynaston Road, N16 0EB (7923 4766/ www.theprincepub.com). Stoke Newington rail/73, 393, 476 bus. **Available for hire** noon-11pm Mon-Thur; noon-midnight Fri, Sat. **Capacity** *Venue* 140 standing. *Private room* 50 standing/50 seated. **Hire charge** *Private room* £25-£75 (£25 charge for bar staff). *Venue* call for details. Gastropub
An amiable mix of young professionals and families flock to this residential gastropub for Sunday roasts, impressive wines and organic cider. Foodie fans can hire the restaurant area but larger parties should venture upstairs to the fabulously shabby chic function room, which, if it wasn't for its own bar, would recall a student's living room with its floral rocking chair, low sofas and mismatched wooden tables. A buffet menu can be tailored to your personal requirements, but usually includes the likes of wild mushroom, spinach and feta cheese filo parcels, risotto balls and lamb kebabs – perfect for soaking up the fizz at a hip but civilised anniversary do.
Catering: in-house. Licence extension possible. Music: MP3 port. Outside space: garden.

EAST

Bistrotheque
23-27 Wadeson Street, E2 9DR (8983 7900/ www.bistrotheque.com). Bethnal Green tube/ rail. **Available for hire** Oak room 6.30pm-midnight Mon-Thur, Sun. *Venue/restaurant* call for details. **Capacity** *Venue* 350 seated/ standing. *Restaurant* 160 seated. *Oak room* 54 seated. **Minimum spend** *Oak room* £500. *Venue/restaurant* call for details.
Restaurant/bar
For review, *see p52.*
Big screen (venue). Catering: in-house. Disabled toilet. Music (venue): DJ equipment; MP3 port. Outside space: yard.

Fox
28 Paul Street, EC2A 4LB (7729 5708/ www.thefoxpublichouse.com). Old Street tube/rail. **Available for hire** noon-11pm daily. **Capacity** *Venue* 250 standing. *Private rooms* 2: 12-40 seated/100 standing. **Minimum spend** *Venue* £1,500. *Restaurant* £750.
Gastropub

VENUES

During the week, City traders and designers flock to this sophisticated yet relaxed gastropub. On weekends, though, the venue is quieter and can be hired out in its entirety. Upstairs is a charming, wooden-furnished restaurant area with candle holders overflowing with wax and fantastic Mediterranean gastro dishes on offer, as well as a selection of canapés. A decent-sized terrace is just begging for summer loving and, due to the surrounding area's low key status, benefits from an unobtrusive, ambient quality. A function room is also available – it's shut off from the bustle and accommodates about a dozen guests. While versatility is the name of the Fox's game – it's great for anniversaries and birthdays and gets rammed with office groups at Christmas – entertainment is limited to an iPod dock.
Catering: in-house. Music: MP3 port. Outside space: terrace (restaurant has access).

Princess
76-78 Paul Street, EC2A 4NE (7729 9270). Old Street tube/rail. **Available for hire** noon-11pm Mon-Fri; 6-11pm Sat. **Capacity** *Restaurant* 45 seated. **Minimum spend** £27.95/person (minimum 25). Gastropub
Wood dominates the scenery in this popular gastrobar, which attracts City professionals and East End hip kids alike. A table on the ample ground floor can be reserved, but for a big, boozy dinner with friends or family, ascend the spiral staircase to the rather more intimate restaurant space which is available for hire. Here, artwork for sale is kept on display, while a large fish-eye mirror and candles add plenty of character. Food offers bold flavours and great quality – lots of meat and fish classics. The room has a stylish, relaxed feel and you can supply your own music, but noise does carry from downstairs, making this somewhere best suited to a party that doesn't mind sharing its pulse.
Catering: in-house. Licence extension possible. Music: MP3 port.

St John
26 St John Street, EC1M 4AY (7251 0848/ www.stjohnrestaurant.co.uk). Barbican tube/ Farringdon tube/rail. **Available for hire** 11am-11pm Mon-Fri; 6-11pm Sat. **Capacity** *Venue* 200 standing. *Restaurant* 110 seated. *Private room* 18 seated. **Minimum spend** *Private room* £30/person (minimum 6). *Venue/restaurant* call for details. Restaurant
For review, *see p53.*
Catering: in-house. Disabled: toilet.

SOUTH

Baltic
74 Blackfriars Road, SE1 8HA (7928 1111/ www.balticrestaurant.co.uk). Southwark tube/ rail. **Available for hire** noon-12.30am daily. **Capacity** *Private rooms* 2: 30 seated/40-70 standing. **Minimum spend** £24-£28/person. Restaurant/bar
Positively dripping with class, Baltic never fails to impress friends, family, bosses and even the local acting community (the Old Vic regularly comes here to celebrate openings and closings). The candlelit private dining room overlooks the gorgeous minimalist restaurant via a window, high in the barn-like roof. Perfect for a glamorous anniversary soirée and increasingly popular with more sophisticated hen dos, the room seats 30 people and is free to hire. Your own waiter and sound system are included and set menus (the restaurant's eastern European cuisine is highly regarded) start at £24. The airy, white restaurant itself, accessed via the deeply seductive cocktail bar, seats up to 120 for big celebrations such as weddings and bar mitzvahs.

IT'S THE GIFT THAT COUNTS

Go traditional, go modern – but for God's sake don't forget.

	Traditional	Modern
1st	Paper	Clocks
2nd	Cotton	China
3rd	Leather	Crystal/glass
4th	Fruit/flowers	Appliances
5th	Wood	Silverware
6th	Sugar/iron	Wood
7th	Wool/copper	Desk sets
8th	Bronze/pottery	Lace/linen
9th	Pottery/willow	Leather
10th	Tin/aluminium	Diamond
11th	Steel	Jewellery
12th	Silk/linen	Pearls
13th	Lace	Textiles/furs
14th	Ivory	Gold
15th	Crystal	Watches
20th	China	Platinum
25th	Silver	Silver
30th	Pearl	Diamond
35th	Coral	Jade
40th	Ruby	Ruby
45th	Sapphire	Sapphire
50th	Gold	Gold
55th	Emerald	Emerald
60th	Diamond	Diamond

Big screen. *Catering: in-house. Music: DJ equipment; MP3 port. Outside space: terrace.*

Bar du Musée
17 Nelson Road, SE10 9JB (8305 3091/ www.bardumusee.com). Cutty Sark DLR. **Available for hire** 7pm-1am Mon-Fri, Sun; 7pm-2am Sat. **Capacity** *Venue* 80 seated/ 250 standing. *Private room* 20 seated/50 standing. **Hire charge** *Venue* call for details. *Private room* £150. Restaurant/bar
Lovely Bar du Musée's George Room doesn't have a dedicated bar or its own loos but does have the sort of classy atmosphere that's perfect for creating a sophisticated sense of occasion. The vibe is relaxed and civilised, with a grand high ceiling, granite-topped tables (which can be arranged or removed as you please) and the sort of leather sofas that make lounging a pleasure. Walls are covered with the sort of lithographs and architects' drawings that look brilliant in markets and hopeless in your own living room – but somehow they work here. Music can be provided courtesy of your iPod – just plug it in and you're good to go. Canapés can be arranged.
Catering: in-house. Disabled: ramp. Music: MP3 port. Outside space terrace.

Chez Bruce
2 Bellevue Road, SW17 7EG (8672 0114/ www.chezbruce.co.uk). Wandsworth Common rail. **Available for hire** noon-2pm, 6.30-10.30pm Mon-Fri; 12.30-2.30pm, 6.30-10.30pm Sat; noon-3pm, 7-10pm Sun. **Capacity** *Private room* 14 seated. **Hire charge** £500 evenings & Sun. Restaurant
For review, *see p52.*
Catering: in-house. No amplified music.

Harrison's
15-19 Bedford Hill, SW12 9EX (8675 6900/ www.harrisonsbalham.com). Balham tube/rail. **Available for hire** noon-midnight Mon-Wed, Sun; noon-1am Thur-Sat. **Capacity** *Private room* 15 seated/40 standing. **Minimum spend** £400 Mon-Wed, Sun; £800 Thur-Sat. Restaurant/bar
Hidden at the bottom of a chic spiral staircase leading off the swanky main restaurant lies the lovely private room at Harrison's. Lined with leather banquettes, and with its own *Barbarella*-ish bar, it's as private as you could want for a party – it even has its own loos. Fitting up to 40 people for drinks, it hits the spot for a really special occasion (an anniversary bash or engagement do would be perfect here). There's no hire fee but a minimum spend applies at weekends. Music comes in the form of an MP3 connection. The cocktails are delicious and food can be organised to suit any celebration.

Catering: in-house. Music: MP3 port. Outside space: terrace.

Rosendale
65 Rosendale Road, SE21 8EZ (8670 0812/ www.therosendale.co.uk). West Dulwich or West Norwood rail. **Available for hire** 10am-11pm daily. **Capacity** *Private rooms* 2: 30-80 seated/50-100 standing. **Minimum spend** £900. Gastropub
Now firmly established on the South London gastro circuit thanks to chef Matthew Foxon, the Rosendale is also a highly versatile party venue, with various spaces to suit events – and, importantly, budgets – of all sizes. It's a large Victorian pub that underwent a stylish refit a coule of years ago. That renovation included the two function rooms upstairs, the larger of which, the Grand Hall, can accommodate up to 100 people for a buffet, or 80 if it's a formal sit-down meal you're planning. The Green room next door is half the size, and offers a more intimate setting for a birthday or anniversary celebration. If you're really pushing the boat out, you can take over the whole pub, upstairs and down. Menus are made-to-measure, and can be as simple or elaborate as you like.
Catering: in-house. Disabled: toilet. Music: MP3 port.

VENUES

The Cow

Bistrotheque

With its bright warehouse space and hidden East End location, Bistrotheque walks the line between street and sophistication. Sumptuous private dinners (not available on Friday and Saturday nights) for up to 54 guests can be accommodated in the antique wood-panelled Oak room. Choose a menu from a tantalising selection of starters, mains and desserts. Options vary according to the season but might include the likes of crab cakes or steak tartare, and for the main event, garlicky roast chicken or grilled lemon sole with samphire. Full-on feast appeal is guaranteed as you can pick three starters, three mains and three desserts for guests to choose from on the night, ensuring everyone's tastes (there are good veggie options) are catered for.

Best for Celebrations requiring good food and an edge.

Must do Give guests good directions – it's a tough one to track down.

Inside tip Make time for cocktails in the hip Napoleon bar.

For listings, see p49.

Chez Bruce

For a really special lunch or dinner, the first-floor dining room at Chez Bruce has sophisticated appeal. A bespoke set or tasting menu can be arranged to suit your requirements or your guests can choose from a simplified version of the day's – predominantly French – restaurant menu. Either way, they won't be disappointed with dishes such as duck magret with spiced pastilla and roast cod with olive oil mash among the options. Service is seamless and professional – even the fussiest family member won't be able to help but be charmed. The wine list is adventurous and reasonably priced for the high quality on offer.

Best for An indulgent family lunch or dinner.

Must do Save room for one of the fabulously indulgent desserts.

Inside tip Turn your mobile off – this is a ringtone free zone.

For listings, see p51.

The Cow

Book the Cow's enchanting upstairs dining room for a private dinner with Gaelic charm. Neutrally decorated with cool touches such as an antler candelabra, it's a space where your parents will feel as much at home as your mates. However, it is the food that really elevates the Cow above other private dining offerings. Oysters are the speciality and there are French and Irish varieties by the half dozen. Mains include an awesome Cow fish stew or Welsh black rump with bubble and squeak, and desserts are gloriously indulgent. Make the most of the space by putting all the

tables together in the centre of the room for an intimate dining experience. We recommend repairing to the downstairs bar for lively after-dinner drinks – after a Guinness or two you'll be on first name terms with half the bar. **Best for** Special occasions and family affairs. **Must do** Sup a Guinness with your oysters. **Inside tip** Keep your eyes peeled for celebs in the bar downstairs. *For listings, see p54.*

St John

The utilitarian private dining room at St John is endlessly popular with groups keen to make the most of the restaurant's fantastic reputation for simple yet delicious British food. Treat your party to the ultimate feast by pre-ordering a whole roast suckling pig (these must be pre-ordered and serve 14-16 guests) – guaranteed to generate gasps of approval as the waiters deliver it to the room. Less brutally carnivorous options include the likes of langoustines and mayonnaise, roast beef with horseradish and whole roast seabass. You choose a menu for your guests in advance (a maximum of two choices of starter, main and dessert) enabling everyone to kick back with a glass of wine and some quality chat until dinner is served. One to impress with.
Best for Foodies who like dishes fuss-free, flavoursome and packing a punch.

Must do Order an extra course of appetisers while you wait.
Inside tip Grab a loaf of raisin bread to take home at the end of the night.
For listings, see p50.

Zuma

This swish Japanese restaurant offers two Kotatsu ('sunken table') rooms for private dining based on the traditional Japanese model where guests remove their shoes and kneel or sit at the table. Both rooms are sectioned off from other diners with antique wooden frames so guests can enjoy the privacy of a private room without missing out on the buzz (and celeb-spotting potential) of the restaurant. Our pick would be the smaller one, which has a view of the kitchen. There is no hire fee, but there is a minimum spend and bookings should be made a minimum of two months in advance. Each of the three set menus features exquisite modern Japanese food that's guaranteed to impress. Perfect for a relaxed celebration requiring something special.
Best for Small celebrations and family catch-ups (kids are welcome in the private rooms).
Must do Order the Zuma tasting menu (£96 pp) to sample all the best dishes.
Inside tip Warn guests in advance that they will have to remove their shoes!
For listings, see p47.

JULIE'S

In contrast to the monied streets beyond its doors, Julie's exudes a homely and inviting warmth. The front wine bar has a convivial ambience, but it's the labyrinth of mismatched rooms below that are the real discovery. Each space is distinct from the next: the terracotta Moroccan dining room is draped in tapestries and antique curiosities, while the bright and breezy Conservatory room features hanging ivy baskets and whitewashed brickwork. The Gothic room has a wonderfully grand feel with crimson walls and high-backed chairs. Most impressive is the Banqueting room with its tapestries, stags' antlers, huge oak table and lectern ready for raucous speeches. The set menus for private dining are packed with crowd-pleasing meat, fish and veggie choices, making this the ultimate stress-free party venue. *For listings, see below.*

WEST

The Cow

89 Westbourne Park Road, W2 5QH (7221 0021/www.thecowlondon.co.uk). Royal Oak tube. **Available for hire** noon-midnight daily. **Capacity** *Private room* 32 seated/50 standing. **Minimum spend** £1,500. Pub/restaurant
For review, *see p52.*
Catering: in-house. Outside space: terrace.

Julie's

rtland Road, W11 4LW (7727 7985/ esrestaurant.com). Holland Park tube.

Available for hire 9am-11.30pm daily.
Capacity *Private rooms* 6: 12-45 seated/ 50 standing (minimum 8). **Minimum spend** £30-£36/person. Restaurant
For review, *see above.*
Catering: in-house. Music: MP3 port. Outside space: terrace.

Lonsdale

44-48 Lonsdale Road, W11 2DE (7727 4080/ www.thelonsdale.co.uk). Ladbroke Grove or Notting Hill Gate tube. **Available for hire** 6pm-midnight Mon-Thur; 6pm-1am Fri, Sat; 6-11.30pm Sun. **Capacity** *Private rooms* 2:

VENUES

a fantastic deluxe tapas menu. The charming staff are happy to arrange bespoke food and cocktail menus that will satisfy even the most fanciful party wish list.

Catering: in-house. Licence extension possible. Music: DJ equipment; MP3 port. Outside space: terrace.

Pig's Ear

35 Old Church Street, SW3 5BS (7352 2908/ www.thepigsear.co.uk). Sloane Square tube, then 11, 19, 22, 319 bus. **Available for hire** 12.30-3pm, 7-10.15pm Mon-Fri; 12.30-4pm, 7-10.15pm Sat; 12.30-4pm Sun. **Capacity** Private rooms 2: 18-35 seated/35-60 standing. **Minimum spend** £1,000. Gastropub
In the four years since its inception, this relaxed Chelsea gastropub has established a fine reputation for high-quality food and great service. Parties are happily catered for in the lovely upstairs dining room – an ideal spot for a big celebration dinner or canapés and drinks reception. Dancing isn't an option – so leave your Abba collection and corresponding dance moves at the door – and due to the residential location, noisy revellers are a no-no. For a fabulous grown-up dinner party, though, it's just the ticket. The inviting feel, roaring fire and twinkling fairylights give it plenty of festive appeal too. Another hire option is the smaller downstairs Blue room. It's partitioned off from the rest of the pub by a curtain and makes a cosy place to get stuck into winter birthday drinks.

Catering: in-house. Disabled: ramp (small room). No amplified music.

Warrington

93 Warrington Crescent W9 1EH (7592 7960/www.gordonramsay.com/thewarrington). Maida Vale tube. **Available for hire** noon-2.30pm, 6-10pm Mon-Thur; noon-2.30pm, 6-10.30pm Fri; noon-4pm, 6-10.30pm Sat; noon-4pm, 6-10pm Sun. **Capacity** Private room 14 seated. **Minimum spend** £500.
Gastropub
If blowing the budget at his namesake restaurant just isn't an option, why not compromise with a spot of Gordon Ramsay gastro fare? The Warrington's private dining Billiard room offers a relaxed space for 14 to dig into the pub's hearty Brit dishes. The emphasis is definitely on the cooking, with rather restrained interior design – cream walls and framed monochrome sports photos – that feels unadventurous contrasted with the stained glass splendour next door. That said, the large oval table provides a convivial space for family banter and wine-fuelled debate. Service is impeccable too.

Catering: in-house. Outside space: garden.

VENUES

24-80 seated/60-200 standing. **Minimum spend** *Restaurant* £7,000. *1st floor* £1,400.
Restaurant/bar
From the outside, this three-floored Georgian townhouse looks like a well-groomed members' bar, but step inside and you'll find a playful clash of '60s retro chic and shiny futurism. The upstairs room, with its chrome space-age wall pods and wood-panelled cocktail bar, makes an unbeatable party venue. The sound system is excellent and your guests will be throwing enthusiastic moves on the carpeted floor before the night is out. The sleek, booth-style restaurant area downstairs can also be reserved for big celebrations and offers

Summer

When the weather starts hotting up and the evenings get brighter, a partygoer's thoughts naturally turn to beer gardens, barbecues and balmy nights on the tiles. Below you'll find a selection of venues we think fit the bill for a fabulous summer bash on account of their balcony, terrace, garden, swimming pool or just a vibe that evokes feelings of fun in the sun. Many of the suggestions in this chapter would also be great for a wedding reception and some are even licensed for ceremonies. And we really shouldn't have to warn you, but do make sure when you're planning an outdoor event that you have adequate back-up for that soul-destroying moment when you realise the Great British Summer is a wash-out once more.

CENTRAL

Boisdale

13 Eccleston Street, SW1W 9LX (7259 1262/www.boisdale.co.uk). Victoria tube/ rail. **Available for hire** noon-12.30am daily. **Capacity** *Venue* 140 seated/230 standing. *Private rooms* 4: 15-60 seated/30-100 standing. **Hire charge** *Private rooms* free-£100. **Minimum spend** *Private rooms* £800. *Venue* call for details. Restaurant/bar

Small, cosy and Scottish-themed, Belgravia's Boisdale offers a number of private areas ideal for hosting a small party or gathering. Decor throughout has a pleasingly trad feel, with lots of tartan for a festive Highland vibe. Among the options are the jazz bar-style MacDonald bar, the private-dining Jacobite room on the first floor (wood panelling, tartan carpets, oil paintings, chandeliers – and happy to accept stags and hens to boot) and the Back bar which is situated next to the lovely Courtyard garden (it has a retractable roof for summer celebrations). The undisputed jewel in the Boisdale crowd, this light and airy conservatory area is the nicest spot for a sit-down dinner and is packed with plants and flowers. Three set menus are available, ranging from £36-£60, or you can plump for a selection of Scottish canapés for something more unusual. Also popular for Christmas events and weddings. *Catering: in-house. Outside space: courtyard (for hire).*

VENUES

The Deck. *See p66.*

Chiltern Street Studios

78 Chiltern Street, W1U 5AB (07768 273858/ www.chilternstreetstudio.com). Baker Street tube. **Available for hire** *Apr-July, Dec* noon-midnight daily. **Capacity** *Venue* 80 seated/250 standing. **Hire charge** Call for details. Studio Founder of the Whistles chain, Lucille Lewin, set up this fashion consultancy, sales and marketing agency with her husband Richard and a couple of colleagues. It represents fashion labels from around the world, but can also be hired out for media launches, fashion shows and press days. It was once a school, and the playground was being turned into a fairytale garden – filled with lush vegetation and viewed through an ornate glass screen from the indoor space – when we visited.

Indoors is a vast open room, presumably the assembly hall, with an open fireplace, ranks of spotlights and distressed floorboards. The lighting set up and runway-friendly shape make it a huge favourite with fashion folk. Hiring the whole space is not cheap, but customers are welcome to use their own caterers. There are full kitchen facilities, a pleasant bathroom and French windows opening out on to a second outdoor space.
Catering: kitchen facilities. Disabled: toilet. Outside space: courtyard (for hire).

Gray's Inn Marquee

The Honourable Society of Gray's Inn, 8 South Square, WC1R 5ET (7458 7960/www.grays innbanqueting.com). Holborn tube. **Available**

for hire *late June-July* 6-11.30pm Mon-Fri; noon-11.30pm Sat, Sun. **Capacity** 150-300 seated/200-500 standing. **Hire charge** from £4,230. Marquee/garden
Organising a fabulous summer party is a breeze with Gray's Inn Marquee as your venue. Set in the society's lovely and expansive gardens, with a picture-perfect marquee erected specially for the summer months, you couldn't ask for a more impressive – or tranquil – party venue. Think relaxed barbecues, alfresco aperitifs and the sun beating down on that happy gathering. Parties of up to 300 can be catered for at dinner; up to 500 for a cocktail reception. Gray's Inn is also a popular summer wedding venue, with a dedicated events team ready to cater for special requests and bridal whims at a moment's notice. Also worth a look for events likely to take place in inclement weather are the huge hall (licensed for civil weddings) and the classy private rooms. *Catering: in-house. Outside space: garden (for hire).*

The Hub
Outer Circle, Regent's Park, NW1 4NR (7935 2458/www.royalparks.org.uk/regents/hub/ thehub.cfm). Baker Street tube. **Available for hire** 7am-11pm daily. **Capacity** *Private room* 60 seated/80 standing. **Hire charge** from £500 + VAT. Sports centre
If you want an unusual location to impress foreign clients, host a team brainstorm or for a work party with a difference, the Hub should fit the bill. From the outside it looks disconcertingly like the *Teletubbies* house, but with its panoramic view of Regent's Park and the London skyline beyond, it

LET'S TAKE IT OUTSIDE

Alexi Duggins looks at London's growing fascination with partying in public.

No longer the preserve of neon glo-stick crusties or White Lightning-clutching bus-stop tweens, getting on down in a public space is right at the centre of London's party scene.

With chain bars popping up like retail *Midwich Cuckoos* working for the forces of blandness, and characterful venues like Stepney's George Tavern having to fight for existence, space hijacking is becoming a much more attractive way to have a party with personality.

'There's a wonderful freedom with this kind of party,' explains Pippa Gueterbock, the founder of Reclaim the Beach – a group who organise mass parties on the Thames beach in front of the Royal Festival Hall. 'The best thing about it is the sense of liberty that you get in the middle of London doing something that's entirely out of the realms of any landowner or landlord. That's what makes it a completely unique experience.'

For all the benefits, public partying is a complex operation. You can hire portable PA systems with in-built CD players from most sound-hire companies, but if you're looking to run anything bigger, you'll need a generator. Trestle tables for picnics with a touch of class are easier, with some companies doing them for as little as £1.50 a day. Getting advance permission is a grey area, with small gatherings almost certainly not a problem and bigger events often tolerated if they're not out of hand. 'We don't worry about permission really,' offers Gueterbock. 'All the authorities have turned a blind eye to us. Which is just as well, because if it was officially above board then it would be more of a pain to organise.'

The key thing to remember is location, however. Try holding a noisy event anywhere within earshot of a residential area, and you can bet your bottom dollar people will complain to the police. What's more, unless you want to live in fear of the rain, you're going to need some shelter, which means warehouses, arches, railway bridges and underpasses for full-scale events, and portable gazebos for posh picnics.

If a little more tricky to organise, space hijacking parties pay dividends in terms of attendance. With dress code, smoking restrictions and kicking-out time all bumped from the agenda in favour of random passers-by joining in with the revelry, you don't need to worry about being stuck with a dull crowd. Anyone worried that this will leave them saddled with enough frothing loons to form a dance troupe should check out the polite passenger participation that occurred when a group of black-tie clad art students made a Youtube video of a dinner party they had on a tube carriage. 'At every party there's always somebody who's the token nutter, but we get all sorts of people,' laughs Gueterbock. 'I think there should be more of these parties in London, because Londoners just love them.' Hear hear.

VENUES

A must for the 'Great British Summer'. **Gray's Inn Marquee.** *See p57.*

can't fail to impress. The venue lends itself well to sport-themed daytime events; there is an underground sports centre and the interior design, while sleek, is slightly anodyne. The outside terrace is a gem and makes a fine spot for surveying the sports fields below. Catering is provided by the excellent Company of Cooks, which specialises in fresh, unpretentious grub at reasonable prices. Special rates available for charities.
Catering: in-house. Disabled: toilet. Outside space: terrace (for hire). Projector.

ICA
The Mall, SW1Y 5AH (7930 0493/www.ica. org.uk). Piccadilly Circus or Leicester Square tube/Charing Cross tube/rail. **Available for hire** *Private rooms/theatre 9am-1am daily.* **Venue/gallery spaces/cinemas** *call for details.* **Capacity** *Venue 600 standing. Private rooms 2: 60-80 seated/80-90 standing. Theatre 120-180 theatre seated/ 350 standing. Gallery spaces 200 standing. Cinemas 45-185 seated.* **Hire charge** *Private rooms from £2,700. Other spaces call for details.* Gallery/bar/cinema
Edgy and elegant in equal measure, the ICA is a classic London venue and perfect for swanky celebrations of all varieties. The high-ceilinged and airy Nash and Brandon rooms are our pick of the private hire options – both are popular for weddings (it's licensed too), cocktail parties and glam dinners. The Nash room's balconies, with views of the Mall and London skyline beyond, give it fabulous summer party appeal. Both rooms have classic decor (off-white walls, wooden floors, orginal John Nash plasterwork) which can

be enchanced with coloured uplighting and banners hung from the built-in hanging system. Food is provided by fabulous caterers Peyton and Byrne and the central location is pretty unbeatable. The two cinemas on the ground floor are popular for corporate presentations and private screenings – they come with a dedicated projectionist. The café bar is available for private hire before midday. The theatre, with the right production and decoration, is great for awards ceremonies, product launches or company balls.
Catering: in-house. Music: DJ equipment; MP3 port. Outside space: balcony (Nash room has access). Projector (cinema).

Momo/Mô Tearoom
25 Heddon Street, W1B 4BH (7434 4040/ www.momoresto.com). Oxford Circus tube. **Available for hire** *Bar noon-3am daily. Restaurant/tearoom noon-1am Mon-Sat; noon-midnight Sun.* **Capacity** *Bar 35 seated/ 100 standing. Restaurant 110 seated/200 standing. Tearoom 35 seated/70 standing.* **Hire charge** *call for details.* Restaurant/bar
This swish Moroccan restaurant offers ample settings for a party to remember. There's the atmospheric restaurant proper, a cosy downstairs bar and an adorable tea room with a bazaar feel and sunny terrace. Laid-back glamour is what Momo is all about, making it an ideal space for bohemian summer parties or exclusive (we're talking the upper end of the private hire scale) festive fun. Christmas parties are particularly popular and prime seasonal celebration dates get booked up well in advance. High quality and memorable food is a given, as is great service,

VENUES

Westminster Boating Base. *See p63.*

live music and entertainment (belly dancers, magicians and tattoo artists can be arranged). The attractive setting is also good for more sedate corporate lunchtime events.
Catering: in-house. Disabled: toilet (ground floor). Music: DJ equipment (bar); MP3 port. Outside space: terrace (restaurant & tearoom have access).

October Gallery
24 Old Gloucester Street, WC1N 3AL (7242 7367/www.octobergallery.co.uk). Russell Square tube. **Available for hire** 9am-11pm Mon-Sat. **Capacity** *Private rooms 3: 40-80 seated/60-150 standing.* **Hire charge** from £50/hr. *Gallery £560/3hrs, then £120/hr.*
Gallery
There has been a gallery in this attractive old schoolhouse five minutes' walk from the British Museum for 29 years. It can be hired, along with its café area and courtyard, by the hour, day or evening. Smaller spaces upstairs include the gorgeous Club, with its high-arched ceiling and

exposed beams, library, decorative rugs and aged leather furniture, and the high-windowed theatre space with its Bechstein and polished floors. Cocktail and birthday parties, launches and arts events are the mainstay. There's a great big kitchen and the sheltered, greenery-filled courtyard looks really beautiful all year round. The theatre is used for performances, launches and smaller receptions; the Club is best suited to sedate events, such as lectures, meetings and script readings.
Big screen (Gallery). Catering: preferred caterer list; kitchen facilities. Outside space: courtyard (for hire). Projector (Theatre Room).

St Giles
60 St Giles High Street, WC2H 8LG (7240 2532/www.stgilesonline.org). Tottenham Court Road tube. **Available for hire** *Private room 9am-11pm Mon, Tue, Thur, Sat; 5-11pm Fri.* **Capacity** *Private room 30 seated/50 standing.* **Hire charge** *Private room £20/hr-£30/hr.* **No credit cards.** Church

THE BEST POOL PARTIES

Brockwell Lido

The future of this lovely lido looked uncertain until Fusion and the Heritage Lottery gave the 1930s art deco Grade II-listed pool and building a beautiful refurb. And it can be all be yours as long as you and your wallet can hold out. Catering is provided on-site and the premises are licensed. The cost ranges from around £75 per hour for one lane to around £5,000 for the entire place for four hours over the weekend (less during the week). It has hosted everything from staff parties to birthdays, wedding receptions to Latin nights.
Best for Big events where budget isn't an issue.
Must do Book well in advance.
Inside tip Take a camera – it's a stunner.
For listings, see p66.

Club Aquarium

It might be indoors and – as London's only nightclub with a swimming pool and Jacuzzi – booked up months in advance, but Club Aquarium still has summery appeal. Catering is on-site and there are various packages available to simplify things (£45 per head gets you a finger buffet and free beer, wine and soft drinks for a five-hour period; swankier options available). Partygoers get access to the pool and Jacuzzi for a three-hour session and towels and lockers are provided.
Best for Parties with a difference whatever the time of year.
Must do Pack your best trunks.
Inside tip For popular nights, book as far in advance as possible.
For listings, see p65.

Hampton Pool

Hampton Pool is actually two pools – one is a 36-metre open air pool, set in two acres of woodland next to Royal Bushy Park, and the other is a learner pool. Both are available for hire, along with a large sunbathing, barbecue and picnic area. On a Saturday evening, the pools can be set up and staffed for up to 250 guests (and the barbecue fuelled and lit) for £1,000. The price, including bouncy castle and inflatables for the pools, is reduced for charity/fundraising events. Bring your own food for the barbie or get the catering manager to sort out a menu – perfect.
Best for Fabulous entertainment and lots of summer fun.
Must do Stick some sausages on the barbie.

Inside tip Pools are pleasingly heated so be the first to dive in.
For listings, see p67.

Haymarket Hotel Pool

Though you're not actually allowed to dive in, parties set around the shimmery water at this sophisticated Firmdale hotel have plenty of glam appeal. Add punchy cocktails, summery tunes and a crowd that isn't likely to leap the minute the staff's backs are turned and you have the ideal swanky pool party.
Best for Upmarket, civilised affairs.
Must do Brief guests on the rules.
Inside tip The canapés are impressive – order in large quantities.
For full review and listings, see p90.

Richmond Pools on the Park

Surrounded by palm trees and pampas grass, these half-lido, half-gym pools are part of a 1970s prefab sports centre and are usually steaming with workers getting on with their laps while planes loom overhead every few minutes from Heathrow. Although they take no bookings over the summer, at other times the outside lido can be hired at weekends. There's a cafeteria, which can lay on barbecues, and a full alcohol licence. There's also access to a music system and you can request a DJ, though both incur additional costs.
Best for Late spring/early autumn parties requiring a summery theme.
Must do Book a DJ for atmospheric sounds.
Inside tip The barbecue is recommended.
For listings, see p67.

Serpentine Lido

In the heart of Hyde Park, the Serpentine Lido (note: it's fresh water and unheated) also boasts a conference room and sun terrace for hire (from £100 to £3,000 depending on time, numbers, and what area is required). The lido is open until 11.30pm (the park gates shut at midnight) and, providing you're not *too* noisy, you are welcome to bring your own music and dance on the terrace. Food and drink can be catered from the kiosk café – anything from pizzas and sandwiches to full-on barbecues.
Best for Maximum impact – who wouldn't want to attend a party here?
Must do Organise some summery sounds.
Inside tip Brace yourself for the cold.
For listings, see p62.

VENUES

Tamsin Egerton
ACTRESS

VENUES

My ideal party guest list would include anyone who's witty, amusing and a good conversationalist. I'd have Jeremy Clarkson beause I think he'd be amusing, and Stephen Fry. Patrick Swayze, who I worked with a couple of years back, would be good fun too. I think the bigger the age range and the more diverse the people, the better.
The best party I've been to recently was the Moët & Chandon party for Fashion Week. They turned a garden into an old-fashioned fairground with a carousel, candyfloss and pancakes. The trees were spray-painted gold and there were twinkling lights everywhere. It was beautiful.
The perfect summer party outfit is a floaty Alexander McQueen dress with some strappy heels and a pashmina.
I'd never go to a party without a gift for the host – maybe a nice bottle of wine. I think it's only polite, if someone's made the effort to entertain you for an evening.
In summer, I always drink Pimm's. It's such a perfect drink in hot weather. And I went to Cuba recently, so mojitos always bring back good memories.
My dream party venue is Kensington Palace. I was invited to a drinks party there recently. It would be a fantastic place to invite lots of friends.
My party piece is going backwards into a crab and then standing up again. It's not the most lady-like thing, so I don't tend to do it very often.
My favourite person to party with is my best friend, Talulah Riley. When you're with your closest friends you know you can be as silly as you like and they won't judge you.
Tamsin Egerton played Chelsea in the recent adaptation of *St. Trinian's*.

This church dates right back to 1101, with the current buildings built in 1734. As a result it has a charmingly worn, historical feel, rare for somewhere so central. It's well positioned for public transport too – only a stone's throw away from Centre Point and Tottenham Court Road tube, which means the lack of local parking isn't too much of an issue. The church's outhouse holds 50 or so people for occasional restrained celebrations and events. It would be great for a family-focused afternoon tea party, for example. Crucially, the garden, shaded by large trees, is big enough to accommodate a marquee, extending the venue's capacity significantly. The main drawback is the curfew: events here need to be finished by 9pm.
Outside space: garden.

Serpentine Lido
Hyde Park, W2 2UH (7706 3422/www. serpentinelido.com). Hyde Park Corner, Lancaster Gate or Marble Arch tube. **Available for hire** 6pm-midnight daily. **Capacity** 200 standing. **Hire charge** from £750; special rates for charities available. Lido
For review, *see p61.*
Catering: in-house. Outside space: poolside terrace; park (for hire).

Wallace Collection
Hertford House, Manchester Square, W1U 3BN (7563 9545/9507/www.wallace collection.org). Bond Street tube. **Available for hire** 6.30pm-11pm daily. **Capacity** *Courtyard* 160 seated/300 standing. *Great gallery* 120 seated. *State room* 40 seated. *Drawing room* 150 standing. *Main galleries* 400 standing. **Hire charge** £6,000-£15,000 + VAT. Gallery Home to 18th-century French paintings and armoury dating as far back as the 10th century, Hertford House is a national museum boasting the lavishness of a baronet's estate. Sir Richard Wallace's collection can be viewed privately during a wedding reception or sit-down dinner, but don't get too comfortable under the warm beam of those gold and crystal chandeliers; receptions are given a time slot of only three hours. Still, the courtyard provides a classy, modern backdrop – it has a retractable glass roof so it's great for evening parties requiring a summery vibe. Various private rooms can accommodate sophisticated dinners for groups of up to 40 too. Corporate and monied clients are the mainstay (it's a swanky venue and the prices reflect this) but it's worth noting that a ten per cent discount is available for registered charities.
Catering: preferred caterer list. Disabled: lift, toilet. Music: no amplified music in Galleries. Outside space: courtyard (for hire).

Westminster Boating Base

136 Grosvenor Road, SW1V 3JY (7821 7389/ www.westminsterboatingbase.co.uk). Pimlico tube. **Available for hire** *9am-midnight daily.* **Capacity** *Venue 150 seated/250 standing.* **Hire charge** call for details. **No credit cards.** Sailing club/charitable trust

Fancy an airy riverside breeze and a lovely garden setting for your party? Then this might just float your boat. Set in the pretty Pimlico Gardens (perfect for wedding photos if that's the kind of bash you're having), this has floor-to-ceiling windows that provide views of the Thames guaranteed to stun your guests. The venue's set-up means it can offer a mix of atmospheres across different spaces – while some let their hair down on the dancefloor in the Edgson room (which has its own covered balcony), others can take in the sights and quietly get to know their fellow guests without being disturbed by thumping bass. The hire fee goes directly to the charitable trust based here, which teaches young people and adults to sail, canoe and kayak. *Catering: in-house; kitchen facilities. Music: DJ equipment. Outside space: balcony; terrace (for hire).*

NORTH

At Proud

Stables Market, Chalk Farm Road, NW1 8AH (7482 3867/www.atproud.net). Camden Town or Chalk Farm tube. **Available for hire** *11am-1am Mon-Wed; 11am-2am Thur-Sat; 11am-midnight Sun.* **Capacity** *Venue 700 standing. Private rooms 3. Gig room 360 standing. Stables 300 standing. South gallery 60 standing.* **Minimum spend** *Venue £5,000. Gig room free-£50,000. South gallery free-£7,500. Stables free-£1,000.* Bar/gallery

If you poke your head around the vibrant fabrics and exotic fragrances of Stables Market, you'll spot the 200-year-old Horse Hospital nestling at the back. The antiquated building is infused with the very contemporary design that coats At Proud's nooks and crannies. Green-spotted leopards freeze in mid leap around the converted stables, each box area a cluttered yet comfortable cushioned hub. There are three areas available for hire, but they don't come cheap. The entire venue could burn a £100,000 hole in your wallet. However, seasonal offers (for most of summer 2008 stables could be reserved free with no minimum spend) mean you could bag yourself a bargain. We love the south gallery: with its exposed beams and white-washed walls, it's fitting for any chic celebration. *Catering: preferred caterer list. Disabled: toilet. Music: DJ equipment; MP3 port. Outside space: terrace (for hire).*

Frederick's

Camden Passage, N1 8EG (7359 3902/ www.fredericks.co.uk). Angel tube. **Available for hire** *noon-2.30pm, 5.45pm-midnight daily.* **Capacity** *Venue 120 seated/250 standing. Private rooms 3: 32-80 seated/45-100 standing.* **Minimum spend** *Venue £4,500.* Restaurant

VENUES

Say it loud. **At Proud** has some amazing seasonal offers.

CONSERVATORY

Ransome's Dock is a curious modern development; and we expected not to warm to this rooftop atrium. But the space is immediately beguiling; the spectacular spiral staircase leads to a conservatory that is not stark but verdant, with Victorian arches, bamboo furniture, classical statues and towering plants. By day, it makes an atmospheric business setting to impress out-of-town clients; the roof terrace has spectacular views across South London, especially at sunset. In the evening, the candlelit ambience make it a romantic choice for a wedding reception, cocktail party or fancy private dinner. We recommend you use the in-house catering team which can create anything from a bespoke finger-food menu to an inventive three-course meal. Note that any music has to be approved by management, the subtext being: this is a classy place so not right for partying into the small hours, repetitive beats or drunken high jinks. *For listings, see p66.*

With its airy and atmospheric Garden room (complete with fabulous vaulted glass ceiling), patio and garden area, Frederick's makes a fantastic summer party venue. The entire space is available to hire – as is a lovely private dining room for smaller events – and the relaxed, civilsed vibe is totally infectious. It's ideal for sophisticated dos (note: loud music is a no-no in the Garden room) such as weddings, anniversaries and special birthdays. Management are happy to clear out the tables for stand-up shindigs, but choosing this option would mean missing out on indulging in one of the impressive bespoke party menus. The food here is too good to miss out on – go for a sit-down dinner, we say.
Catering: in-house. Outside: garden (for hire).

Pineapple

51 Leverton Street, NW5 2NX (7284 4631). Kentish Town tube/rail. **Available for hire** *noon-11pm Mon-Sat; noon-10.30pm Sun.* **Capacity** *Conservatory* 30 seated/50 standing. **Minimum spend** Call for details. Pub
The Pineapple used to have a wonderfully anarchic feel; particularly if you were lucky enough to end up at one of the hedonistic parties upstairs. Unfortunately, since the refurbishment, the function room is no more (plagued by noise complaints by neighbours). Instead the airy back-room conservatory can be used as a private space, and for a larger fee (and total privacy) you can hire the adjoining walled beer garden as well

– although you may have to fend off a few disgruntled pipe-smoking locals. Thai food has booze-soaking appeal, while a decent selection on tap (Hoegaarden, Leffe, Pedigree) should satisfy the needs of most beer fans. A good choice summer party option for those seeking a country pub ambience in the heart of Kentish Town.
Catering: in-house. Outside: garden (for hire).

EAST

All Hallows by the Tower

Byward Street, EC3R 5BJ (0845 618 7274/ www.beyondboyle.com). Tower Hill tube/ Fenchurch Street rail. **Available for hire** 10am-midnight daily. **Capacity** *Venue* 70 seated/120 standing. **Hire charge** £750 + VAT. Restaurant
The fact that the oldest church in the City adjoins the modern building acquired by the Beyond Boyle organisation for their first London venue is of particular relevance, because BB displays a certain missionary zeal in its dealings with corporate and media clients. Simon Boyle, founder of the company, believes in 'bringing people together over food'. His food-based team-building, conference and party experiences, tailor-made for clients, are also training opportunities for homeless and vulnerable people in the local community. A grassy outdoor space allows for summer barbecue parties and spillover from the modern, glass-and-chrome space by the Tower of

London. The company's working relationship with the church means that an area near the north aisle of the ancient building, with its sculptures and famous monuments, as well as an atmospheric upstairs board room, can also be hired.
Catering: in-house. Disabled: toilet. Music: MP3 port. Outside space: garden (for hire).

Club Aquarium
256-264 Old Street, EC1V 9DD (7253 3558/ 07838 360990/www.clubaquarium.co.uk). Old Street tube/rail. **Available for hire** 9am-3am Mon-Wed; Thur 9am-Mon 3am 24hrs. **Capacity** 550 standing. **Minimum spend** £2,000 Mon-Wed; Thur-Sun call for details. Nightclub
For review, *see p61.*
Big screen. Catering: in-house. Music: DJ equipment; MP3 port. Pool & Jacuzzi (for hire).

Corbet Place
The Old Truman Brewery, 15 Hanbury Street, E1 6QR (7770 6028). Liverpool Street tube/ rail. **Available for hire** 10am-11pm Mon-Wed; 10am-5pm Thur, Fri. **Capacity** *Venue* 300 standing. **Hire charge** from £150/hr. **Minimum spend** £700. Bar
Hidden behind two large wooden doors, this excellently located warehouse conversion is surprisingly large inside. A dancefloor, long bar and sofas arranged around individual coffee tables, striking antler chandeliers, a retro stamp

vending machine and a pond leading from the venue into the conservatory all feature – in fact, there are innumerable quirks to this characterful space. Size-wise it's perfect for a large party of any persuasion, though the early closing time might put some off. The outside space and relaxed feel make it perfect for summery sessions – a barbecue is possible on the decked area at the front. And you can always carry on down Brick Lane until the wee hours.
Disabled: toilet. Music: DJ equipment; MP3 port. Outside space: garden; terrace (for hire). Projector.

Little Ship Club
Bell Wharf Lane, Upper Thames Street, EC4R 3TB (7251 7171/www.littleshipclub.co.uk). Mansion House tube/Bank tube/DLR. **Available for hire** *Club/dining room* 6-11pm daily. *Private rooms* 8am-11pm. **Capacity** *Club room* 120 standing. *Dining room* 120 seated/ 150 standing. *Private rooms* 8-50 seated/70 standing. **Hire charge** *Club room* £450 +VAT. *Dining room* £450 +VAT. **Minimum spend** £24/person + VAT. Sailing club
Just a few steps from the heart of the City, the LSC has a superb riverside location – and plenty of sailing history and tradition to add a touch of watery character to your party. The largest space for hire is the dining room (up to 250 guests can be catered for if you join this with the Club room), which boasts large windows overlooking the

Paradise By Way of Kensal Green. See p69.

Thames and great views of Southwark Bridge. It makes a great party space whatever the weather but for a summer celebration we recommend checking out the Club room, which has large windows and doors that can be opened to allow access to the Thames Path. Food is provided by preferred caterer Chester Boyd – an array of menus from formal sit-down meals to buffets and canapés are on offer.

Catering: in-house. Licence extension possible. Outside space: terrace (Club room access).

SOUTH

Brockwell Lido

Brockwell Park, Dulwich Road, SE24 0PA (7274 3088/www.brockwelllido.com). Brixton tube. **Available for hire** *6.30am-8pm Mon-Fri; 8am-10.30pm Sat, Sun.* **Capacity** *400 standing.* **Hire charge** *from £750/hr.* Lido For review, *see p61.*
Catering: in-house. Outside space: poolside terrace (for hire).

Conservatory

Ransome's Dock, 35-37 Parkgate Road, SW11 4NP (3265 0115/www.theconservatoryvenue. co.uk). Bus 49, 170, 319, 345. **Available for hire** *9am-1am daily.* **Capacity** *Venue 50 seated/120 standing.* **Hire charge** *Venue £200/hr.* Conservatory

For review, *see p64.*
Catering: kitchen facilities. Outside space: terrace (for hire).

The Deck

National Theatre, South Bank, SE1 9PX (7452 3796/www.nationaltheatre.org.uk/thedeck). Waterloo tube/rail. **Available for hire** *Apr-Oct 9am-midnight daily.* **Capacity** *120 standing.*
Hire charge *from £2,000 + VAT.* Bar
This flatpack venue above the National Theatre proved the hottest party destination in town in summer 2008 (get straight on the phone if you want to secure a summer 2009 booking). Check out its perfect location, between the cultural triumvirate of the Oxo tower, BFI Southbank and Somerset House, and it's easy to see why. Outside decking makes it ideal for a relaxed summer barbecue, while the in-house sound and lighting team from the National Theatre guarantee a fantastically customisable space. The opaque panelled walls and ceiling can be lit in a range of different colours, and a wash of light can change the floor's hue if required. Speakers line the outdoor terrace and DJs can play inside, although it's not a venue that suits dancing or loud music. Still, as this is one of the prettiest places in the capital to take in a relaxing day's sunshine, it hardly matters.
Big screen. Catering: in-house. Disabled: lift; toilet. Licence extension possible. Music: MP3 port. Outside space: terrace.

Hampton Pool

High Street, Hampton, Middx TW12 2ST (8255 1116/www.hamptonpool.co.uk). Hampton rail. **Available for hire** *Summer* 5-7pm Tue; 5.30pm-midnight Sat. *Winter* call for details. **Capacity** 600. **Hire charge** from £650. Pool For review, *see p61.*
Catering: in-house. Disabled: toilet. Outside space: poolside terrace; picnic area.

North Pole

131 Greenwich High Road, SE10 8JA (8853 3020/www.northpolegreenwich.com). Greenwich DLR/rail. **Available for hire** *Club* noon-midnight Mon, Tue, Sun. *Garden* noon-11pm daily. *Restaurant* noon-midnight Mon-Thur, Sun; noon-1am Fri,Sat. *VIP room* noon-midnight Mon-Wed, Sun; noon-1am Thur; noon-2am Fri, Sat. **Capacity** *Venue* 148 seated/235 standing. *Private rooms* 5: 25-83 seated/25-90 standing. **Minimum spend** *Club* £500. *Garden* call for prices. *Restaurant* £1,000. *VIP room* free (cancellation fee applies).
Restaurant/bar
Tucked away and surprisingly suave, North Pole does party glam with style. The downstairs (South Pole) club is antarctically cool, with curvy sofas, smooth moulding and atmospheric lighting; it's pumping sub-woofers are also handily DJ-friendly. For a small but funky get together, or an elitist staging post for a party downstairs, look no further than the ground-floor VIP area – surely the best combination of wood and cowhide this side of the Thames. Upstairs, the Piano restaurants Red and Green rooms provide a classier, more traditional take on the party venue, perfect for an intimate private dinner to remember. Think high, airy windows, curly architraves and pleasingly seamless service. A garden area for hire completes this venue's good all-rounder status and would be brilliant for a sunny evening do. *Big screen. Catering: in-house. Licence extension possible. Music: DJ equipment, MP3 port. Outside: garden (for hire), terrace.*

Princess of Wales

1A Montpelier Row, SE3 0RL (8852 5784/ www.princessofwalespub.co.uk). Blackheath rail. **Available for hire** noon-11pm daily. **Capacity** *Conservatory* 45 seated/75 standing. *Garden* 200 standing. **Minimum spend** *Conservatory* from £150. *Garden* from £1,000. Gastropub
This large Victorian boozer – all dark wood and heavy lampshades – commands a wonderful vantage point, with a terrace overlooking the wide open spaces of Blackheath. At the back, a large, light conservatory and intimate paved garden make it a perfect summer party venue too. It's

impressively versatile: the conservatory can accommodate more formal sit-down affairs, with a menu offering the usual gastropub staples, while in fine weather, the garden comes into its own – it's just the place for a celebratory barbecue. There's another area inside, the Snug, that's also available for hire. Look no further than the leather armchairs and rugby memorabilia in here if your sports club is planning an end-of-season awards do.
Catering: in-house. Disabled: toilet. Licence extension available (conservatory). Music: DJ equipment. Outside space: garden (for hire).

Richmond Pools on the Park

Old Deer Park, Richmond, Surrey TW9 2SF (8940 0561/www.springhealth.net). Richmond tube/rail. **Available for hire** 7.30pm-1am daily. **Capacity** *Venue* up to 500 (with marquee up to 3,000). **Hire charge** *Venue* approx £5,500 (inc DJ, staff), call for further details. Pool For review, *see p61.*
Catering: in-house. Disabled: toilet. Licence extension possible. Outside space: grounds; poolside terrace (for hire).

Westbridge

74-76 Battersea Bridge Road, SW11 3AG (7228 6482/www.thewestbridge.co.uk). Bus 19, 49, 239, 319, 345. **Available for hire** 9am-1am daily. **Capacity** *Private rooms* 2: 14-40 seated/60-80 standing. **Hire charge** free. Gastropub
A beautifully updated pub, the Westbridge has two great upstairs rooms for hire. The smaller Cabinet room is great for a sit-down dinner and

---

PLAYLIST

FESTIVAL VIBES FOR SUNNY DAYS
FrankMusik, www.myspace.com/
frankmusik

- Everybody Loves the Sunshine – Roy Ayers
- Summer Madness – Kool and the Gang
- Gabriel – Roy Davis Junior
- Expansions – Lonnie Liston Smith
- What a Fool Believes – Doobie Brothers
- Yah Mo B There – James Ingram
- My Feeling – Junior Jack
- Summer in the City – Quincy Jones
- Sultans Of Swing – Dire Straits
- Anything by Kenny Loggins

suits civilised gatherings such as wedding receptions or christening parties. Next door, however, is a totally different affair. The Bridge bar is sumptuously opulent, dimly lit by red-shaded lamps and boasts its own very well-stocked bar: hundreds of bottles glimmer in the half light. A set of decks is available for hire, or you can simply opt to plug in an iPod. There is direct access to the lovely garden (so summer dos are a must) and a stage should you want to do the 'Locomotion' accompanied by your mate's band. For a big bash you could even combine the two spaces. Whatever you choose, this is a fine place to raise a glass to anything.
Big screen (cabinet room). Catering: in-house. Music: MP3 port. Outside space: garden.

WEST

Aragon House
247 New King's Road, SW6 4XG (7731 7313/ www.aragonhouse.net). Parsons Green tube. **Available for hire** *House & basement bar* 9am-11pm Mon-Sat. *Ted Bentley bar* 9am-midnight Mon-Sat. **Capacity** *House* 100 seated/250 standing. *Basement bar* 80 standing. *Ted Bentley bar* 100 seated/200 standing. **Hire charge** *Basement bar* from £125. *Ted Bentley bar* from £400. **Minimum spend** *House*

£8,000. *Basement bar* £1,000. *Ted Bentley Bar* £4,000. All prices + VAT. Bar
For review, *see below.*
Catering: in-house. Licence extension possible. Music: MP3 port. Projector (Ted Bentley bar). Outside space: garden.

Grand Union
45 Woodfield Road, W9 2BA (7286 1886) Westbourne Park tube. **Available for hire** noon-11pm Mon-Thur; noon-midnight Fri, Sat; noon-10.30pm Sun. **Capacity** *Private room* 60 standing. **Minimum spend** call for details, minimum 20. Pub
Less flashy than the Metropolitan nearby, the Grand Union has nevertheless stayed in with the in crowd. At weekends you'll find the bohemian Notting Hillbilly overspill chattering away in large well-groomed groups, but there's no attitude here. Just as well, as if you hire the downstairs room you may have to share the outside canal-side space. For a price though it can all be yours; and there's no better spot to tuck into a jug of Pimm's or the pub's renowned barbecue grill in the summer. Just make sure you squint your eyes to obscure the bus depot opposite. As the night draws in you can retire into your snug hire space, which has its own bar and selection of board games. Great for a low-key summer celebration. Parties can be catered for on request.

ARAGON HOUSE

This discreetly located, posh period house/ bar offers the perfect venue for those looking for something elegant, extravagant and off the beaten track. The whole shebang, including the lovely garden, can be hired for a big, landmark celebration – think wedding receptions and big birthday dos. Alternatively, sofas, the basement bar (with access to a cute patio) and the private hire Ted Bentley bar are all up for grabs. An instant hit for sophisticated engagement and birthday dos, the Ted Bentley has an intimate and decadent feel with inky blue walls, plush carpets, dark leather furniture and chandeliers. The space also has a projector and big screen for films, and you can either use their in-house DJ or bring your own. The basement bar is great for an informal summery affair, but to make the most of the garden – and the venue's legendary barbecues – you need to think exclusive hire. There's an impressive canapé menu or, if you plump for the Ted Bentley, go for a buffet. But it's the capacity for music, dancing and good-natured debauchery that sets this place apart. *For listings, see above.*

Catering: in-house. Licence extension possible. Outside space: terrace (for hire).

London Rowing Club
Embankment, SW15 1LB (8788 1400/07976 671398/www.londonrc.org.uk). Putney Bridge tube/Putney rail. **Available for hire** 9am-11pm daily. **Capacity** *Long room* 100 seated/150 standing. *Members' room* 20 seated/40 standing. **Hire charge** *Long room* Mar-Sept £470-£1,200; Oct-Feb call for details. *Members' room* £300. Rowing club
Those seeking a party venue with a difference should head down the Thames to the London Rowing Club. With a balcony overlooking the start of the Boat Race at Putney Bridge, the main Long room can easily fit 100 revellers for a sit-down meal courtesy of the venue's recommended caterers – the club itself has space for some 250. Along with a fine chef, the LRC also has some decent contacts in the world of event styling, as images of wedding receptions past pay testament. The aforementioned balcony is great for barbecues and any kind of summer bash, while the rowing photographs on the main wall add an air of history to proceedings.
Catering: in-house. Disabled: lift; toilet. Outside space: balcony (long room & members' room have access).

Number Sixteen
16 Sumner Place, SW7 3EG (7287 4434/ www.firmdale.com). South Kensington tube. **Available for hire** 1-10pm daily. **Capacity** *Conservatory* 10 seated. *Conservatory & garden* 40 standing. **Hire charge** *Conservatory* £75/hr. *Conservatory & garden* £150/hr (both + VAT). Hotel
A tranquil conservatory stands small, tall and proud in the confines of this five-star hotel. An intimate sit-down dinner for ten can be served on dusky-brown tables (barbecue facilities also available), while tribal decorations give the place an earthy feel. Guests may spill out into the private garden (which can be hired in addition to the conservatory, but not on its own), where a fountain, camouflaged sculptures and white marble tables evoke a sense of English splendour. It's a popular venue for summery christenings and baby showers, possibly due to its natural ambience and canopy of trees, though party animals should note the garden closes at 10pm. Wedding ceremonies can also be held here.
Catering: in-house. Civil ceremony licence. Disabled: toilet. Outside space: garden (for hire).

Paradise By Way of Kensal Green
19 Kilburn Lane, W10 4AE (8969 0098/www. theparadise.co.uk). Kensal Green tube/Kensal

Rise rail. **Available for hire** noon-midnight Mon-Wed, Sun; noon-1am Thur; noon-2am Fri, Sat; noon-midnight Sun. **Capacity** *Reading room* 14 seated/40 standing. *Dining room* 20 seated/ 70 standing. *Music room* 50 seated/150 standing. **Minimum spend** *Music room* £3,000 Fri; call for details Mon-Thur, Sat, Sun. *Dining room* £1,000. *Reading room* £300. Gastropub
This killer party venue makes many a Notting Hill dweller wish they lived on the other side of the canal. With a choice of three distinct rooms, the Paradise suits both seasoned promoters and amateur hosts wanting to impress. Downstairs there's a book-lined dining room where the pub's 'host a roast' concept (the kitchen provide your roast of choice and you carve it up at the table) proves popular. For those seeking more privacy, upstairs boasts a private room, provocatively drenched in flocked purple wallpaper with brightly coloured chaise longues and sofas at one end. A door out onto a decking-clad roof terrace completes a very appealing picture. However, the pièce de resistance is the large Music room next door, with the same fun decor – deers' antlers, a stuffed peacock and a quirky lamp shade/chandelier centrepiece. It's large enough for a proper party and has a professional quality sound system, decks and a raised stage area.
Catering: in-house. Music: DJ equipment; MP3 port (Music room). Outside space: garden; terrace (private room has access).

Roof Gardens
99 Kensington High Street (entrance on Derry Street), W8 5SA (7937 7994/www.roof gardens.com). High Street Kensington tube. **Available for hire** 6pm-1.30am Mon-Thur, Sun; 8am-5pm Fri, Sat. **Capacity** 180 seated/500 standing. **Hire charge** £3,000. **Minimum spend** £2,000 day; £15,000 evening. Restaurant/bar
If your budget allows, this is an impressive, historic and slightly surreal venue for an unforgettable event. Nestled high above High Street Ken, guests can relax in the woodland, Tudor and Spanish gardens, and the space can also be dramatically transformed if you want to impose your own theme. Although a sit-down meal is possible, allowing guests to wander with canapés or barbecued nibbles gives them a chance to explore and take in the stunning surroundings, plus you can fit far more people in (up to 500). Just make sure you give clear instructions on how to get in – the entrance is easily overlooked at street level.
Catering: in-house; kitchen facilities (Sun). Disabled: lift; toilet. Licence extension possible. Music: DJ equipment; MP3 port. Outside space: garden (for hire).

Christmas

Mulled wine, tinsel, mistletoe and oranges speared with cloves; there's nothing like the onset of the Christmas season to get a person in the mood for some festive partying. Below you'll find a selection of venues that we think make the grade for seasonal shenanigans of the celebratory kind. All of them are, of course, suitable for other types of party too. It's also worth browsing through the other chapters in this book as many of the venues featured are great for Christmas parties too. In particular, check out Boisdale (*see p56*), Momo (*see p59*), Fox (*see p49*) and Silver Sturgeon (*see p95*).

CENTRAL

Albannach

66 Trafalgar Square, WC2N 5DS (7930 0066/www.albannach.co.uk). Charing Cross tube/rail. **Available for hire** *Venue noon-1am daily. Lower ground floor bar noon-3am daily.* **Capacity** *Venue 420 standing. Restaurant 50 seated. Dining room 20 seated. Bars 2: both 150 standing.* **Minimum spend** £35/person if dining.* Restaurant/bar
This haven to all things Scottish is surprisingly versatile and makes a cosy party venue for all sorts of occasions. Decorated in a tribute to a Highland hunting lodge, Albannach is popular for both corporate dos (there's a 50-inch plasma screen for presentations) and private social events such as wedding receptions, Christmas (it has a particularly festive feel) and birthday parties. On offer are four distinct areas: the main bar, the mezzanine dining level, a boardroom-style private dining room and an underground vaulted lounge bar called Doon (free to hire during the week with no minimum spend). Special set menus can be tailored to suit your event and start at £35 per head. The mezzanine level overlooks the main restaurant but still feels quite private. It's good for larger sit-down dinners or laid-back cocktails and canapés at the small tables. *Big screen (dining room & lower ground floor bar). Catering: in-house. Disabled: toilet (ground floor). Licence extension possible (venue). Music: DJ equipment (lower ground floor bar); MP3 port.*

Studio Valbonne. See p74.

Bam Bou

1 Percy Street, W1T 1DB (7323 9130/ www.bam-bou.co.uk). Tottenham Court Road tube. **Available for hire** *Private rooms* noon-3pm, 6pm-1am Mon-Fri; 6pm-1am Sat. *Red bar* 6pm-1am Mon-Wed, Fri. **Capacity** *1st floor* 35 seated. *Private rooms* 4: 9-20 seated. *Red bar* 60 standing. **Minimum spend** *1st floor* £1,800. *Private rooms* £300. *Red bar* £1,100. Restaurant/bar
This exotic hotspot, just off Tottenham Court Road, boasts scenery worthy of the 'Oscar for best cinematography', and does indeed offer its premises for filming. Warm colours emphasise the varied artwork on display, while small treasures including birdcages add quirky appeal. Private dining spaces are no side act for this upmarket venue: there are five areas ranging in size and mood. The stylish Ante room is a great space to gather friends for an indulgent anniversary celebration (the oriental food here is fabulous and the party menus are no exception), while the Red bar (no children allowed) has everything you need for a great gossip-over-canapés Christmas do. Another feature are the slanting stairs that add a touch of shambolic character to an otherwise opulent venue.
Catering: in-house. Music: MP3 port. Outside space: terrace.

De Hems

11 Macclesfield Street, W1D 5BW (7437 2494). Leicester Square or Piccadilly Circus. **Available for hire** 10am-midnight Mon-Sat;

noon-10.30pm Sun. *Private room* 80 seated/ standing. **Minimum spend** £500 Mon, Sun; £600 Tue; £1,000 Wed; £1,500 Thur; £2,000 Fri, Sat. Restaurant/bar

De Hems, located spitting distance from Chinatown, offers its upstairs level for private hire. It has a boisterous, lively feel that works well for stag/hen shenanigans, big birthday get-togethers and upbeat Christmas bashes. Originally an 'Oyster Bar', the walls are lined with 500,000 oyster shells, and the sizeable room has a relaxed, loungey feel. Food comes in the form of fuss-free buffets or you can order specific dishes off the main menu. With that sorted, all you have to do is turn up and make your acquaintance with the venue's excellent selection of Benelux beers. Music is controlled downstairs, with a DJ on Friday and Saturday nights. Note that while there is no designated dancefloor, you are welcome to shift the furniture around to create one. There's also a big screen TV available. Hire is restricted to groups of 40 or more – if your group is smaller consider hiring a few tables (they seat ten). Its central location means it's also a good vantage point for continuing into the night round Soho way. *Big screen. Catering: in-house.*

The Ivy

1 West Street, WC2H 9NQ (7307 5783/ 5784/www.the-ivy.co.uk). Covent Garden or Leicester Square tube. **Available for hire** 8-10.30am, noon-5pm, 6.30-midnight daily. *Private room* 60 seated/120 standing. **Minimum spend** £1,800-£4,500 + 15% service charge. Restaurant

Even in these days of smoking bans you'd swear the smoke lingers from Churchill's cigar, so old school is the green carpet, leather-backed chairs and oak panelling of London's most famous restaurant; but as the diamond stained-glass windows withstood the Blitz, the Ivy's private room withstands vogueish follies to deliver to a loyal crowd eschewing the celebrity-gawpers downstairs. A reception with bar, cloakroom and piano fronts a main dining area, where a choice of ten enticing set menus is offered, along with an atmosphere that'll make your guests feel right at home. This being Theatreland, live entertainment is de rigueur, and Esther Williams and her jazz trio are on hand with the classics (no dancing though). Beloved of gourmets and gourmands, the Ivy is perfect for sit-down feasts, book launches, wrap parties and swanky 60th

LIBERTY

Liberty, London's grandest department store, is an eccentric mishmash of traditional British design; from the tudor façade to the ornate wooden panelling and labyrinthine rooms. The beauty is in the detail; with fantastic in-house catering, florists and designers at its disposal, the events team can create the perfect bespoke event. A popular option is to have a cocktail party or private dinner on the fourth floor where guests can admire the intricate skylights and lounge on designer furniture. For a price, the whole store can be hired for private shopping events; DJs, bands and performers can also be installed. For those seeking something more intimate, try hiring the Heritage Suite, a mid-sized room with charming period features – drinks cabinets and a dressing room hidden behind panelling and ornate Georgian stained-glass windows. With a separate entrance, this is perfect for ladies seeking a discreet shopping experience, a high class 'hen afternoon', imaginative PR bashes or baby shower. This place is perfect for work events where somebody else is paying – Christmas at Liberty? Bring it on. And don't limit yourself to the options listed; consult the in-house events team who will help you pull off your dream party.
For listings, see p73.

celebrations. The private room really comes into its own for Christmas lunches, with a tree, classic greenery and traditional decorations.
Catering: in-house. Music: MP3 port.

Liberty

Regent Street, W1B 5AH (7734 1234/www. liberty.co.uk). Oxford Circus tube. **Available for hire** *Venue/personal shopping 6.30-11pm daily. Heritage suite 7am-11pm daily.* **Capacity** *Venue 500 standing. 4th floor 60 seated/500 standing. Personal shopping suite 35 seated. Heritage suite 20 seated/30 standing. Tea room 30 standing. Restaurant 60 seated/80 standing.* **Hire charge** *Venue £25,000. 4th floor £15,000. Personal shopping suite £5,500. Heritage suite £1,500.* Department store
For review, *see p72.*
Catering: in-house; kitchen facilities available. Disabled: lift; toilet. Licence extension possible.

Old Crown

33 New Oxford Street, WC1A 1BH (7836 9121/www.theoldcrownpublichouse.com). Holborn or Tottenham Court Road tube.

Available for hire 10am-midnight Mon-Wed, Sun; 10am-2am Thur-Sat. **Capacity** *Private rooms 2: 20-40 seated/40-90 standing.*
Minimum spend call for details. Pub
Not to be confused with the other Old Crown (a Sam Smith's pub) on New Oxford Street, this light-filled boozer is an excellent place to throw a party. There are two private spaces available: a lounge on the first floor and a larger function space on the second. Both areas are fantastically good-looking, with big windows, floorboards and a twinkly, shabby chic feel, and work well for leaving dos, birthday bashes and spectacular Christmas shindigs. Book the lounge for a smaller, more intimate do – it has an open fire, leather sofas and makes a fine spot for a laid-back meal or drinks and canapés. For a big bash (up to 90 people), the second floor is your best bet, with a private bar, its own lavatory, screening facilities and DJ equipment. Unpretentious canapés can be provided (bowls of olives and spiced broad beans, dim sum, falafels, mini chipolatas), as can three-course set menus. A fine choice.
Big screen (2nd floor room). Catering: in-house. Music: DJ equipment; MP3 port.

Only Running Footman

5 Charles Street, W1J 5DF (7499 2988/ www.therunningfootman.biz). Green Park tube. **Available for hire** *7.30am-11pm daily.* **Capacity** *Private rooms 2: 14-30 seated.* **Minimum spend** *Function room £1,000-£1,500. Chef's table £750.* Gastropub

This restored Mayfair town house offers intimate private dining opportunities and has the capacity to host small parties as well. The main private room, situated above the pub, is light and airy, with pale wood floors and exposed bricks creating a rustic feel. Three-course set menus start at £40 per person; canapés and buffet-style catering can also be arranged. A chef's table and private kitchen space, located in another private room, is also a popular option for parties. Here you can have one of the pub's chefs talk you through a five-course meal they'll then prepare in front of you – a great way to add an interactive twist to a Christmas or birthday gathering. Choose from six different chefs who each create their own signature menus.

Big screen (function room). Catering: in-house. Licence extension possible. Music: MP3 port.

Studio Valbonne

62 Kingly Street, W1B 5QN (7434 0888/ www.studiovalbonne.co.uk). Oxford Circus tube. **Available for hire** *10am-4am Mon-Sat; 10am-12.30am Sun.* **Capacity** *Venue 500 standing. Club 150 seated/420 standing. VIP room 35 seated/80 standing.* **Minimum spend** *Club £50/person (minimum 150); VIP room £50/person (minimum 30).* Nightclub

SECRET SANTA

A cheat's guide to getting the annual gift gamble right.

It's that time again. Yes, Christmas is around the corner and some bright spark in the office has suggested you all do a 'secret santa'. Chances are, you won't know the person you're buying for very well, which means that Christmas must become the season of pigeonholing people – into the one who never leaves her desk, he who fancies himself as the office funny-man, and that well-meaning person who nags everyone about recycling. And if it's the boss's name you pick out of the hat, tread very carefully by choosing a gift which demonstrates the appropriate deference...

The Boss

Around £5: 'Get to the Point' pencils, 60p, by Smart Women (www.tattydevine.com).
Around £10: Freshly made gourmet truffles from Paul A Young, at 33 Camden Passage, N1 8EA (7424 5750/www.payoung.net).

The New Girl

Around £5: London in a Bag by Muji, £5.95 (www.muji.co.uk).
Around £10: Mini bottle of Pommery Pop pink Champagne, £10.95 (www.thefinewinecompany.co.uk).

The Work Experience Boy

Around £5: Dr Who TARDIS keyring, £7.50 (www.marksandspencer.com).
Around £10: Sonic Grenade alarm clock, £9.95 (www.firebox.com).

The Office Fashionista

Around £5: Star print kirby hair clips, £6 (www.topshop.com).
Around £10: Ring keyring, £10.50 (www.grahamandgreen.co.uk)

The About-to-Retire Colleague

Around £5: Travel speakers, £5.95 (www.iwantoneofthose.com)
Around £10: 1955 Gadgets Annual, £10 (www.labourandwait.co.uk).

The Eco Warrior

Around £5: Metal-saving eco stapler, £5 (www.nhm.ac.uk).
Around £10: Plant a tree in a Devon wood (and receive a seed mat for planting), £12.50 (www.carbonneutral.com).

The Comedian

Around £5: Pick Your Nose Party Cups, £5.95 (www.iwantoneofthose.com).
Around £10: Deliverance-style false teeth (banjo music not included), £11.95 (www.comedy-zone.net).

The Workaholic

Around £5: Personalised photo mouse mat, £6.99 (www.snapfish.co.uk).
Around £10: USB port massager, £10.99 (www.gadgetsquick.co.uk).

VENUES

The best family restaurant in London

SAGAR

BEST VEGETARIAN RESTAURANT

www.gosagar.com

'One of the Best South Indian Vegetarian Restaurants in London'
- **Time Out**

Time Out's Top 50 places you must eat before you leave London.
- **January 2008**

Sagar Hammersmith
157 King Street
Hammersmith
London W6 9JT

Reservations:

020 8741 8563

Sagar West End
17A Percy Street,
off Tottenham Court Road
London W1T 1DU

Reservations:

020 7631 3319

Sagar Twickenham
27 York Street
Twickenham
London TW1 3JZ

Reservations:

020 8744 3868

NEW

New to Percy Street

* Private room for parties.
* We cater for Weddings, Christmas Parties & **Family Parties.**

Please call Percy Street below for details.

After two decades, the Valbonne – nightclub to the stars of the '80s, including Madonna, George Michael and Boy George – has been gorgeously revamped and now includes a classy restaurant/bar. It also boasts a VIP room, and a dancefloor surrounded by velvety booth seating – perfect for lounging on after a particularly hectic strut. Christmas parties can be tailor-made to your unique specifications – Moulin Rouge, pearls and diamonds, winter wonderland, to name but a few, but this venue would also be great for a special birthday or big corporate event.
Big screen. Catering: in-house. Music: DJ equipment; MP3 port.

NORTH

Dartmouth Arms

35 York Rise, NW5 1SP (7485 3267/www. dartmoutharms.co.uk). Tufnell Park tube/ Gospel Oak rail. **Available for hire** 11am-11pm Mon-Fri; 10am-11pm Sat, Sun. **Capacity** *Private room* 60 seated/85 standing. **Hire charge** £20 Mon-Thur, Sun; £50 Fri, Sat. Gastropub

Tucked away in a leafy Dartmouth Park side street, the Dartmouth Arms oozes a mellow charm. The decor is understated – wood panels and faded crimson wallpaper – and the books on the shelves are reassuringly well-thumbed. The back dining room can be hired as a private space that can come with a well-selected sit-down set

menu (try the speciality 21-day organic steak) or a variety of canapé choices ranging from £5 to £14 a head. The room is best suited to private dining but with its high ceilings and roof atrium it feels large enough for a more ambitious party (the gentrified locals have taken to hosting wine tasting evenings here). The helpful staff are open to requests and redecoration, so long as you bring the props yourself.
Catering: in-house.

Island Queen

87 Noel Road, N1 8HD (7354 8741). Angel tube. **Available for hire** noon-11pm Mon, Sun; noon-11.30pm Tue, Wed; noon-midnight Thur-Sat. *Private room* 45 seated/60 standing. **Hire charge** free. Pub

Far from the madding Islington crowds, the ivy-clad Island Queen is a dapper Victorian pub redolent with intimations of faded grandeur, from the huge floor-to-ceiling windows and splendid horseshoe bar to the intricately painted wall mirrors. The function room upstairs, however, is rather less grand and more like something you'd find in a Working Men's Club; clean, functional, with lino flooring and a pool table in one corner. There's no separate bar but the room is free to hire and lends itself to all kinds of creative possibilities; a boisterous Christmas quiz night, a book club gathering, pool tournament or even a meeting of minds for an 'overthrow Boris' revolution? Either way, this is a fine place.
Catering: in-house. Pool table.

Positively 4th Street

119 Hampstead Road, NW1 3EE (7388 5380/www.positively4thstreet.co.uk). Warren Street tube/Euston tube/rail. **Available for hire** 5-11pm Mon-Thur; 5pm-1am Fri; 7pm-1am Sat. **Capacity** 120. **Hire charge** £135. **Minimum spend** £1,500. Bar

While not located in the most salubrious of surroundings, Positively 4th Street is a gem among the NW1 high rises. Bathed in deep red decor, the bar immediately screams 'decadence' at the 120-odd people you'll cram into the basement and ground-floor bars. Bring your own decks to thump out the tunes or simply plug in the old iPod and hit shuffle. Perfect for off-kilter, bohemian gatherings, after-show gigs (there is a mic and projector) or a cool cat Christmas party, the key selling points are the unpretentious vibe, edgy feel and fantastic oriental canapés available for private parties. All this and it's just a swift five-minute walk from Warren Street tube – what more can you ask for? Note: a relaunch is currently being planned so get your booking in as soon as possible.
Catering: in-house. Music: MP3 port.

William IV

7 Shepherdess Walk, N1 7QE (3119 3012).
Old Street tube/rail. **Available for hire** noon-
11pm Mon-Wed; noon-midnight Thur-Sat;
noon-10.30pm Sun. **Capacity** *Private rooms*
2: 12-40 seated/70 standing. **Minimum
spend** £25/person. Gastropub
Upstairs at William IV continues the pub's ground-
floor theme of old English decadence with aplomb
– think stuffed birds in glass boxes, framed maps
of the old country and standard lamps casting a
warm glow over the dark wooden furniture (and
check out the owners' family pictures as you go
up the stairs). There are two separate rooms for
hire that together can host 100 for a party. A
waiter is included to keep the drinks topped up,
as there's no bar upstairs. The Geography room
– the larger of the two – has sash windows across
one wall and is sumptuously decorated in dark
green and cream. Next door, the classic private
dining room boasts black-and-white striped
wallpaper and a large round table. Carefully
chosen buffet food can be provided and both
rooms can also be used for exclusive dining.
William IV is perfect for Christmas gatherings –
enjoy the log fires and candlelit atmosphere. It's
also worth noting that the smaller private dining
room can be hired free of charge to diners.
*Catering: in-house. Licence extension
possible. Music: DJ equipment; MP3 port.*

EAST

Bar Kick

*127 Shoreditch High Street, E1 6JE (7739
8700/www.cafekick.co.uk). Liverpool Street
or Old Street tube/rail.* **Available for hire** noon-
midnight Mon-Thur; noon-11pm Sun. **Capacity**
Basement 80 seated/150 standing. **Hire
charge** Mon-Wed, Sun £200 + VAT. Thur
£350 + VAT. **Minimum spend** £2,000. Bar
The theme here is a winning one: table football,
flags of all nations and the essential plasma
screen make this venue a refined football haven
and perfect for laid-back affairs requiring an
injection of fun. The large basement bar is
regularly hired out for birthdays, Christmas and
office parties, and boasts comfy brown couches,
a cinema screen, spotlights and foosball tables
galore. DJ equipment is available but if you want
a DJ on the night you'll need to apply for a licence.
Mediterranean cuisine is created in an open
kitchen on the ground floor. The atmosphere is
contagiously chilled and evokes the exciting,
communal elements of a hip students' union. Get
the foosball rolling with Kick's prized mojitos.
*Big screen. Catering: in-house. Licence
extension possible. Music: MP3 port.*

Jem Frazer
PROFESSIONAL SANTA

**The best parties are at Christmas
because** it's the one time of year when
everyone is full of goodwill and trying to be
nice to each other. That's the best possible
starting point for having a good time.
**The most amazing party I've ever been
to** was for a businessman who flew us all
out to Monaco. He'd had a big marquee built
overlooking the bay and there was an ice bar
and a ship that came into the cove with
fireworks exploding off it. Jonathan Ross
compèred and Stevie Wonder sang.
The key to being a good Santa is never,
ever patronise the kids. Make them feel like
you're really interested in what they have to
say, and listen to them. You have to believe
in the act yourself, too – when I'm Father
Christmas, I truly become Father Christmas.
Some children truly believe I can bring
them the impossible. I've had kids who
think I'm going to bring them a sports car
or arrange a trip to a moon. But I never
tell them I can make their wish come true,
because it might not happen and you
don't want to disappoint a kid.
The hardest thing about being Santa
is the pushy parents who want to force their
children on you. Some kids just don't want
to go anywhere near a strange bearded man
and they'll be kicking and screaming, but the
parents will insist the child sits on my knee.
In this day and age, Santa needs
to make sure he's got security back-up.
When you're switching on the lights in a
town centre there's always one kid who
wants to pull Santa's beard off and post
the video on YouTube. Santa is a celebrity
and therefore he's a target.
Jem Frazer has been playing Santa for
20 years. www.contrabandevents.com

VENUES

FESTIVE FEASTS

For when quality turkey and a nice sit down is all you want out of the festive season. The below are also open for Christmas Day 2008.

Christmas Lunch Cruise
Westminster Pier, Victoria Embankment, SW1A 2JH (7740 0400/www.citycruises.com). Westminster tube.
For a refreshing change, enjoy a traditional Christmas lunch on the Thames with City Cruises. The 'RiverLiner' sets sail at 8pm during the festive season and 12.30pm on the day itself, offering a three-course traditional lunch on board. The cost? £72.50 a head, £92.50 on Christmas Day.

Devonshire
126 Devonshire Road, W4 2JJ (7592 7962/www.gordonramsay.com). Turnham Green tube.
This cosy Gordon Ramsay gastropub is a great option for Christmas lunch and perfect for a family get-together. The traditional British food won't disappoint either. Lunch with all the trimmings is priced at £65 per person for three courses. Finish off with coffee, mince pies and a feeling of festive joy.

Little Bay
171 Farringdon Road, EC1R 3AL (7278 1234/www.little-bay.co.uk/london.html). Farringdon tube/rail.
Got a big crowd to organise for *and* want to work within a tight budget? Then head for this popular Mediterranean eaterie in Farringdon (there are also branches in Battersea, Kilburn, Fulham and Croydon. For a frankly ridiculously low cost of £26 a five-course set menu is served from noon until 6pm in a cosy, quirky space with a wonderfully convivial atmosphere.

Narrow
44 Narrow Street, E14 8DP (7592 7950/ www.gordonramsay.com). Limehouse DLR.
Another Gordon Ramsay affair, Narrow makes a fine choice for festive dining. The atmosphere is warm and relaxed (there are fireplaces and armchairs) so it's as good for couples as it is for family, friends or even a bigger crowd. The private 'Captain's Table' room upstairs can seat up to 14 guests and drinks can be served in the room or at the bar. Past Christmassy delights have included chicken liver pâté with own-made piccalilli, braised root vegetable pie and mash and pear and cinnamon crumble in a three-course menu for £60 per person.

The Vine
86 Highgate Road, NW5 2PB (7209 0038/ www.thevinelondon.co.uk). Kentish Town tube/rail/Gospel Oak rail.
This laidback gastropub is perfect for a stress-free lunch – whether with chums, family, or the whole crew from work. You can book the entire place out (up to 200 people) or just an area – choose from the Moroccan, Paris, Media and Garden (covered) spaces or go for the cosy Fireside spot. The traditional turkey lunch (there's always a decent veggie option too) costs £50 for three courses (£20 for children).

Waterfront
Baltimore House, Juniper Drive, SW18 1TZ (7228 4297/www.waterfrontlondon.co.uk). Wandsworth Town rail/297 bus.
This classy looking riverside gastropub with huge outdoor terrace serves quality fare at reasonable prices. All tall windows, drapes, glass and sleek woods, Waterfront is happy to cater for up to 100 people with bespoke menus for canapés or a full sit-down, or you could simply book the Christmas lunch which is certain to be a hearty three-course menu (around £45), followed by petits fours and tea or coffee.

Winter Garden
Landmark Hotel, 222 Marylebone Road, NW1 6JQ (7631 8000/www.landmark london.co.uk). Marylebone tube/rail.
This is one cool venue. The striking restaurant stands at the base of the Landmark Hotel's glass-roofed atrium and, as well as music from a harp and piano, and a glass of Taittinger champage, you can dine on a five-course Christmas lunch or a four-course dinner for £165 and £100 a head respectively. Alternatively, you could book out one of the rooms (the ballroom is perfect for big dos) and create your own theme. Ice sculptures, a winter wonderland, a mock up of the *Titanic*? Let your imagination (and your wallet) run riot.

VENUES

Christ Church Spitalfields

VENUES

Cat & Mutton

76 Broadway Market, E8 4QJ (7254 5599). London Fields rail. **Available for hire** 6-11pm Mon; noon-11pm Tue-Thur, Sun; noon-1am Fri, Sat. **Capacity** *Private room* 40 seated/ 70 standing. **Hire charge** £150 Thur-Sat.
Gastropub

You'll bring the party to the party at this bustling gastro boozer next to London Fields. It's hardly ever empty, but you can escape up the iron, spiral staircase to the quaint function room for christenings, birthdays, wedding celebrations or anything else you care to raise a glass to. You'll need to book well in advance for a Christmas lunch or dinner as it's a popular local choice. Known for their rustic twist on contemporary pub fare (although the service is just as famous for being a bit flaky), the chef can also conjure magnificent buffet nibbles at the drop of a hat. DJ decks are available (Disco Bloodbath DJs spin here at weekends) but live music isn't allowed, so you'll have to kick that karaoke session out to the overcrowded kerb.
Big screen. Catering: in-house. Disabled: toilet. Music: DJ equipment; MP3 port.

Christ Church Spitalfields

Commercial Street, E1 6QE (7377 2440/ www.spitalfieldsvenue.org). Aldgate East tube/Liverpool Street tube/rail. **Available for hire** 9.30am-11.30pm Mon, Wed-Sat; 4-11.30pm Tue. **Capacity** 300 seated/600 standing. **Hire charge** £5,500 (50% discount for charities; performance and community rates also available). **No credit cards**. Church

For a truly spectacular event, this beautifully restored church takes some beating. It was designed by Nicholas Hawksmoor between 1714 and 1729 as one of a planned 50 new churches in what was then the outskirts of London. There's ample outside space available under the portico and next to the church, and the stunning vestibule (use it for cloakroom facilities or receiving guests) makes all the right first impressions. The nave itself has high ceilings, dramatic pillars, stone floors, chandeliers and oak-panelling – all this before you even start setting about dressing the venue to suit your specific event. We think it'd be fabulous for a grand-scale festive lunch or dinner (think mulled wine under the portico), but it also

NOTE

ULTIMATE MULLED WINE
- 600ml or 1 pint orange juice
- 300ml or 1/2 pint water
- 3 cinnamon sticks
- 6 cloves
- 60g dark muscovado sugar
- 1 orange (sliced)
- 1 lemon (sliced)
- 1 star anise
- 1 ltr or 1 3/4 pint red wine
- 300ml or 1/2 pint brandy or
  fruit liqueur.
Heat gently until hot. Don't boil
(the alcohol evaporates). Remove
from heat. You can keep adding all
or some of the ingredients as you go.

has the size and drama required for a truly fabulous wedding reception or corporate bash. Charity discounts are available.
Catering: preferred caterer list. Civil ceremony licence. Disabled: toilet. Outside space: portico (for hire).

Lowlander Grand Café
18-20 Creechurch Lane, EC3A 5AY (7623 8813/www.lowlander.com). Aldgate or Bank tube/Liverpool Street tube/rail. **Available for hire** *Venue noon-midnight Sat, Sun. Basement noon-midnight daily.* **Capacity** *Venue 200 seated/400 standing. Basement 60 seated/100 standing.* **Minimum spend** call for details. Bar
The basement bar at this clean-cut Belgian/Dutch style café – all warm polished woods and retro beer posters – is well set up for City grafters seeking a pint worth savouring. Lowlander's adventurous range of 16 speciality draughts and 50 bottles – including the much treasured Trappist Westmalle Dubbell – is guaranteed to put even a Leffe in its place. Ask for a 'Samples Tray' – three or six smaller measures of any draught. And for non-beer drinkers in your party, Lowlander guarantees to help find a beer they'll like (or offer you something else). The friendly management specialise in a range of 'Beer Degustation' events – boozy fun for a leaving do or Christmas party – and the emphasis on quality extends to the cuisine, where top chefs prepare anything from platters of Belgian charcuterie and cheeses to five-course feasts, each with a complementary brew. Free hire, DJ decks and an LCD screen for sporting events are added bonuses.
Big screen. Catering: in-house. Disabled: toilet (ground floor). Music: DJ equipment. MP3 port.

NOTE

HALLOWEEN PARTIES
A haunted pub should fit the bill. Both Soho's John Snow (39 Broadwick Street, W1F 9QP; 7437 1344) and Hampstead's Spaniards Inn (Spaniards Road, NW3 7JJ; 8731 6571) have suitably spooky presences (a 19th-century cholera victim and Dick Turpin respectively). Both also have function rooms (120 for John Snow and 50 for the Spaniards). Alternatively, the Old Operating Theatre Museum and Herb Garret (9a St Thomas Street, SE1 9RY; 7188 2679) is available for private hire, conjuring freaky mental images of horrors past in its operating theatre.

L'Oasis
237 Mile End Road, E1 4AA (7702 7051/ www.loasisstepney.co.uk). Stepney Green tube. **Available for hire** noon-11pm Tue-Sat; noon-10.30pm Sun. **Capacity** *Private room 30 seated/40 standing.* **Hire charge** £75 (room only). Bar
This far up the Mile End Road you might expect to find the party venue bar set rather low, but L'Oasis is an unexpectedly fine space for celebrating in style. Upstairs you'll find a smart, well-decorated room in which the very friendly, very flexible management will let you do, well, almost anything you want. That makes it a great place for a quirky club meeting or a cosy Christmas do. There's art for sale on the walls (a different exhibition every month), a large screen and an HD projector for film clubs, or presentations, or even just showing off your holiday pics to their best potential. There's good food, good beer, and as long as your party indulges in some of it and treats the place well, they won't charge you for the room. Perfect.
Catering: in-house.

Old Gringo
8 Tysoe Street, EC1R 4RQ (7278 7678/ www.clerkenwellbar.com). Angel tube/ Farringdon tube/rail. **Capacity** *Venue 100 standing. Private room 15 seated/26 standing. Private area 80 standing.* **Hire charge** *Private room £80.* **Minimum spend** call for details. *Venue £250 deposit.* Bar
The Mexican/Brazilian themed Old Gringo has risen from the ashes of this venue's previous incarnation – dim sum joint the Old China Hand – but is still a great place for an alternative Christmas event. The decor has been suitably tweaked (there's a subtle South American vibe) and a crop of Mexican lagers and South American wines add to the Latin flavour. Up to 100 people can be catered for here and best of all, there's no hire charge. The entire ground floor can be reserved for larger gatherings, while more intimate get-togethers can be held at the back of the bar in the skylight room; there is also an upstairs room (up to 26 people), which is ideal for karaoke parties (all the equipment hire can be arranged).
Big screen (venue). Catering: in-house. Music: MP3 port.

Prenelle Gallery
Dutch Barge Prins, West India Dock, off Hertsmere Road, E14 4AE (7093 0628/ 07779 724 636/www.prenelle.co.uk). West India Quay DLR. **Available for hire** 7am-midnight daily. **Capacity** 60 seated/110 standing. **Hire charge** £1,000. **No credit cards**. Gallery/boat

VENUES

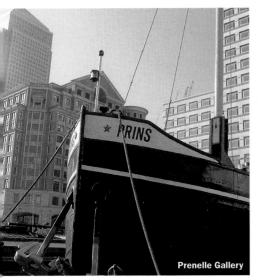

Prenelle Gallery

This attractive Dutch barge and gallery space moored in West India Quay makes a fabulously quirky venue for a party. Particularly popular for Christmas celebrations, on account of its pleasingly festive atmosphere, Prenelle's outdoor deck also means plenty of potential for summery fun. Assistance with catering, decorations and the like can be provided if you so desire, and screening equipment is also available. Book early for the Christmas season as it's a popular choice for seasonal festivities in these parts.
Catering: kitchen facilities.

Three Kings of Clerkenwell
7 Clerkenwell Close, EC1R 0DY (7253 0483). Farringdon tube/rail. **Available for hire** noon-11pm daily. **Capacity** *Venue* 150 standing. *Private rooms* 2: 20-30 standing. **Hire charge** *Venue* £500. *Private rooms* call for details. Pub
Rhino heads, Egyptian felines and Dennis Bergkamp may not be to everyone's taste but those looking for something a little less ordinary will appreciate the decorative backdrop of the Three Kings. Private parties can be held in the two small upstairs rooms (up to 50 guests), which have a laid-back vibe and an outstanding 7" jukebox, or these and the downstairs can be hired out for up to 150 people. Prices start from £500 (if you want the whole venue) depending on the night, numbers and rooms required, and parties can be catered for with substantial buffet or finger food. The Three Kings is perfect for a Christmas bash as, once the tables are pushed back, there's even a little space for groovers to ping around to the tunes of brought-in DJs or the jukebox.

Catering: in-house. Licence extension possible. Music: jukebox (private room); MP3 port.

Troxy
490 Commercial Road, EC1 0HX (7790 9000/www.troxy.co.uk). Limehouse DLR/rail. **Available for hire** noon-2am daily. **Capacity** *Venue* 2,600 seated/standing. *Private room* 200 seated/standing. **Hire charge** call for details. Cinema/theatre
The Clapham Grand meets Miami Beach circa 1924 in this vast, kaleidoscopic art deco venue. Built in 1933 as a cinema, and used variously as a practice facility for the Royal Opera and a Mecca Bingo hall, this huge space retains its original, wonderfully kitsch decor and provides one of the largest, most flexible venues in London. Grade II-listed, but run with modern efficiency by a hugely helpful, client-friendly management, Troxy is perfect for all large events on a small budget: Christmas parties, concerts, club nights, corporate events, exhibitions, conferences and award ceremonies. Caterers, AV companies and the like can all be recommended, and there are numerous dressing rooms and a backstage area, including the White room VIP area, a bling-tastic marble-floored room with flat-screen TVs.
Catering: preferred caterer list; kitchen facilities. Disabled: toilet. Licence extension available. Music: DJ equipment; MP3 port. Projector.

SOUTH

Boot & Flogger
10-20 Redcross Way, SE1 1TA (7407 1184). Borough tube. **Available for hire** 11am-8pm Mon-Fri. **Capacity** *Private rooms* 2: 6-8 seated. **Hire charge** free. Wine bar
This marvellously Dickensian wine bar has a loyal clientele and a small private room (seats eight) hireable throughout the year for lunches, meetings and evening dos. Advance booking for Christmas is essential as those who hire it usually re-book for the following year so, barring a death (and as the average punter is way over 21, a clog-popping is always possible) it's often booked solid. There is a also a smaller glass enclosed space (the 'office') within the bar seating four to six people. Friendly waitress service and a small outside courtyard for smokers are a big draw. Average prices charged for the traditional British fare (think potted shrimps, roast beef, treacle tart) are around £25 per head, excluding wine (house wines start at £13.80). This is a wonderful old-school establishment perfect for small, sedate

Garrison

gatherings and annual reunions, meetings, post-work drinks or a boozy Christmas lunch, but remember, it does close at 8pm.
Catering: in-house. No amplified music. Outside space: courtyard.

Garrison

99-101 Bermondsey Street, SE1 3XB (7367 6351/www.thegarrison.co.uk). London Bridge tube/rail. **Available for hire** 8am-11pm Mon-Fri; 9am-11pm Sat; 9am-10.30pm Sun. **Capacity** *Private room* 25 seated/30 standing. **Hire charge** £50 Mon-Wed; £100 Thur-Sun.
Gastropub
The basement of this Bermondsey gastropub is home to a spot-on intimate party venue. Low lighting, vintage lampshades and battered sofas provide a boho backdrop for laid-back celebratory dinners or classy bashes of all varieties – we think it works fantastically for a birthday meal or anniversary do, while the subterranean setting feels cosily festive for Christmas events. Convivial banquette seating and long table set-ups ensure the space is suitable for large groups and the pub's culinary credentials (bistro-style meat and fish dishes, good veggie options) mean top-notch food is a given (the well-thought out set menus change seasonally). The room comes complete with a big screen (great for gathering a crowd for sporting events, films or the family camcorder archives), while an eclectic jukebox offers ample opportunity for an embarrassing post-dinner singalong. The room can be hired for drinks and canapés if a sit-down dinner doesn't appeal.
Big screen. Catering: in-house. Disabled: toilet. Music: jukebox.

Prince of Wales

138 Upper Richmond Road, SW15 2SP (8788 1552/www.princeofwalesputney.co.uk). East Putney tube/Putney rail. **Available for hire** noon-midnight daily. **Capacity** *Restaurant* 45 seated/60 standing. *Dining area* 30 seated/70 standing. **Minimum spend** call for details.
Gastropub
This bright and breezy gastropub pulls a sizeable crowd throughout the week. They're not just here for the booze either – the Prince is known for its fresh, seasonal food, sourced from independent, organic farmers. The dining room, which doubles as a function area, is gamely decorated with images of, erm, meat and makes a great spot for a private dinner. Perfect for a gathering of civilised souls for birthday gluttony or a satisfyingly hearty Christmas lunch with family and friends. Canapés and drinks are also an option but not overly encouraged. Note: there's no capacity for dancing so this is a venue best considered for relaxed eat, drink and make merry type affairs. Outside space is available and, though not for exclusive hire, makes a pleasing spot for a fag break.
Catering: in-house. Music: MP3 port. Outside space: pavement.

WEST

Bowler

2A Pond Place, SW3 6QJ (7589 5876/ www.bowlerbarandgrill.co.uk). South Kensington tube. **Available for hire** noon-midnight Mon-Thur, Sun; noon-1am Fri, Sat.

VENUES

Capacity *Venue* 80 seated/200 standing. *Private areas* 2: both 80 standing. **Minimum spend** *Venue* £2,500. *Private areas* call for details. Restaurant/bar

This suave bar and restaurant offers a fine setting for a civilised cocktails-and-canapés or private dining do. Decor is restrained and tasteful and the management are open to all manner of party requests. Think champagne receptions, fancy Christmas buffets and the loud guffaws of well-to-do SW3 types making it their mission to have a good time. The space can be hired in its entirety or in part, and the food is particularly high-quality, with the emphasis on seasonal and locally sourced produce (the steak is fantastic). Unfortunately, thanks to arcane licensing laws you won't be allowed a DJ, but you can stick your iPod on and play music through their soundsystem. And to be fair, when you can host a Henry VIII-style banquet (presumably without the swans), who cares about a lack of pumping bass? *Catering: in-house. Licence extension possible. Music: MP3 port.*

Cross Keys

1 Lawrence Street, SW3 5NB (7349 9111/ www.thexkeys.co.uk). Sloane Square tube. **Available for hire** noon-midnight Mon-Sat; noon-11.30pm Sun. **Capacity** *Private rooms* 2: 40 seated/80 standing. *Restaurant* 64 seated. **Minimum spend** *Private rooms* £300. *Restaurant* £1,500. Gastropub

An eclectic mix of styles means Cross Keys has something to offer most tastes. The open-plan Gallery, a vividly decorated area (think leopard print sofas and gilt chandeliers) overlooking the main bar is certainly a talking point – great for a bash of the canapés, cocktails and crazy moves on the dancefloor variety. The upstairs function room has a long medieval banqueting table, huge lion's head fireplace and its own bar. Its privacy makes it ideal for work Christmas bashes with higher than average embarrassment potential (so most of them then). The restaurant downstairs is light, airy and altogether more sophisticated, with old fashioned church pews and interior hedges. Perfect for a more formal birthday bash or wedding reception. *Catering: in-house. Civil ceremony licence (restaurant). Disabled: toilet (restaurant). Music: MP3 port.*

Defectors Weld

170 Uxbridge Road, W12 8AA (8749 0008/ www.defectors-weld.com). Shepherd's Bush tube. **Available for hire** *Venue & private room* noon-1am Mon-Tue, Thu-Sun. **Capacity** *Venue* 300 standing. *Private room* 50 seated/70 standing. **Minimum spend** *Venue* £3,500. *Private room* £300. Pub

Hidden away from the after-work throng downstairs, ascending to the Defectors Weld's private room feels like you've stepped into an Edward Hopper painting – all muted greens and pools of light. In fact, it's much-aped country gent decor has recently become a hip photo-shoot location (the Arctic Monkeys did one here not long ago, £50 per hour). By night, this cosy hideaway makes an intimate party venue, as equally suited to sedate dining and conversation as raving (party food can be catered for on request). You can bring your own DJs (decks provided) or just enjoy the

OFFICE CHRISTMAS PARTY

Swanky dos for the season of goodwill to all workers.

You've worked like a slave all year so it's important to remember the one consistent, regular upside of the business world. Yep, it's the annual opportunity to get giddy on too much advocat and tell your boss exactly what you think of his new photocopying policy.

Banqueting House

Whitehall, SW1A 2ER (3166 6150/ www.hrp.org.uk). Westminster tube. **Available for hire** 4.30pm-1am daily. **Capacity** 370 seated/400 standing. **Hire charge** £12,500 + VAT.

With what promises to be an interesting opportunity for ordinary mortals – rather than visiting royals or ministers of state – to actually enjoy a banquet at Banqueting House, events' organisers the Ultimate Experience (7940 6060, www.the-ultimate. co.uk) offer a 'Classical Christmas' party in one of Whitehall's oldest buildings. It's a first for this type of event in the building's remarkable history, apparently. Designed in Palladian style for Charles I by Inigo Jones in the 17th century as part of the royal palace of Whitehall, it was the setting for the beheading of that king in 1649. From 3-11 December, parties of between 200-400 (prices start from £119 per head) can be wined and dined in the Great Hall, with its astonishing ceiling painted by Rubens depicting the awesome *Apotheosis of James I.*

Chartered Accountants Hall

1 Moorgate Place, EC2R 6EA (7920 8771/ www.cahall.co.uk). Bank or Moorgate tube. **Available for hire** 8am-11pm daily. **Capacity** 200 seated/500 standing. **Hire charge** £10,000.

Fancy bringing a touch of financial precision – flair, even – to your Christmas bash? Then the obvious choice must be the Chartered Accountants Hall, the illustrious home of all those wannabe lion-tamers. This pompous but charming mock-Baroque building, designed by Sir John Belcher in 1890, is bang in the middle of the City near Bank. The Russian Ambassador's Ball is the theme for 2008, which sees the Grand Hall decked out in Russian whites to evoke the glory days of St Petersburg. Hire packages for the night range from £80-£100 per person.

Foundling Museum

40 Brunswick Square, WC1N 1AZ (7841 3608/www.foundlingmuseum.org.uk). Russell Square tube. **Available for hire** 9am-midnight Mon; 6pm-midnight Tue-Sun. **Capacity** 30-100 seated/200 standing. **Hire charge** from £1,500.

Celebrate Christmas like Hogarth. The Foundling Museum's rococo Court Room, sumptuously decorated and filled with fine paintings from one of London's first public art collections, designed by Hogarth himself in the 1740s, makes a splendid setting for smaller Christmas parties. The museum's moving history, as one of the first homes for abandoned children in the world, makes it an appropriate setting for yuletide celebrations with a conscience. Parties of up to 30 can be catered for in the Court room. The Picture Gallery seats 100 along its full length, hung with the portraits that formed the core of the collection, including Hogarth's of the Foundling Hospital's founder, rubicund seafarer Sir Thomas Coram.

The HAC

Armoury House (next to 32-36 City Road), EC1 2BQ (7382 1533/www.hac.org.uk). Old Street tube/rail. **Available for hire** *Long room* 4.30-11pm daily. *Prince Consort rooms* 9am-midnight daily. **Capacity** *Long room* 150 seated/220 standing. *Prince Consort rooms* 350 seated/700 standing. **Hire charge** *Long room* from £1,500 + VAT. *Prince Consort rooms* £5,250 + VAT.

For a stress-free Christmas party, try the brisk efficiency at the HQ of the Honourable Artillery Company, one of the oldest regiments in the British Army. The castle-like Armoury House has at its heart, the oak-panelled Long room, the setting for the HAC's Christmas party, promising a kind of white riot of pearl, deep reds and designer steelwork. The Prince Consort rooms are another option. Between them they can cater for up to 700 guests. In the grounds, the tented Winter Gardens, set up specially for the season by European Events (0845 2000 234, www.europeanevents.co.uk), can seat up to 900 or accommodate 3,000 standing. Ultimate Experience (www.the-ultimate.co.uk) will be taking the reins for Christmas 2009.

music that can be piped up from downstairs. The friendly and unfazed staff give this all the feel of a private club at half the price.
Catering: in-house. Disabled: toilet (Venue). Music: DJ equipment (Venue); MP3 port.

Mestizo
103 Hampstead Road, NW1 3EL (7387 4064/www.mestizomx.com). Warren Street tube/Euston tube/rail. **Available for hire** noon-midnight Mon-Wed, Fri-Sun. **Capacity** *Private rooms* 2: 50-70 seated. **Minimum spend** from £1,000.
A good option if the company budget's tight, Mestizo serves up authentic Mexican cuisine of a quality that's rarely found so far from the Americas. It can lay on spreads of tacos and tamales, and perhaps even the house special, *molcajete*: a stone bowl filled with spiced beef, chicken or vegetables, with cheese, chorizo, spring onions, avocado and salsa. The restaurant caters for up to 120 guests.

Saatchi Gallery
Duke of York's HQ, King's Road, SW3 4RY (8968 9331/www.saatchigallery.com). Sloane Square tube. **Available for hire** Call for details. **Capacity** 1,100 seated/1,500 standing. **Hire charge** *Daytime* £17,500 +VAT. *Evening* £15,000 + VAT.
From October 2008, the pristine 70,000 sq ft of the new Saatchi Gallery will be available for hire. It occupies a large part of the imposing neoclassical Duke of York's HQ in Chelsea, formerly the HQ of the Territorial Army and originally built in 1801 as the Royal Military Asylum for military orphans. With a capacity of up to 1,500, this place is guaranteed to be the wow-factor venue of 2008 – get in their early for peak-season dates. Most events will be organised by GSP (8968 9331) and offer exclusive viewings of the gallery's artworks.

Wimbledon Stadium
Plough Lane, SW17 0BL (0870 840 8905/www.lovethedogs.co.uk). Bus 44, 77, 156, 493. **Available for hire** 6-11pm Tue, Fri, Sat. **Capacity** 20-28 seated/standing. **Hire charge** from £35/person.
A fun venue for your Christmas do (and the chance to enjoy an evening of live racing action) is one of the executive suites at Wimbledon Stadium. Each suite holds a minimum of 20 and a maximum of 28 people and there are three packages to choose from (silver, gold and platinum). For larger events, the inter-connecting doors can be removed to accommodate parties of up to 112 people. Every booking includes admission, room hire, race card and a hot and cold buffet.

Under the Westway
Westbourne Studios, 242 Acklam Road, W10 5JJ (7575 3123/www.underthewestway.com). Westbourne Park tube. **Available for hire** Mon-Thur, Sun 6pm-1am; call for details Fri, Sat. **Capacity** *Bar & courtyard* 350 standing. *Screening room* 82 seated/150 standing. **Hire charge** *Venue* from £1,200. **Minimum spend** £2,000. Member's club
Hit party guests hard with 'wow factor' by hosting your event at UtW. There's a courtyard space with a cosy bar area, a 100-seater cinema, a 350-capacity bar space and room for up to 60 for sit-down dining – so it's a venue worth considering for your Christmas capers, especially as extras include a dressing room, in-house catering (from canapés to the works) and PA system, plus a 1,000 sq ft studio/band venue. The whole shebang is available from Sunday to Thursday and features palm trees, huge lounge areas, a pool and football table, and the Westway as its roof. Most suitable as a party venue, it can also be used for launches, fashion shows, and has even been decorated with half-pipe skate ramps and supercars. There is a team to help with organisation. Contact the venue for a 'temporary membership' on a Saturday night so that you can see the venue before booking for private hire.
Catering: in-house; kitchen facilities. Disabled: toilet. Music: DJ equipment; MP3 port. Projector (screening room & courtyard).

NOTE
OTHER SEASONAL SHENANIGANS
Valentine's Day – see p45 for our romantic restaurant recommendations.
Chinese New Year – try one of the cool private rooms at Drunken Monkey (see p29) or Hakkasan (see p90).
Thanksgiving – PJ's Grill (52 Fulham Road, SW3 6HH; 7581 0025) usually comes through with a decent Thanksgiving spread and has a party room to boot. Or try the all new but resolutely old school Chicago Rib Shack (145 Knightsbridge, SW1X 7PA; 7591 4664) for a full-on taste of step-back-in-time Americana.
Burns Night – Albannach (see p70) and the Boisdale (see p56) offer private spaces and haggis-related fun.

Corporate

Arranging a corporate function or work do doesn't have to be a drag. The choice of interesting and exciting London venues – from waterside terraces to towers, subterranean vaults to historical haunts – is limitless. Here you'll find a selection of venues (some large, some small) that make great spots for corporate parties. It is worth scanning the other chapters in this guide for venues that might also be suitable. The likes of the Wallace Collection (*see p62*), All Hallows by the River (*see p64*), Cinnamon Club (*see p44*), the Deck (*see p66*), Studio Valbonne (*see p74*), Christ Church Spitalfields (*see p79*), the ICA (*see p59*) and the new Saatchi Gallery (*see p85*) all have plenty of corporate appeal. Also check out the party planners listed in Organisation & Planning (*see p196*).

CENTRAL

Absolut Ice Bar/Belowzero

31-33 Heddon Street, W1B 4BN (7478 8910/ www.absoluticebarlondon.com). Oxford Circus tube. **Available for hire** *Bar* 3.30pm-10.15pm Mon-Thur, Sun; 3.30pm-12.30am Fri, Sat (45 minute sessions). *Restaurant* noon-12.30am daily. **Capacity** *Bar* 60 standing. *Restaurant* 270 standing. *Private rooms* 3: 25-60 seated/50-100 standing.

Restaurant/bar

If you're out to impress or want to organise an event with both novelty factor and impact, London's Ice Bar is just the ticket. Redesigned completely each year (for the 2008 season former Karl Lagerfeld jewellery designers David & Martin have taken the reins), the bar is made entirely from ice (even the 'glass' your drink comes in is frozen) and kept at a frosty minus five degrees – thermal capes are provided! Bookings are recommended for small groups and the bar is also available for larger events. It's too chilly for the whole night, though, which is where the pleasingly warm belowzero restaurant and lounge comes into play. This swanky venue has various areas available for hire, including the Moose dining room which also boasts a cosy drinking area called the Husky Vault. *Catering: in-house. Licence extension possible. Music (restaurant): DJ equipment; MP3 port.*

VENUES

Namco Station. *See p90.*

Amuse Bouche
21-22 Poland Street, W1F 8QG (7287 1661/www.abcb.co.uk). Oxford Circus tube. **Available for hire** noon-11.30pm Mon-Thur; noon-midnight Fri, Sat. **Capacity** *Private room* 50 seated/80 standing. **Hire charge** *Private room* £100. **Minimum spend** call for details.
Restaurant/bar
This dazzling bar and restaurant makes a fantastic venue for a relaxed but glamorous corporate event or upmarket birthday bash. Upstairs is an elegant and airy champagne bar, perfect for kicking off the night in style. Downstairs, there's a function room with a relaxed, bohemian vibe, deep red walls, squashy leather sofas and twinkling fairy lights. The DJ booth, small dancefloor and intimate atmosphere make it the ideal choice for buzzy business gatherings, leaving dos or special celebrations. Should you want to hire the entire venue for more large-scale corporate entertaining, the bar can hold up to 225 for standing drinks and canapés, and up 50 seated for dinner. A great spot for socialising Soho-style.
Big screen. Catering: in-house. Licence extension possible. Music: DJ equipment.

Café des Amis
11-14 Hanover Place, WC2E 9JP (7379 3444/www.cafedesamis.co.uk). Covent Garden tube. **Available for hire** 11.30am-1am Mon-Sat. **Capacity** *Venue* 100 seated/250

SILVER STURGEON

Silver Fleet has four vessels for hire but if you really want to push the boat out, you might want to look at hiring the *Silver Sturgeon* river cruiser. This impressive vessel was refurbished in 2007 and boasts a glass staircase, oak dancefloor and a swanky open-air deck. You want impressive? You've got it – but it doesn't come cheap. For exclusive hire, this venue is best for corporates with plenty of cash to flash or brides looking for a sophisticated nautical theme for the big day. Bargain hunters and smaller groups could always book one of the party cruises (a shared Christmas dinner cruise starts at £115).
For listings, see p95.

standing. *Wine bar* 70 standing. *Restaurant* 70 seated/100 standing. *Dining room* 20 seated/25 standing. **Minimum spend** *Venue* £10,000. *Wine bar* £2,000. *Restaurant* from £1,500. *Dining room* from £800.
Restaurant/bar
Pleasingly off Covent Garden's beaten track, this unpretentious restaurant/bar has more to offer than the usual Long Acre suspects. There are several floors of party potential and a sizeable overall capacity. As such, this attractively decorated space (think mini chandeliers and monochrome prints) makes a satisfactory venue for relaxed corporate dos, wedding parties or fancy birthday celebrations. The central location is a definite bonus too. There's a separate music system for each floor and even a grand piano for those whose musical tastes stretch further than the latest fads. What Café des Amis does best, though, is food; there's an enticing array of party menus to choose from, including reasonably priced set menus, canapés and buffets.
Catering: in-house. Music: MP3 port.

Crazy Bear
26-28 Whitfield Street, W1T 2RG (7631 0088/www.crazybeargroup.co.uk). Goodge Street tube. **Available for hire** *Bar* noon-midnight Mon-Fri; 6pm-midnight Sat. **Capacity** *Bar* 80 standing. **Minimum spend** £4,000-£10,000. Bar
London's outpost of Oxfordshire's upmarket hotel and bar, Crazy Bear offers its deliciously designery downstairs (padded alcoves, swivel cowhide stools and low-slung leather armchairs) lounge bar for exclusive hire as long as you guarantee a certain minimum spend (dependent on numbers, day of the week and time of year). The venue's tucked-away location, hidden signage and hip feel offer instant edge to any celebratory event. And whatever the occasion, cocktails are a speciality here and must be sampled. As an alternative to exclusive hire, there are three booths available in the bar that seat between eight and 12 people (no minimum spend). Note: there are no decks, but you can plug in an iPod – just don't think about hitting the

dancefloor (there isn't one); this is a place for posing and mingling, rather than moshing and pinging about. But that's not a problem – five minutes spent in the desperately glam loos (hidden doors, mirrored floor, walls, even urinals…) can have a wonderfully disorientating *Alice in Wonderland* effect.
Catering: in-house. Music: MP3 port.

5th View

5th floor, Waterstone's, 203-206 Piccadilly, W1J 9LE (7851 2468/www.5thview.co.uk). Piccadilly Circus tube. **Available for hire** 10am-10pm Mon-Sat; noon-6pm Sun.
Capacity *Private areas* 2: *bar* 180 seated/ 140 standing; *reading room* 40 seated/70 standing. **Minimum spend** *Bar* £4,000. *Reading room* £2,500. Bookshop
The 'sweeping' view is slightly overhyped, but the historical credentials, literary theme and cosmopolitan array of beers at the top of Europe's largest bookstore attract a steady flow of media events and high-profile book launches. A bright, open-plan bar with a higgledy-piggledy view across the rooftops to Big Ben is just the place for noisy chatter at café tables or on 1950s chartreuse sofas, while the classier, sleeker Reading room on the edge of the shop floor is a more intimate choice for smaller groups. Key here is the 'Author's Table', where perching punters can flick through selected tomes. Homemade dips and tapas come from in-house caterers Digby Trout, but the real winner is a frisky and mouthwatering library of cocktails.
Catering: in-house. Disabled: lift; toilet. Music: MP3 port.

14 Henrietta Street

14 Henrietta Street, WC2E 8QH (7558 8797/ www.14henrietta.com). Covent Garden or Leicester Square tube. **Available for hire** 7am-11pm daily. **Capacity** *Private rooms* 6. *Atrium* 60 seated/120 standing. *Main studio* 60 seated/120 standing. *Patio & roof terrace* 40 standing. *Breakout studio* 30 seated/ 60 standing. *Green rooms* 10 seated/15 standing. **Hire charge** call for details.
No credit cards. Townhouse
'We don't want to attract crazy parties,' states the events manager firmly when we look round this bright, blank-canvas venue. The spaces for hire, which include a pleasant roof garden (where cocktails can be served) and balcony area, are generally reserved for big-shot clients. Nike use the house for their annual 'Rock Star' product launch, because the basement area has a sprung dancefloor and floor-to-ceiling mirrors. Other clients include PR and publishing companies, possibly because the elegant

Georgian House was once the home of George Orwell's publisher, Gollancz. So, wild bashes are a no no, but the rooms, which each seat 35 for dinner or 50 standing, as well as the interview rooms, kitchen areas and receptions, are perfect for sedate media happenings. Projectors, screens and surround sound make it perfect for screenings too. A list of caterers and other suppliers can be provided.
Catering: in-house; kitchen facilities. Music: MP3 port. Outside space: patio; terrace (for hire). Projector.

Gaucho

25 Swallow Street, W1B 4DJ (7734 4040/ www.gauchorestaurants.co.uk). Piccadilly Circus tube. **Available for hire** noon-midnight. **Capacity** *Basement* 120 seated/130 standing. *Private rooms* 2: both 14 seated.
Minimum spend *Basement* from £12,000. *Private rooms* from £39.50/person. Restaurant/bar
There's cowhide everywhere you look in this flagship branch of the glitzy Argentinian steakhouse chain, and that which isn't covered in the skewbald pelt is shiny black-and-white and chrome. The preponderance of statuesque, black-suited female staff talking into collar microphones as customers arrive for their steak dinners ratchets up the slick factor a notch too. Certainly, the two larger party hire options – one a huge padded and mirrored basement cocoon with bar, decks and loads of white leather; the other a glamorous second-floor restaurant – attract glamorous clients capable of guaranteeing sizeable minimum spends. More intimate celebrations can take place in the 'Cavas de Gaucho' – the pleasantly appointed and cow-skin-free wine

NOTE

CHARITY CASES
If you're hosting a charity event, be sure to let your preferred venue know when you first make contact. Many will happily offer a hire discount for charities. Of the venues listed in this guide, the following made a point of noting their charity-friendly credentials when we called to check details: the Hub (see p58), the Wallace Collection (see p62), All Hallows (see p64), Hampton Pool (see p67), the Serpentine (see p62) and Whitechapel Art Gallery (see p101). This doesn't mean other venues listed don't provide similar discounts so it's always worth asking.

VENUES

boutique (Argentinian only), with its wooden floors and shelves. This seats up to 14 for private tastings and functions (be sure to make use of the free sommelier service). The private dining room, just off the main first floor restaurant is perfect for a special dinner date for up to nine people. Pan-Latin glam is evident in the menus; the steaks are highly recommended.
Catering: in-house. Music (basement): DJ equipment; MP3 port.

Hakkasan
8 Hanway Place, W1T 1HD (7907 1888). Tottenham Court Road tube. **Available for hire** noon-12.30am Mon-Wed, Sun; noon-1.30am Thur-Sat. **Capacity** *Venue* 210 seated/300 standing. *Private areas* 3: 16-150 seated. **Minimum spend** call for details. Restaurant
The bladder-scented alley location's probably about as incongruous a setting as you could get for this jewel in the crown of London's Chinese restaurant scene. However, once inside, it's all wafting sandalwood incense and low lighting. Black wooden screens separate the two dining areas from each other, both of which are exercises in dark-hued refinement. The Ling Ling room's soft leather benches make for a more comfortable group dining environment, with the separate snug at the end particularly cosy. It's better suited to smaller parties, as the narrow bar space isn't available for hire, and groups of eight or over are required to pre-select from a range of set menus. Gourmands wanting to celebrate with some of the capital's finest oriental cuisine won't be disappointed, though. A tip: sample their exquisite cocktails before eating, and read the menu in advance as some dishes are only available with 24 hours' notice.
Catering: in-house. Disabled: toilet. Music: DJ equipment (venue).

Haymarket Hotel Pool & Bar
Haymarket Hotel, 1 Suffolk Place, SW1Y 4BP (7287 4434/www.firmdale.com). Piccadilly Circus tube. **Available for hire** 9am-1am Mon-Sat; 9am-midnight Sun. **Capacity** *Pool & bar* 220 standing (pool covered); 100 standing (pool uncovered). **Hire charge** £500/hr; £4,000 day; £2,000 evening. All + VAT. Hotel
You could be forgiven for thinking that a poolside party means plenty of watery frolics, but safety considerations mean staff 'encourage you to think of it as a water feature' in Kit Kemp's fabulously lit, ultra hip venue – as perfect for West End wrap parties and New Year's celebrations as it is for corporate dos. Certainly the stunning 18-metre pool is very worthy of aesthetic contemplation. Martin Richman's light installation (ask for gradually morphing colours)

casts a magenta hue across the deep blue waters, tiny pin-prick lights kindle the ceiling, while tribal artefacts and contemporary artworks make for a funky, hedonistic vibe. Pricey cocktails are served from the pewter bar, guests wave perfectly painted toenails while lounging on glam gold sofas and canapés are spread out on shell-studded sideboards or in one of the adjacent private rooms. Add a comprehensive sound system and it's easy to see why this venue gets booked up so fast. Tempting as it is, a jump in the pool will lead to an embarrassing lights up/music off/loudspeaker scenario, so brief unruly guests in advance.
Catering: in-house. Music: DJ equipment; MP3 port.

Horse Hospital
Colonnade, WC1N 1HX (7833 3644/ www.thehorsehospital.com). Russell Square tube. **Available for hire** noon-11.30pm daily. **Capacity** *Venue* 90 seated/150 standing. **Hire charge** *Venue* £50/hr day; £100/hr evening. **No credit cards**. Arts space
This charming former – you guessed it – Horse Hospital retains most of its historic allure (the space has been operating since 1797) with a DIY edge. Even manager Roger claims that sometimes, 'it still smells of horses.' Neon paint highlights the steep ramp leading up to the lofty space – not great for elderly partygoers – but once inside there are TV screens, a DJ booth and a bring-your-own-booze, donation-only bar to ensure that gallery parties (there is usually an exhibition on), dinner soirées, and fancy themed events go off with a bang. Deep ridges on the stone floor mean the room is not ideal for dancing, so think modest and sophisticated rather than drunken and raucous. Best for arty or corporate parties that require an interesting space – but warn guests not to wear heels.
Music: DJ equipment. Projector.

Namco Station
County Hall, Riverside Buildings, Westminster Bridge Road, SE1 7PB (7967 1067/www. namcostation.co.uk). Westminster tube/ Waterloo tube/rail. **Available for hire** 10am-midnight daily. **Capacity** *Venue* 1200 standing. *Private rooms* 6: 20-300 standing. **Hire charge** call for details. Bar/entertainment
The constant rattle of coin slots and the garbled blare of computer effects isn't music to everyone's ears, but corporate gangs (or even stags) with fond memories of afternoons wasted in front of the NES or Megadrive will relish an afternoon at Namco Station. Here the latest and the greatest video arcades jostle for space – from

GATE

The Gate Restaurant, Bar and Club form the hub of Notting Hill's social scene. Spread over two venues dominating the junction at the very heart of Notting Hill, the Gate offers everything one could need for a great night out.

The establishment comprises a restaurant, bar, lounge, club and private rooms with many options available for private hire. Enjoy a light bite, a full dinner or delicious canapés with a wine list that compliments the food perfectly and an extensive cocktail selection. With a different DJ every night of the week offering up everything from R&B, Hip Hop and Funky House to Salsa, Soul and Pop classics, the party never ends at the Gate...

Gate Restaurant, Bar and Club

Gate Bar and Private Rooms, 90 Notting Hill Gate W11 3HP
Gate Bar and Lounge, 87 Notting Hill Gate W11 3JZ
Gate Restaurant and Club, 87 Notting Hill Gate W11 3JZ

Website: www.gaterestaurant.co.uk

For restaurant reservations, guestlist, party bookings and private hire contact Chloe Campbell on 020 7727 9007
Email: general@gaterestaurant.co.uk

Village Underground

VENUES

Beaconsfield

A former ragged school, sympathetically restored from a dilapidated state in 1995, when Beaconsfield took it over, this venue was built to inspire awe. Its day job is as a contemporary art space with charitable status (claiming to be the first and only arts organisation to be powered by 100% green electricity), so it's financed by its other role as high-end, big bash venue, mostly used by corporate clients (Nike, Jack Daniels, Budwar, Soho House) who want to make a splash. It's a diverse space: there's the high-ceilinged gallery floor, a more intimate lower space (with kitchen) which is perfect for standing about with cocktails, and an Arch space, which has a bare-brick, urban aesthetic. The yard outside is gated and has space for lorries bringing in party sets. The building is dry hire only so clients are expected to organise their own props, music, eats and drinks – perfect for those wanting a free rein with planning and visuals.
Best for Unusual but totally spectacular product launches.
Must do Have cash to flash.
Inside tip The company can advise on themes and decor if you require.
For listings, see p101.

Hempel

World-famous for its serene, minimal and innovative interiors, the Hempel Hotel regularly draws an eye-popping cast of patrons from fashion and entertainment

circles. Essentially a blank canvas for the most whimsical of whims, its Zen-style garden consists of three square ponds, each with clean, symmetrical borders of grass and stone, dramatically relocated into a marquee of your specification– voluptuous swathes of black and ivory drapes, colourful Mongolian yurts, or even pure glass, with stunning lighting and floral creations can be achieved. Optimistic forecasters can go for simpler canopies, or just the garden itself, with its topiaries and smooth round pebbles. In-house chefs specialise in modern Thai fusions and sushi, and tai chi classes, chocolate tastings or Uluvka martini masterclasses can be arranged for corporate parties.
Best for Bespoke corporate events and big budget weddings.
Must do Let your imagination run wild.
Inside tip Employ the talents of in-house mixologist, Joel Miguel.
For listings, see p104.

Old Billingsgate

Catwalk show, conference, cabaret or Christmas party, Old Billingsgate offers the sort of look that guarantees to make your guests 'ooh' and 'aah'. With a number of spaces, it has the versatility to fulfil just about any party requirement. The main space has triple-height ceilings, a steel mezzanine gallery, acres of plate glass and is capable of hosting up to 2,400 people. For a quirky place to party, we love the vaults – a subterranean

cellar with atmospheric interlinked arches. The space is expandable so can cater for anything from a relatively modest company dinner to the blow-out bash to end all bashes. Best of all, there's a team of support (lighting, sound, security) who can tailor-make your event to your budget.

Best for Superb river views.

Must do Get ideas from the events management team.

Inside tip Impress guests with a bit of past event name-dropping – the *Sex and the City* premiere bash was held here.

For listings, see p98.

Village Underground

Cultural and corporate wet dream alike, Village Underground is a massive warehouse that is as comfortable hosting progressive theatre as it is the launch of a new hedge fund. Walking through the industrial entrance, the expansive space is breathtaking. What was until recently a rickety, burnt-out Victorian building housing a few clapped-out old cars is now a ten-metre high-ceilinged, bare-bricked, light and airy empty shell that can be morphed into the venue you desire. Natural light spills through the roof in the day, and at night uplighters illuminate the walls. The vaults coming off the main space house the toilets (more of which have just been added) as well as a food preparation area. The space is perfect for setting out lots of tables for a big celebratory meal and so is

also ideal for weddings. Whatever you intend to use this venue for, it can't help look anything less than stunning. Book well ahead.

Best for Cultural events and company parties.

Must do Check out the tube carriages (stripped out and used as artist studios) on the roof.

Inside tip Anything's possible – this is the ultimate cool blank canvas.

For listings, see p101.

Vinyl Factory Shoreditch

Be the first to hire this brand spanking new, cutting edge, contemporary art venue from Vinyl Factory (for the Soho venue, *see p95*), which opens in October 2008. Inspired by NYC's counter-culture spaces, it's a vast, loft-style 7,000 sq ft set over two levels and featuring bright white walls, wooden flooring and plenty of natural light. Designed to host corporate media, music and fashion events and shows alongside parties, exhibitions, presentations and dinners, the festivities bustle around the three (yes, three!) bars. Downstairs is where live bands and DJs can take advantage of the in-built sound system and wicked acoustics, and both in-house and external caterers will be available.

Best for Hoxtonites with their fingers on the pulse.

Must do Get some killer live bands in.

Inside tip Head to the mezzanine smoking terrace for sophisticated 'smirting'.

For listings, see p101.

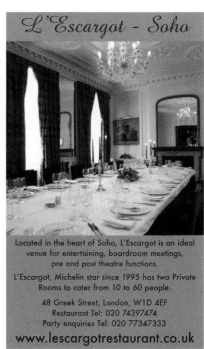

cutting-edge racing simulators and shooting games to bloodthirsty beat-'em-ups, and with a good range of slot machines for more 'mature' gamers. The 35,000 sq ft arena is also home to seven full-size pool tables (20p per minute) and a crash-happy dodgem car course (£2 per car), plus there's a menu of suitably Americanised meals and snacks at the bar.
Big screen. Catering: in-house; preferred caterer list. Disabled: lift; toilet. Music: DJ equipment (sub station). Projector.

Planet of the Grapes
9 New Oxford Street, WC1A 1BA (7405 4912/ www.planetofthegrapes.co.uk). Holborn tube. **Available for hire** noon-midnight daily. **Capacity** *Private room* 18 seated. **Minimum spend** £250. Shop
Marc, Matt and Sam, who run this singular wine shop, recently had the builders in to refurbish their tasting cellar. Their mission is to hold regular tastings to give their customers the chance to taste 'great, rare, interesting and damn good wines at reasonable prices with people who know what they are talking about'. Private tasting parties are a speciality. Clients from all walks of life – from corporations wishing to bond over the bottle, to family-and-friend groupings united in their love of the vine – book the cellar and a wine tutor (additional tutors cost from £75) and sample about eight types of wine, from a 700-variety collection that covers everything from bargain bin tipples (from £5.50/bottle) to the rare and precious (£2,000/bottle). Food can be provided (usually locally produced charcuterie, cheese and bread, for around £10/head) or clients can bring their own nibbles. For bigger crowds, consider the Planet of the Grapes bar (9-10 Bull's Head Passage, EC3V 1LU, 7929 7224). It's open until 2am daily and holds 30 seated, 50 standing (minimum spend £1,500).
Catering: in-house. Music: MP3 port.

Quo Vadis
26-29 Dean Street, W1D 6LL (7440 1463/ www.quovadissoho.co.uk). Leicester Square, Piccadilly Circus or Tottenham Court Road tube. **Available for hire** noon-2.30pm, 5.30-11pm Mon-Fri; 5.30-11pm Sat. **Capacity** *Private rooms* 2: 12-25 seated. **Minimum spend** from £32.50/person. Restaurant
The refurbished private rooms above this revamped Soho stalwart (now owned by Sam and Eddie Hart of Spanish restaurants Fino and Barrafina) really look the part for upmarket leaving dos, parties, small weddings and corporate shindigs. Quo Vadis takes its private hire seriously and offers the kind of flexibility party planners lust after. Tables can be decorated

as per any chosen theme and visual props can be brought in for business functions. The smaller room seats up to 12 and has an airy and sunny feel, while the larger room fits 25 and offers a projector, plasma screen, pull-down screen and a sound system. Champagne buckets lining the floors of both areas give the place a luxury feel and there are fabulous specialist menus to choose from. The management can organise a private meal anytime, from breakfast to dinner, and flowers can be provided on request.
Big screen. Catering: in-house. Projector.

Silver Sturgeon
Woods River Cruises, Wapping Pier, King Henry's Stairs, Wapping High Street, E1W 2NR (7481 2711/www.silverfleet.co.uk). Bus D3, 100. **Available for hire** 7am-1am daily. **Capacity** *Venue* 458 seated/550 standing. **Hire charge** *Venue* from £3,700 (day); from £6,200 (evening). **Minimum spend** *Venue* (peak season, evening) £22,000 + VAT. Boat For review, *see p88*.
Catering: in-house. Outside space: deck (for hire).

Vinyl Factory
Entrances: Phonica Records, 51 Poland Street & 45 Foubert's Place, W1 (7025 1385/www.vinylfactorygallery.co.uk). Oxford Circus tube. **Available for hire** 8am-11pm daily. **Capacity** *Venue* 450 standing. *Main gallery* 250 standing. *Studio* 200 standing. **Hire charge** from £1,000/day. **No credit cards**. Gallery space
Cunningly situated beyond the hippest music store in London – Phonica Records (although there is also a back entrance on Foubert's Place) – the Vinyl Factory is undoubtedly one of Soho's coolest venues. With a client list reading like a who's who of fashion, design and business (Nike, Hilfiger, Nokia and T-Mobile to name but four), there are clearly a lot of people who see the 4,500 sq ft main room as *the* place to host catwalk shows, gigs and press launches. But there's more: a 200-capacity back room can either be hired separately or together with the main space. to up the capacity significantly. This is a 'dry venue' – meaning you will be supplying the alcohol for your event.
Catering: kitchen facilities. Disabled: toilet.

Wellington Arch
Hyde Park Corner, W1J 7JZ (7973 3292/ www.english-heritage.org.uk). Hyde Park Corner tube. **Available for hire** 11am-11pm Mon, Tue; 6-11pm Wed-Sun. **Capacity** *Venue* 36 seated/80 standing. **Hire charge** from £1,700. Heritage building

Commissioned by George IV as an entrance to Buckingham Palace, the Wellington Arch was moved to Hyde Park Corner in 1882. Today, as well as providing a convenient tourist landmark, it opens its doors for corporate and other events. There's a wide selection of caterers to choose from (flower arrangements can also be provided), lots of plush chairs and the option of either long or round tables to suit your plans, but it's the illumination of the Arch's exterior with your own choice of lighting that really takes some beating. Drinks can be served upstairs (where an arresting view can be enjoyed from the balcony) before a sit-down dinner below. If your guest list tops the capacity threshold, then neighbouring Apsley House, the first Duke of Wellington's London pad, can offer additional space with its interior boasting works by Velázquez and Goya. *Catering: preferred caterer list. No amplified music.*

NORTH

Garden Café

Inner Circle, Regent's Park, NW1 4NU (7935 5729/www.thegardencafe.co.uk). Baker Street or Regent's Park tube. **Available for hire** *Oct-Mar noon-11pm daily.* **Capacity** *Venue 300 standing/160 seated.* **Hire charge** *Venue £1,000-£1,500.* Café
This quirky 1960s turreted café has an enchanting setting adjacent to St Mary's Rose Garden and the open air theatre in Regent's Park. The light-filled interior and alfresco dining area make it a perfect spot for summer evening parties; for private hire the café stays open past park opening hours – effectively your very own

park lock-in. The unpretentious menu, tasty food and friendly service also lift this venue above the ordinary. Ignore the slightly cramped toilets, peeling paintwork and marooned piano inside and head to the fabulous gardens where you can relax among the neon flowerbeds with a glass of rosé. Sections of the café can be hired for lunch – perfect for office dos and horticultural book launches – with a two-course set menu starting at £15.80. Book early and catch some theatre or play a bit of team-building rounders first. *Catering: in-house. Disabled: toilet. Outside space: garden (for hire).*

Roundhouse

Chalk Farm Road, NW1 8EH (7424 6771/ www.roundhouse.org.uk). Chalk Farm tube. **Available for hire** *call for details.* **Capacity** *Venue 1,800 seated/standing. Private room 200 seated/standing.* **Hire charge** *Venue £43,000 + VAT. Private room £1,250 + VAT.* Performing arts centre
This striking Grade II-listed building started life as an engine shed before going on to host legendary performances from the likes of Jimi Hendrix and Pink Floyd in the 1960s and '70s. Following £29.7 million worth of development, the Roundhouse is thriving once more as a landmark centre for the performing arts. The space is available for hire for around 40 events per year and makes an impressive setting for any celebration. Capable of hosting a reception for 200 or a huge gathering of 1,800 there's lots of flexibility and, of course, state-of-the-art audio-visual equipment. Get in there early and check out the availability online. *Catering: preferred caterer list. Disabled: toilet.*

Take your party back to a more elegant time at **4 Princelet Street**.

EAST

4 Princelet Street

4 Princelet Street, E1 5LP (7377 5550/ www.princelet.co.uk). Aldgate East tube/ Liverpool Street tube/rail. **Available for hire** call for details. **Capacity** 60 seated/140 standing. **Hire charge** call for details. House Set in a quiet conservation area in Spitalfields, this unique space – a double-fronted Georgian merchant's house, with period features throughout – is a wonderful place to host a lunch or dinner (up to 60) or a launch (up to 140). Any or all of the 15 rooms can be hired as locations for photography or filming and can be fitted out with period furniture and textiles if you want to achieve an authentic historical look. If you're looking for a summer venue, there are two outside roof terraces (connected by an original spiral staircase) while in winter all the rooms have original working fireplaces. For DIY catering, there is a kitchen, or recommended caterers can take care of requirements.
Catering: preferred caterer list; kitchen facilities. Outside space: roof terrace.

Gun

27 Coldharbour, E14 9NS (7515 5222/ www.thegundocklands.com). Canary Wharf tube/DLR/South Quay DLR. **Available for hire** 11am-midnight Mon-Sat; 11am-11pm Sun. **Capacity** *Venue* 108 seated/200 standing. *Private rooms* 3: 14-35 seated. *Terraces* 90-200 standing. **Minimum spend** *Venue* from £10,000. *Others* call for details. Gastropub This award-winning gastropub continues to go from strength to strength. Reopened in 2004, after a fire gutted what had been a pub for 250 years, this Grade II-listed building, with its fabulous riverside location, makes the ideal place for a power breakfast, a business lunch, an anniversary dinner or a small party. Almost every part of the pub can be hired out: the restaurant; the wonderfully cosy fireside room; an intimate ground-floor private dining room; the majority of the terrace and possibly the best of the lot – the upstairs dining room, reputedly where Lord Nelson 'entertained' Lady Hamilton. In addition, A Grelha, the Gun's alfresco Portuguese offshoot next door, can be hired out in its entirety. The terrace has the same great view of the O2 and comes with its own dedicated bar and barbecue.
Catering: in-house. Licence extension possible. Outside space: terrace (for hire).

Mary Jane's

124-127 Minories, EC3N 1NT (7481 8195). Tower Hill tube/Tower Gateway DLR. **Available for hire** *Venue* noon-3am Sat; noon-midnight

Guy Rodger
CO-FOUNDER OF THE ULTIMATE EXPERIENCE

My favourite corporate party venue is Old Billingsgate. It's a Grade I-listed former fish market on the north bank of the Thames and it's a big, beautiful space with a fantastic riverside view. All the large banks and solicitors firms have their parties there.

On a more modest scale somewhere like Delfina on Bermondsey Street, Southwark is great. It consists of four white gallery spaces that are great for product launches.

One of the best parties we've organised was a rodeo party at a client's home. We had 20 carpenters build a whole Wild West town and then we had a live rodeo with knife-throwing and lassoing. It was quite cheesy in many respects, but it was fantastic.

The most unusual place we've ever organised a party is the Hellfire Caves at West Wycombe. They're a long way down and we had to get everything carried there without any lights.

For our own company's party we took over a prep school and everyone stayed in dormitories. It started with an assembly in the morning, at which one of our directors played 'All Things Bright And Beautiful', then we had a sports day with hockey and rounders and in the evening there was a big disco.

If you want to guarantee attendance choose a landmark venue like the V&A or the National History Museum. Somewhere with a good reputation that's very central and convenient to get to, so that when people get the invitation they'll think, 'I'd like to go there'.

Ultimate Experience (www.the-ultimate. co.uk) organises events for clients including Diageo and Merrill Lynch.

VENUES

Sun; *private areas* noon-midnight Mon-Wed; noon-2am Thur, Fri. **Capacity** *Venue* 400 standing. **Minimum spend** *Venue* £5,000. Bar
A plush and airy two-floor haunt populated by City workers looking for a sniff of speakeasy-style after-office debauchery. Subdued red lighting, an aquarium, a wrought-iron staircase and chandeliers set the scene, and there are plenty of party spaces to choose from. Entering from the Minories, a ground-floor bar suits birthday shenanigans, a small balcony area is great for cosy three-course meals, canapés and party platters, while the private, outdoor Sky Bar comes complete with a plasma screen. Mary Jane's in-house events team can rope in anything from burlesque to circus performers to give your party wow factor. Girls, remember to hold your skirts as you totter over the mezzanine's glass floor.
Catering: in-house. Disabled: toilet. Music: DJ equipment; MP3 port. Projector.

Old Billingsgate

1 Old Billingsgate Walk, 16 Lower Thames Street, EC3R 6DX (7283 2800/www.old billingsgate.co.uk). Monument tube. **Available for hire** 6am-3am daily. **Capacity** *Venue* 1,700 seated/3000 standing. *Private rooms* 3: 150-600 seated/600-1000 standing. **Hire charge** £5,000-£20,000 + VAT. Historic building
For review, *see p92.*
Catering: preferred caterer list. Disabled: toilet. Outside space: terrace (for hire).

1 Lombard Street

1 Lombard Street, EC3V 9AA (7929 6611/ www.1lombardstreet.com). Bank tube/DLR. **Available for hire** noon-1am daily. **Capacity** *Venue* 200 seated/450 standing. *Private room* 40 seated. **Minimum spend** *Venue* from £8,000. **Hire charge** *Private room* £450. Restaurant/bar
A domed skylight over the bar, a Michelin star in the kitchen and an events organiser on hand throughout, make this a luxurious choice of venue. What was once a banking hall is now a thoughtfully decorated Grade II-listed building that houses a bright and spacious brasserie and bar. This area accommodates 200 seated and 450 standing and has proved a sophisticated destination for corporate events, weddings and bar mitzvahs. The events team is experienced and will guide you through wine and food tastings and remain in situ on the night with 20 other staff to make sure everything goes smoothly. The separate restaurant at the back can be used for pre-party drinks, and there's a private dining room downstairs for formal dinners and meetings. You'll need to book up to a year in advance.
Catering: in-house. Disabled: toilet.

Rookery

Peter's Lane, Cowcross Street, EC1M 6DS (7336 0931/www.hazlittshotel.com). Farringdon tube/rail. **Available for hire** 8am-7pm daily. **Capacity** *Private rooms* 2: 10-14 seated. **Hire charge** *Drawing room* £295-£450. *Library* £195-£350. Hotel
If you were to step into a time machine and seek out a destination where a tastefully quirky scholar with a penchant for Georgian and Victorian articles lived, you would likely end up in a place like the Rookery. While its private rooms' special features (presentation screens, Wi-Fi, DVD players) have a distinctly business edge, the venue exudes warmth thanks to its caringly designed interior – think Persian carpets, antiques and gold detailing. The drawing room seats fourteen guests and is home to a small lounge area with a stone fireplace. In the smaller library area, colours turn a shade darker and a large bookcase adds a serious, intellectual vibe.
Big screen. Catering: in-house. Disabled: toilet.

Roost

142 Sandringham Road, E8 2HJ (07767 836221/www.theroost.co.uk). Hackney Downs rail. **Available for hire/hire charge** call for details. House
One of the most unusual venues we've found available for hire is east London's Roost. Primarily used for commercials, photographic shoots and pop promos, it offers several floors and an outside space – all individually decorated with antique or retro pieces of furniture and accessories. Hand-printed wallpapers, fabulous French beds, Italian lights and antique leather sofas create a hip, sophisticated backdrop to whatever event you are looking to host – and if you really adore that pouffe you were perching on, you might be able to buy it afterwards, as much of the furniture is for sale. The basement has a glam white marble floor, while the upstairs floors would make a unique venue for a small wedding, launch (Sony Walkman had one here in 2007) or cocktail party (photographer Tim Walker had one here recently). However, as the owners stress, 'this is not a "bang bang" kind of place'. Rates vary according to numbers and whether an event would go into the following day (clean up and re-dress).

Shoreditch House

Ebor Street, E1 6AW (7749 4530/ www.shoreditchhouse.com). Liverpool Street tube/rail. **Available for hire** noon-3am Mon-Sat; noon-midnight Sun. **Capacity** *Private room* 70 seated/120 standing. **Hire charge** £600. **Minimum spend** £5,000. Members' club

de Wintons a passion for food

Decadent Food Design & Event Production

Innovative Drinks and Refreshing Cocktails

Outstanding Service & Attention to Detail

Call Jacqueline or James on 0207 627 5550 for more information
www.dewintons.co.uk

Definitely not the last ditch party venue: **Shoreditch House**. *See p98*.

Two years after it first opened, this sleek Tom Dixon-designed modernist temple still has an abundance of the wow factor. The Biscuit Tin space with its exposed brickwork, industrial pipes and drop cylindrical chandeliers is the perfect size for entertaining; whether that be a fashion launch, a company dinner or a cooler-than-thou wedding bash. For a decadent girls' night out, the Cowshed spa rooms put on inspired 'pretty parties' – an evening of pampering, champagne and delicious food. If you want to hire the rooftop pool (which is available in the winter only), opulent private dining room or raucous bowling alley with its own bijou bar, you'll need to become a member – worth it if you can face the try-hard membership form. Occasionally even non-members can negotiate use of the off-limits spaces; make an appointment and check out the place in person. Even non-smokers should head upstairs to check out the rooftop terrace for wonderful views across east London.
Disabled: lift; toilet. Catering: in-house. Music: DJ equipment; MP3 port. Outside space: roof terrace.

30 St Mary Axe

30 St Mary Axe, EC3A 8EP (7071 5009/ www.30stmaryaxe.com). Bank tube/DLR. **Available for hire** 6.30pm-11.30pm Mon-Thur; noon-11.30pm Sat, Sun. **Capacity** *Venue* 90 seated/260 standing. *Private rooms* 5: 2-15 seated. **Hire charge** *Venue* £3,500-£10,500 + VAT. Landmark building
Deep pockets buy more than just a light head at the dizzying apex of London's rocketing modern icon. The gleaming blue-blacks and slate greys of the interior match the astonishing city views, and reflect the light that fills the room through the diamond-mullioned, one-way glass. The split-level nature of the suite lends versatility – special dinners and weddings, ostentatious product launches or business presentations can take place at the northern aspect of the lower floor, before wowing the guests with champagne and breathtaking panoramas from the glass cupola. A wireless PA system caters to corporate or musical requirements, and bespoke European cuisine comes in-house from Searcy's, who can also hire in anything – from a seafood bar to

cocktail flairers and an ice sculpture of your company logo. It's worth noting that smaller, private rooms are available for dinner at a fraction of the price. Book this place from sunset until late to experience the movement of the city by night. *Big screen. Catering: in-house. Civil ceremony licence. Disabled: lift; toilet.*

Village Underground

54 Holywell Lane, EC2A 3PQ (0787 806 2436/www.villageunderground.co.uk). Liverpool Street or Old Street tube/rail. **Available for hire** 9am-2am daily. **Capacity** *Venue* 200 seated/600 standing. **Hire charge** call for details. **No credit cards.** Art space
For review, *see p93.*
Catering: kitchen facilities.

Vinyl Factory Shoreditch

32-37 Cowper Street, EC2A 4AP (7025 1385/www.vinylfactorygallery.co.uk). Old Street tube. **Available for hire** 8am-3am daily. **Capacity** *Private rooms* 2: both 400 standing. **Hire charge** call for details. **No credit cards.** Gallery
For review, *see p93.*
Catering: in-house; kitchen facilities. Outside space: terrace (for hire). Music: DJ equipment; MP3 port.

Whitechapel Art Gallery

80-82 Whitechapel High Street, E1 7QX (7522 7877/www.whitechapel.org). Aldgate East tube. **Available for hire** *Café/other galleries* 9am-11pm Mon; 6-11pm Tue, Wed, Fri-Sun. *Tom Bendhem gallery* 9am-11pm Mon-Wed, Fri-Sun; 9am-5pm Thur. **Capacity** *Café* 30 seated/110 standing. *Tom Bendhem gallery* 16 seated/50 standing. *Other galleries* 60-360 standing. **Hire charge** *Café* £350-£450. *Tom Bendhem gallery* £250-£350. *Other galleries* £250-£2,500. Gallery
This hip East End art space is going through a massive renovation so its current hire spaces are limited until its reopening at the end of March 2009, by which time there'll be a large variety of options on offer. Still, the vast historic space (it was Britain's first purpose-built contemporary art gallery in 1901) can offer a whole floor of three glacially cool box rooms, linked by a foyer, to host leftfield arty parties in. Live bands can rock out in the Liam Gillick-designed café area, where tables can also be arranged for tasty bites from their in-house caterers, or you can set up the decks in the Tom Bendhem gallery and get the crowd spinning under the dimmer lights. Stylish, low-key bashes are more suited to the giant lofty spaces, where you can sophisticatedly sup a cocktail while perusing the gallery's art

installations. Projectors and screens are also available at an extra cost. Tip: book well ahead if you want to hire out one of the larger spaces in between exhibitions – they are only completely bare a few times a year.
Catering: in-house. Disabled: lift; toilets. Licence extension possible. Music: DJ equipment; MP3 port.

SOUTH

Beaconsfield

22 Newport Street, SE11 6AY (7582 6465/ www.beaconsfield.ltd.uk). Lambeth North tube/Vauxhall tube/rail. **Available for hire** noon-1am daily. **Capacity** *Venue* 500 standing. *Private rooms* 3: 100-350 standing. **Hire charge** *Venue* from £1,800. *Private rooms* from £1,200. **No credit cards.** Art space
For review, *see p92.*
Catering: kitchen facilities. Disabled: toilet. Outside space: courtyard (for hire).

Delfina

50 Bermondsey Street, SE1 3UD (7564 2400/www.thedelfina.co.uk). London Bridge tube/rail. **Available for hire** *Café gallery* 5pm-midnight Mon-Fri; 9am-midnight Sat, Sun. *Exhibition gallery* 9am-midnight daily. **Capacity** *Galleries* 2: 130-250 seated/ 200-350 standing. **Hire charge** from £2,000 + VAT. Gallery
Delfina has hosted events for the likes of the Tate Modern, Givenchy and the BBC so the management know what an events space needs to make an impact. Up to 525 square metres of light, white-walled, versatile open space is available until midnight (licence extensions by arrangement) for all types of events, from launches and exhibitions to awards and parties. The galleries can be hired separately or all together, up to a maximum of 130 for lunch/dinner or a reception for 200. The hire charge includes the use of on-site facilities, but catering and event management is charged for separately according to each client's specific needs. The space is now licensed for marriage ceremonies, and Delfina is already booking for its exquisite Christmas party.
Catering: in-house. Disabled: toilet. Licence extension possible. Outside space: garden.

Design Museum

28 Shad Thames, SE1 2YD (7940 8262/ www.designmuseum.org). Tower Bridge tube/Tower Gateway DLR. **Available for hire** *Riverside hall & design gallery* 6-11pm daily;

VENUES

Royal Observatory

museum space 8am-11pm daily. **Capacity** *Private rooms* 3. *Riverside hall* 120 seated/250 standing. *Design gallery* 150 seated/150 standing. *Museum space* 80 seated/200 standing. **Hire charge** £2,000-£7,000 + VAT. Museum

Perfect for aesthetes wanting to surround themselves with cutting-edge design, the contemporary design gallery allows guests the opportunity for a champagne mingle around a glass display case of innovative products set in front of a panoramic river view, prior to a stroll around the current exhibition (although depending what's on, drinks may need to be left at the entrance). Downstairs the baby-blue walled Design Museum space can be set up to accommodate an 80-person sit down meal or reception for 150. Food is available from the renowned and stylish Blueprint Café. The ground-floor lobby space is also available, with the option of a cloakroom for guests.

Catering: preferred caterer list. Disabled: lift, toilets. Music: MP3 port (riverside hall & design gallery). Projector (museum space). Outside space: terrace (for hire).

Royal Observatory
Greenwich Park, SE10 9NF (8312 6693/ www.rog.nmm.ac.uk). Cutty Sark DLR/ Greenwich DLR/rail/Maze Hill rail. **Available for hire** 5pm-midnight daily. **Capacity** *Planetarium* 110 seated/160 standing. *Octagon room* 60 seated/100 standing.

Queen's house 120 seated/150 standing. **Hire charge** *Planetarium* £4,000. *Octagon room* £4,000. *Queen's house* £5,000. All + VAT. Museum

For an event that ascends past the usual hot air into the stratosphere, it would be hard to improve on the Royal Observatory as a venue. After all, you don't get to hire out parts of a World Heritage site very often. The Octagon room, in Flamsteed House, is a fabulous, grand room with views of Canary Wharf that can only be described as 'sweeping'. It is the sort of room that makes you feel more intelligent just for standing in it and would make a brilliant, unusual venue for an important dinner or a meeting. The entrance to the Planetarium is a rather more functional, modernist space, but can be used in conjunction with the Planetarium for an event that would be, well, out of this world. The piéce de resistance, however, is the Queen's House, down the hill towards the river, who's orangery and Great Hall would combine to make a wedding venue that Jane Austen might have written about. This sensational building was commissioned in 1616 by Queen Anne of Denmark and designed by Inigo Jones. It has a parquet marble floor, vaulted roof with balcony, two large ante-rooms, views up to the observatory and of the river, and a gravelled outside space. Wonderful.

Catering: in-house; preferred caterer list. Disabled : toilet. Licence extension possible. Outside space (Queen's House): balcony; grounds.

Hempel

31-35 Craven Hill Gardens, W2 3EA (7298 9000/www.the-hempel.co.uk). Bayswater tube/Paddington tube/rail. **Available for hire** *Private rooms 9am-1am daily. Garden 9am-10.30pm daily.* **Capacity** *Private rooms 6: 16-80 seated/30-180 standing. Garden 350 seated/600 standing.* **Hire charge** call for details. Hotel
For review, *see p92*.
Catering: in-house; kitchen facilities (venue hire). Disabled: lift; toilet.

Jasmine Studios

186-188 Shepherd's Bush Road, W6 7NL (7751 1157/www.jasminestudios.com). Hammersmith tube. **Available for hire** 10am-1am daily. **Capacity** *Venue 300 standing. Private rooms 5: 20-200 standing.* **Hire charge** £500-£5,000 + VAT. **No credit cards.** Studio space
Winner of a RIBA award for design in 2007, Jasmine Studios are über-swish photographic studios by day, but can be hired for your do by day and night. What started life as a Victorian school building that has been rendered light, bright and quirky – and now has a large outside area, with innocuous planted pots around the edge – is easy to do up with candles, lights, greenery and a marquee for a summer party (evening licence until 1am, or 4am on special application). The vast main studio has natural light from the vast, angular ceiling and interlinking doors to further studios, bar, kitchens (clients must use Jasmine Street-preferred caterers) and reception area. Each studio can be hired individually; the smallest, studio five, with a standing capacity of 30, is good for intimate gatherings. Jasmine Studios has already attracted several big-cheese clients for promotions, notably Land Rover – who drove one of their jalopies into the main studio – and Sky. Check out the art – some is for sale.
Catering: preferred caterer list. Disabled: toilet. Licence extension possible (Fri/Sat).

Kiasu

48 Queensway, W2 3RY (7727 8810). Bayswater or Queensway tube. **Available for hire** noon-11pm daily. **Capacity** *Private room 40 seated.* **Minimum spend** £200 Fri-Sun. Restaurant
The name means 'afraid to be second best' and this purveyor of uncommonly good food from the Straits of Malacca offers a first-rate dinner party service in its comfortable, semi-formal upstairs dining room. The fact that it's a favourite venue

for beanos held by the Singaporean Embassy and Singapore Airlines is testament to the excellence of food and service. Smartly appointed in royal blue, with stereo speakers and a large screen, the room works well both for conferences and family parties. Clients plan the menu with the chefs, but the diverse oriental menu is suitable for most tastes: old favourites like chicken satay and spring rolls can be interspersed with more unusual dishes from the Straits, such as pai tee (pastry cups with yam bean), bamboo shoots, pork and prawn.
Big screen. Catering: in-house.

Natural History Museum

Cromwell Road, SW7 5BD (7942 5000/www.nhm.ac.uk). South Kensington tube. **Available for hire** *Hall/Earth galleries 6pm-1am daily; theatre 9am-5pm daily.* **Capacity** *Hall 650 seated/1,200 standing. Earth galleries 200 seated/400 standing. Theatre 209 seated.* **Hire charge** *Hall from £15,200. Earth galleries £8,525. Theatre £2,800.* Museum
If you're really looking for a venue to make guests gasp, there can't be many more impressive spaces than the central hall of the Natural History Museum with its cathedral-like proportions and enormous diplodocus. Space-wise it can accommodate dinner for up to 650, dancing (in the adjoining North Hall) for up to 450, buffets for up to 850 and receptions for an impressive 1,200. The Earth galleries provide a fun, star-studded space with their 'galactic' connections, while the Flett theatre and Mary Anning room are perfect for conferences, lectures and presentations. The team who organise London Fashion Week here can give you whatever help you need for your own show-stopping event.
Catering: preferred caterer list. Disabled: lift; toilet. Licence extension possible.

Townhouse

31 Beauchamp Place, SW3 1NU (7589 5080/www.lab-townhouse.com). Knightsbridge tube. **Available for hire** 4pm-midnight daily. **Capacity** *Venue 180 standing. Private rooms 3: 25-90 standing.* **Minimum spend** *1st-floor bar from £1,500 Thur-Sat.* Other prices on request. Bar
Retaining almost all the original features of the town house it once was, this attractive Mayfair bar is a classy spot for private events. Cocktails are a speciality (the in-house mixologists can create a drink for your party), there's good equipment for DJs and a feeling of exclusivity. Its location on a side street off Knightsbridge means there's a popular misconception that it's a members' bar. Despite being a fairly small venue,

VENUES

20th Century Theatre

VENUES

there are a number of options for a private party. The front bar area has floor-to-ceiling windows looking out on to the residential street outside and suits pre-party welcome drinks or networking events. Upstairs is a smaller, quieter bar area, good for corporate events, family gatherings and engagement parties – you can hire a few tables or the whole room. Below the ground floor is a snug little room, complete with cushions, sofas and a karaoke machine, perfect for an intimate celebration or a novelty team-building event. *Big screen. Catering: in-house; kitchen facilities. Music: DJ equipment.*

20th Century Theatre

291 Westbourne Grove, W11 2QA (7229 4179/www.20thcenturytheatre.com). Notting Hill Gate tube. **Available for hire** 8am-11pm daily. **Capacity** *Venue* 140 seated/250 standing. **Hire charge** £2,000 + VAT. **No credit cards**. Historic building
Laurence Olivier made his professional debut at this Grade II-listed theatre building and a sense of history and glamour prevails today. This is a dry venue (meaning you supply pretty much everything yourself) and, as such, works best for special bespoke events such as weddings, product launches, film shoots and landmark parties. The venue has a reputation for providing the backdrop to really impressive events – its sweeping staircase and high ceilings certainly look the part. Let your imagination run riot. *Catering: in-house; kitchen facilities.*

V&A

Cromwell Road, SW7 2RL (7942 2628/ www.vam.ac.uk/corporateevents). South Kensington tube. **Available for hire** *Dome/ garden* 6.30pm-2am daily. *Galleries* 6.30-11pm daily. *Theatre* 10am-11pm daily. **Capacity** *Dome* 250 seated/700 standing. *Garden* 700 standing. *Galleries 5:* 150-400 standing. *Theatre* 300 seated. **Hire charge** *Dome & garden* £7,000-£16,000. *Galleries* from £5,000. *Theatre* from £1,000. Museum
As well as being one of the world's great museums, this magnificent Victorian building offers a myriad different possibilities for entertaining in sumptuous style. Rooms and galleries can be hired here and at the newly refurbished Museum of Childhood at Bethnal Green (*see p112*). The spectacular domed entrance is an elegant and impressive setting for receptions and dinners, while the John Madejski garden is a peaceful oasis for a summer reception; pre-dinner drinks can be held in the Sculpture Galleries, but it doesn't get more classy than a reception in the Raphael Gallery, where guests are surrounded by seven of the artist's works. A private view of current exhibitions can be combined with evening receptions and dinners. Services include catering, lighting, flowers and entertainment. The maximum number for dinner is 400 and for drinks 600. *Catering: preferred caterer list. Disabled: lift; toilet. Outside space: garden (for hire).*

Children

Gone are the days when you could con six-year-olds into believing 'sleeping lions' constituted party fun before letting them gorge themselves on Skittles and Wagon Wheels. Nope, the kids of today expect quality entertainment and their parents want them sent home giddy on organic carrot batons not E numbers. It's enough to have your average parent reaching for the gin. Make it a double as you browse the reviews below for inspiration. Also check out the Party Shops & Decorations (*see p178*) chapter for fancy dress goods, balloons and party bags, Music & Entertainment (*see p148*) for children's entertainers and Organisation & Planning (*see p196*) for party organisers.

VENUES

PARTY VENUES

CENTRAL

Coram's Fields
93 Guilford Street, WC1N 1DN (7837 6138). Russell Square tube. **Available for hire** *Summer* 10am-5pm Sat, Sun. *Winter* 10am-4pm Sat, Sun. **Capacity** *Private rooms* 2: both 25. **Hire charge** £65. **No credit cards.** Playground
For review, *see p108*.
Catering: kitchen facilities available. Disabled: toilet. Outside space: Coram's Fields.

Dragon Hall
17 Stukeley Street, WC2B 5LT (7404 7274/ www.dragonhall.org.uk). Holborn tube. **Available for hire** 9am-11.30pm daily. **Capacity** *Private rooms* 3: 15-200. **Hire charge** £30-£50/hr. **No credit cards.** Community centre
This simple, airy hall is handily located in the centre of town. It's a community centre (special rates available for local residents and charities) on a quiet side street and has a range of different sized (and priced) rooms. The main hall, which can fit up to 200 people on its semi-sprung wooden floor, comes with tables and chairs, a small stage and a PA system (at extra cost), all of which can be stored away if need be. It's essentially a sports hall so you're allowed to

Science Museum. *See p117.*

decorate the place as you see fit, providing, of course, that it's all cleared out at the end of the night. The place has to be empty by 11.30pm. *Catering: kitchen facilities. Disabled: lift; toilet. Piano (hall).*

Oasis Sports Centre
32 Endell Street, WC2H 9AG (7831 1804/ www.camden.gov.uk). Tottenham Court Road tube. **Available for hire** 4.30-5.30pm Sat, Sun. **Capacity** 20. **Hire charge** £134.70.
Swimming pool
Swimming parties prove endlessly popular (with kids at least) and between 4.30pm and 5.30pm at weekends you can hire out the indoor pool at Holborn's Oasis Sports Centre. The hire fee

includes a lifeguard and there's an on-site café where the kids can chow down after exhausting themselves in the pool. If you've got enough folk to keep an eye on them, you could even take a dip yourself in the heated outdoor pool.

NORTH

Caxton House Community Centre
129 St John's Way, N19 3RQ (7263 3151/ www.caxtonhouse.org). Archway tube. **Available for hire** 9am-11pm daily. **Capacity** *Hall* 150. *Café* 60. **Hire charge** call for details. **No credit cards**. Community centre

VENUES

Coram's Fields

Centre for Wildlife Gardening

This is a magical place for a children's party: there are secluded bowers that are great for hide and seek, a sandpit, a pond buzzing with dragonflies (and home to several wild newts) and a creepy-crawly area favoured in recent years by stag beetles. Parties have to be self-catering, but there's room in the Visitors' Centre (which is lined by tanks full of stick insects) for up to 20 kids, and there's a kitchen in which to prepare food. For an additional fee, the Centre's staff can supervise educational activities, such as insect hunts and pond dipping. Book your own children's entertainer.
Best for Nature trails and bug hunts.
Must do Brace yourself for muddy footprints.
Inside tip Book well in advance.
For listings, see p113.

Clown Town

If proof of the popularity of soft play centres were ever required, Clown Town is it. Three separate play areas, graded according to age, make it ideal for siblings (and their friends) tagging along with the birthday boy or girl. The 'crawler' and 'toddler' areas have a bouncy castle, toy cars and soft shapes for babies. The main section – a three-level multi-activity frame featuring slides, ball ponds and rope climbs – is heaven for energetic kids. Several menus, from healthy sandwiches,

carrots and juice, to chips and chicken can be eaten in several party rooms. Prices from £8.95 each (including food and drink).
Best for Mixed age groups.
Must do Get a high level of noise tolerance.
Inside tip Kids love the healthy menu.
For listings, see right.

Coram's Fields

A short walk from Russell Square tube, Coram's Fields is run by an independent charitable trust as a drop-in play zone, with two rooms available for cheap hire (£65) at weekends. Both the rooms are large enough (42 x 26ft, and 35 x 18ft) for you to lay on your own entertainment: clowns, balloons, food, drink and cake (and there's a small kitchen to keep things warm or cold). Coram's Fields will also supply tables and chairs, and kids can make use of the large outdoor area with its many nooks and crannies for young explorers.
Best for Sunny days when you can make the most of the playground.
Must do Pack the kitchen with party food.
Inside tip Be prepared for repeat visits.
For listings, see p106.

Finsbury Leisure Centre

If your little ones are after a sporty party, Finsbury Leisure Centre is just the ticket. It offers two rooms for hire (the smaller starts

Caxton House is an independent community centre charity with a large sports hall which can be rented out for parties and other events. The main hall's capacity is 150 and it has a sprung floor and dimmable lighting. There's a PA system and stage as well as tables and chairs, and there's also an adjacent café which holds 60 and can be rented out separately or with the main space. It won't win any awards for atmosphere – though with a load of balloons strung up no child would notice – but in terms of size, price and practicality (there's even a small car park) – it's hard to beat.
Catering: kitchen facilities. Disabled: toilet.

Clown Town
Unit 3, Coppetts Centre, North Circular Road, N12 0QS (8361 6600). New Southgate rail. **Available for hire** 10am-4pm Mon-Fri; 10am-4.30pm Sat, Sun. **Capacity** 25. **Cost** £8.95/child (inc food & drink). Soft play centre
For review, *see left.*
Catering: in-house. Disabled: toilet.

Finchley Lido Leisure Centre
Great North Leisure Park, Chaplin Square, N12 0GL (8343 9830/www.gll.org). East Finchley tube. **Available for hire** 4.30-6.30pm Sat, Sun. **Capacity** *Leisure pool* 30. **Hire charge** £129/hr. Swimming pool
The original outdoor pool here closed in 1992, but was redeveloped four years later with a Vue multiplex cinema, bowling centre and several restaurants. The lido is now far smaller, but still has a pleasing grassy terrace. Indoors, swimmers can plough up and down the main pool or enjoy the leisure pool's wave machine and picture windows. The leisure pool is available for children's parties and can be hired between 4.30pm and 6.30pm at the weekends.
Outside space: terrace.

Gill's Cookery Workshop
7 North Square, NW11 7AA (8458 2608/ www.gillscookeryworkshop.co.uk). Golders Green tube. **Capacity** 12-20. **Cost** from £30. **No credit cards**. Cookery workshop
It's never too early to get the little darlings working in the kitchen. Parties of between 12 and 20 children can decide on their own themes or menus to make on the day at the Cookery Workshop, under the capable supervision of Gill Roberts. What you do with their new-found skills when they get home is up to you – but don't be surprised if they're keen to help out with the cooking. Two-day holiday classes for six to 13 year-olds and Saturday morning sessions for three- to eight- year-olds are also available.

at just £20 per hour), both ideal for children's birthdays. Tables can be provided, but parties must be self catered. The basement area easily accommodates up to 100 children and comes fully equipped for a disco, with wall mirrors for admiring those dance moves. Various sports (football and badminton are especially popular) can be incorporated into a party. Dads, dust off those trainers!
Best for Older kids.
Must do Rope in parents prepared to help out.
Inside tip Last-minute bookings are not unheard of – give them a call.
For listings, see p112.

Puppet Theatre Barge
A children's party venue with an unusual twist, the Puppet Barge is moored on the Grand Union Canal near Warwick Avenue, though in summer (July-Oct) it can be found on the River Thames. The whole boat may be rented out for an hour of fun, with the parents providing the food and cake (£50). Or you can book a masterful puppetry performance to go with your party hour. The barge is delightfully colourful, heated in the winter (and cooled in the summer), and can seat up to 50 people.
Best for A party with a difference.
Must do Splash out on a performance.
Inside tip Send invites with a watery theme.
For listings, see p117.

VENUES

Highbury Fields One & Two O'Clock Club

Bandstand, Highbury Fields, near Baalbec Road, N5 1UP (7704 9337/www.islington. gov.uk). Highbury & Islington tube/rail. **Available for hire** *Summer* noon-6pm Sat, Sun. *Winter* 10am-4pm Sat, Sun. **Capacity** 20 (more if using outdoor area). **Hire charge** (plus £150 returnable deposit) *Summer* £80. *Winter* £70. Play centre

Tucked away in Highbury Fields – a green oasis in built-up Islington – is this drop-in children's centre with indoor and outdoor play areas for high-octane kids. The salubrious location makes it perfect for summer parties, and the hall can be hired out at weekends. Self-catered parties get full use of the equipment, including drawing kits inside, and climbing frames, play houses and toys outside. The field is enclosed, with convenient benches for worn-out parents, and it's only a ten-minute walk from Highbury & Islington tube.

Catering: kitchen facilities. Outside space: play area (for hire).

Kentish Town City Farm

1 Cressfield Close, off Grafton Road, NW5 4BN (7916 5421/www.ktcityfarm.org.uk). Kentish town tube. **Available for hire** 2-4pm Sat, Sun. **Cost** £50 (plus £50 returnable deposit).

For review, see p112.
Outside space: farm.

Topsy Turvy World

Brent Cross Shopping Centre, NW4 3FP (8359 9927/www.topsyturvyworld.com). Brent Cross tube, then 210 bus/Hendon Central tube, then 143, 186 bus. **Available for hire** *Venue* 6-8pm Mon-Sat; 5.30-7pm Sun. *Private rooms* 10.30am-6pm daily. **Capacity** *Venue* 25-300. *Private rooms* 4: 10-35. **Hire charge** *Venue* £150 plus charge per child; call for details. *Private rooms* from £10.50/child. Soft play centre

Located near Brent Cross Shopping Centre, this soft-play centre allows kids to let off steam while their parents sip cappuccinos. The equipment on offer is many and varied, including foam ball shooters, spinning platforms and big slides. The clean and spacious party room caters for a minimum of ten children, with classic buffet food being served up by attentive staff. All party bookings allow for 90 minutes of free play, giving the tykes time to tire themselves out. There's a pulsating laser tag option for the over-sixes, and you can also hire out the whole venue (minimum 25 children).

Catering: in-house. Disabled: toilet.

EAST

Delta Force

Aveley Road, Upminster, RM14 2TW (0844 477 5050/www.paintballgames.co.uk). Upminster tube/rail. **Available for hire** *Private games* 9.15am-4pm daily. **Cost** £17.50/person (minimum 40). Paintball

Want your young teenagers to get active and messy with a vengeance? Paintball giant Delta Force has several branches close enough to the M25 to be convenient for Londoners. The sites at Billericay and Upminster in Essex are both within walking distance of train and tube stations. Children have to be over 11 to don their fatigues and participate in the fun. They get 150 paintballs to fire between 9.15am and 4pm, plus a pizza lunch – all for £17.50 per head. If you're planning a particularly large manoeuvre, every 15th person goes free.

Catering: in-house.

Departure Art Centre

649 Commercial Road, E14 7LW (7702 8802/www.depart.in). Limehouse DLR/rail. **Available for hire** 5-10pm Mon; 5.30-11pm Sat; call for details Sun. **Capacity** *Hall* 40-60. **Hire charge** £150. **No credit cards.** Community centre

Departure is a Christian Mission community centre in east London, which hosts exhibitions, classes and meetings. It has a bright and modern café which serves halal food and a hall which can accommodate up to 60. The hall can be hired out

NOTE

ORGANISING A NAMING CEREMONY
1. Choose a name
   (www.babycentre.co.uk/pregnancy/naming)
2. Find a venue
   Most local register offices (www.gro.gov.uk) now offer simple civil naming ceremonies for children. Many parents also choose to host a celebration at home or in a small, child-friendly venue such as the ones listed in this chapter.
3. Choose a celebrant
   You can lead the ceremony yourself or the British Humanist Association (www.humanism.org.uk) can provide a trained 'celebrant', who can help you to prepare the ceremony and lead it on the day.
For more information:
www.civilceremonies.co.uk

VENUES

for birthday parties and wedding receptions, but because of the centre's own religious affiliation and links with the local, mainly Muslim, community, it's better suited to children's birthday parties and low-key events than riotous shindigs (alcohol is neither served nor permitted on the premises and all brought-in food must be halal). *Catering: in-house; kitchen facilities (£50 hire charge). Disabled: toilet. Outside space: roof terrace (for hire).*

Finsbury Leisure Centre
Norman Street, EC1V 3PU (7253 2346/ www.aquaterra.org). Old Street tube/rail. **Available for hire** Sat, Sun; call for details. **Capacity** *Activity room 30. Basement 100.* **Hire charge** *Activity room £20/hr. Basement £40/hr.* Sports centre
For review, *see p108.*
Catering-in-house. Disabled: lift; toilet.

Golden Lane Leisure Centre
Golden Lane Estate, Fann Street, EC1Y 0SH (7250 1464/www.cityoflondon.gov.uk). Barbican tube/rail. **Available for hire** 2-3pm Sun. **Capacity** 40. **Hire charge** £65; £85 with party room. Swimming pool
Situated a two-minute walk away from the Barbican tube station, Golden Lane Leisure Centre hires out its 20-metre pool for children's parties on Sundays. Two lifeguards supervise the pool session for an hour, then the kids can retire to the party room for another hour (for an extra £20). Here they can tuck into whatever food you care to provide or take part in further activities. There is a music system available.
Disabled: toilet.

St George's Pools
221 The Highway, E1W 3PB (7709 9714/ www.towerhamlets.gov.uk). Shadwell DLR. **Available for hire** 4.30-5.30pm Sat, Sun. **Capacity** 20 (plus 10 adults). **Hire charge** £30.20/hr. Swimming pool
On Saturdays and Sundays, St George's 'baby pool' can be hired for watery children's party fun at a rate of £30.20 per hour. The maximum numbers allowed is 20 but there's space for parents to come along and supervise too. A lifeguard is included in the price. You can bring your own food for afterwards and there are rooms available for hire to set it all up in (an additional £20). A music system can be provided.

V&A Museum of Childhood
Cambridge Heath Road, E2 9PA (8983 5200/ recorded info 8980 2415/www.vam.ac.uk/ moc). Bethnal Green tube/rail. **Available for hire** 10am-5pm Sat, Sun. **Capacity** *Private rooms 2: both 25.* **Hire charge** £100. Museum
A frisbee throw from Bethnal Green tube, the Museum of Childhood is an outpost of the V&A, paying homage to childhood past and present. As well as the intriguing displays of games, toys, dolls and the like, there's a great birthday space downstairs, with seating for 15-25 children. Bright and colourful, it has a film projector and a sink for cleaning up those inevitable spills. Available for hire at weekends in three-hour slots, prices vary depending on the package, which can include menus from their café, special activities involving arts and crafts, or a story trail around the museum (£100 per story trail assistant). *Catering: in-house. Disabled: toilet. Outside space: picnic area.*

KENTISH TOWN CITY FARM

Founded in 1972, Kentish Town City Farm is London's oldest and stretches way beyond the farmyard into precious pasture and well-tended vegetable gardens by the railway line. Livestock includes farmyard ducks, goats, pigs, horses, cows, chickens, a cat, dogs and sheep. There's also a pond with a dipping platform that is full of frogs. But best of all, the farm now has a brand new space – usually reserved for teaching schoolchildren – that it can rent out for children's parties. Slots are available between 2pm to 4pm on Saturday's and Sunday's. Hire is for the classroom only, but there is a kitchen where you can prepare the kids' food (and make yourself and your helpers innumerable cups of tea).
For listings, see p110.

VENUES

SOUTH

All Fired Up Ceramics Café

34 East Dulwich Road, SE22 9AX (7732 6688/www.allfiredupceramics.co.uk). East Dulwich rail. **Available for parties** 9.30am-6pm Mon, Tue, Sat; 9.30am-10pm Wed-Fri; 10.30am-4.30pm Sun. **Capacity** 8-20. **Cost** £10-£12.50/child. *Café/pottery centre*

As the name suggests, All Fired Up Ceramics Café gives children a fine opportunity to release their creativity and have a party with art at its heart. A full range of different, ready-to-paint ceramics are on offer, from plates and cups, to robots, planes and treasure boxes. Every party gets personalised invitations, balloons, painting instruction and supervision, and a personalised plate for the birthday boy or girl. Sessions last an hour and a half and you can bring your own cake (buffets can be arranged on request). *Catering: in-house (£5/child).*

Centre for Wildlife Gardening

28 Marsden Road, SE15 4EE (7252 9186/ www.wildlondon.org.uk). East Dulwich rail. **Available for hire** 2-4.30pm Sun. **Capacity** 20. **Hire charge** £60. **No credit cards**. *Garden*
For review, *see p109.*
Catering: kitchen facilities. Outside space: wildlife gardens.

Crawley Studios

39 Wood Vale, SE23 3DS (8516 0002). Forest Hill rail. **Available for parties** call for details. **Capacity** 5-10. **Cost** from £8/child. **No credit cards**. *Pottery studio*

Smaller, more intimate pottery-painting parties can be arranged at Marie-Lou's studio which is attached to her home. The cost usually depends on what's to be painted; selections range from popular animal ornaments (around £8) to cups and bowls (£10-£15 including firing charge). Items are ready for collection a week later. Refreshments are provided free (tea and coffee, and hot chocolate for the kids).

East Dulwich Community Centre

46-64 Darrell Road, SE22, (8693 4411/ 3810/www.eastdulwichcommunitycentre.org. uk). East Dulwich rail. **Available for hire** 9am-11pm Sat; 11am-9pm Sun (available to community groups/charities Mon-Fri). **Capacity** 120. **Hire charge** £35-£40/hr. **No credit cards**. *Community centre*

It's not exactly swish but this community centre's hall for hire is fairly indestructible and excellent value for money. It fits up to 120 people and has a raised stage at one end and access to a large playground. This, and the fact that there are ample toilets, makes the place ideal for kids' parties. There is also a kitchen, which is useful for preparing and storing any food and drink you bring along to fuel 'em with.
Catering: kitchen facilities.

Pavilion Café Dulwich

Dulwich Park, off College Road, SE21 7BQ (8299 1383/www.pavilioncafedulwich.co.uk). West Dulwich rail/P4 bus. **Available for parties** 8.30am-6pm Mon-Fri. **Capacity** 20. **Cost** from £5.50/child. **No credit cards**. *Park café*

VENUES

If the British weather could be relied upon, then summer children's parties in this corner of south London would be easy to organise: make a picnic and let the kids wear themselves out tearing around Dulwich Park's verdant, carefully landscaped acres. But you can't rely on the weather, and that's where the Pavilion Café comes in. Rent one half of this airy single-storey building in the middle of the park, then you've got somewhere for the children to shelter if the rain sets in. The café offers excellent, healthy (low-salt) party food, with lots of fruit and fresh vegetables, and they'll bake you a cake to your specifications (or even erect a tower of individually decorated fairy cakes). It's worth noting that the café is licensed, and is happy to make a jug of Pimm's for worn-out grown-ups. *Catering: in-house. Outside space: park.*

WEST

Campaign Paintball
Old Lane, Cobham, Surrey KT11 1NH (01932 865999/www.campaignpaintball.com). Effingham Junction rail. **Available for hire** *Private games 9am-4.30pm Sat, Sun.* **Cost** £24.95-£34.50/person (minimum 25). Paintball
This battle-ready outfit in the heart of rural Surrey has a junior wing called Campaign Young Gunz. Paintballing days for ten- to 15-year-olds take place at weekends and school holidays (see the website for details). For £24.95 per child including 300 paintballs (£34.50 for 500 balls) you receive eight to ten games, tuition, a battlesuit with body armour, semi-automatic paintball guns and a barbecue lunch. Campaign trophies and team photographs are handed out after all the fun. *Catering: in-house.*

Eddie Catz Wimbledon
42 Station Road, SW19 2LP (0845 201 1268/ www.eddiecatz.com). South Wimbledon tube. **Available for hire** *Venue 6-8pm Mon-Fri; 6.30-8.30pm Sat, Sun. Private room 10am-6pm daily.* **Capacity** *Venue 100. Private rooms 4: 10-49.* **Hire charge** *Venue from £200. Private rooms £8-£13.99/child.* Play centre
As larger-than-life tigers go, Eddie is more pussycat than big cat and his huge play centres (there's also one in Putney) make birthday parties a doddle. A variety of equipment is on offer for all ages, from babies and toddlers (padded soft play area and bouncy chairs) to kids up to 10 (a huge play frame, video games, a disco room and a reading zone). Party bookings require a minimum of ten children (accompanied by

unlimited adults and babies) and the centre offers private rooms, free invitations and a choice of hot or cold menus. Optional extras include a personal visit from Eddie himself, balloon modelling and face painting. *Catering: in-house.*

Gambado
7 Station Court, Townsmead Road, SW6 2PY (7384 1635/www.gambado.com). Fulham Broadway tube, then 391 bus. **Available for hire** *9.30am-6.30pm daily.* **Capacity** *Private area 30.* **Hire charge** £18.50-£26/child. Play centre
Gambado is pretty much the king of play centres. All the stuff that experienced party organisers expect – colourful climbing frames and slides – are present and correct, but Gambado goes the extra mile with its dodgems and a carousel. Party packages include invitations, a throne for the party boy or girl, balloons, a party host, and, of course, a choice of hot or cold food. There's a large café area for over-stretched parents, and after their 80 minutes of full-on fun, you can guarantee the children will be grateful for those seats too. *Catering: in-house.*

Pottery Café
735 Fulham Road, SW6 5UL (7736 2157/ www.pottery-cafe.com). Parsons Green tube/ 14, 414 bus. **Available for parties** *11am-6pm Mon; 10am-6pm Tue-Fri; 10-11am Sat; 11am-noon Sun.* **Capacity** *30.* **Cost** £19.95/child. Café/pottery centre
Paint-a-pot centres have mushroomed in the UK, but this place was among the first to offer a paint-your-own crockery deal. Children's parties can

BABY SHOWERS

Kate Riordan investigates the latest gift-gathering ploy.

Berkeley

If you're not sure what a baby shower is, quite honestly where have you been? Predictably American in origin (though an ancient Hindu ritual bears similarities), a baby shower is a (generally) female-only gathering where a pregnant mother-to-be is showered with baby gifts by her friends. In almost all cases, lots of cake, games, tummy rubbing and a glass of champers is involved. The cynical among us would say that it's just another manipulative ruse to part us from our cash; a more positive approach is that any excuse for a party, especially one that involves lots of cake, should be welcomed.

Traditionally a shower was held at home but it has become de rigueur to spend the afternoon in a luxury hotel, being waited on hand, foot and bump. Both the Berkeley (Wilton Place, SW1X 7RL; 7235 6000, www.the-berkeley.co.uk) and Hertfordshire's the Grove (Chandler's Cross, Hertfordshire WD3 4TG; 01923 807807, www.thegrove.co.uk) hotels – 25 minutes by train from Euston – offer baby shower packages that combine beauty treatments with a themed spread of treats. Meanwhile, Cupcake (Unit 6, Riverside Quarter, Point Pleasant, SW18 1GG; 8875 1065, www.cupcakemum.com), a spa and members' club in Wandsworth for new and expectant mums, also hosts afternoon teas with beauty treats (non-members can book).

Minutely less indulgent are Mamas & Papas baby shower buffets at Cibo (256-258 Regent Street, W1B 3AF; 01484 438476, www.mamas andpapas.co.uk), the flagship store's cafe on Regent Street.

Websites a-plenty have sprung up to cater to those organising their own do, from which you can order themed tableware, set up gift lists, and consider investing in a nappy cake – a tiered display of real nappies intended as a table decoration (honestly). Free ideas for games to play is another area covered comprehensively on the internet. One 'traditional' game, presumably for the unsqueamish, involves blind-tasting baby food out of a (clean) disposable nappy. For the uninitiated, there's an entire baby-crazy alternative world out there.

USEFUL WEBSITES

Babbee Baby Showers
www.babbee.com
Useful site covering questions of etiquette as well as supplying games ideas, recipes and even poems.

Baby Concierge
Studio 109, 300 Kensal Road, W10 5BE (8964 5500/www.babyconcierge.co.uk).

A one-stop shop for baby garments, gear and gifts. Book an advisory consultation on what you need for your nursery or set up a gift list.

Baby Shower Games
www.baby-shower-games.org
Lots of games ideas, including ice breakers, as well as tips on themed showers and a handful of gift ideas.

Baby Shower Host
01225 819988/www.babyshowerhost.co.uk
Styles itself the UK's largest site for shower decorations, games, cakes and favours.

Elias & Grace
158 Regents Park Road, NW1 8XN (7449 0574/www.eliasandgrace.com).
Designer togs for babies, kids and expectant yummy mums. Labels include Petit Bateau, Stella McCartney and the in-house brand.

Home Mummy
0844 800 9498/www.homemummy.co.uk
Glam evening dresses, chic wrap dresses and slimming trousers all designed to flatter the bump for that perfect baby shower outfit.

Jellybabys
01737 550844/www.jellybabys.co.uk/ free_baby_shower_games.php
Gifts to order online, plus a page of 40 free games ideas.

John Lewis Nursery List
0845 600 2202/www.johnlewisnurserylist.com
Ever-reliable John Lewis has a great choice of nursery equipment.

Parties in a Box
0113 282 8162/www.partiesinabox.co.uk
Cheap and chirpy tableware, decorations and baby shower bingo.

Shower my Baby
0845 224 0514/www.showermybaby.co.uk
This dedicated site has everything, from guest signing books to personalised satin sashes and the obligatory nappy cake.

Snowflake Showers
0777 571 2250/www.snowflakeshowers.co.uk
Baby shower kits including invitations, table decorations and a 'rule book' (£160, 10 guests).

be arranged for £19.95 per head, which includes invitations, party food (bring your own cake) and all the necessary materials and staff. Alternatively, you can bring your own sandwiches. You collect the children's works of art after they've been glazed and fired. The café also sells fruit juices, Byron Bay cookies and Union coffee. *Catering: in-house.*

Puppet Theatre Barge
Opposite 35 Blomfield Road, Little Venice, W9 2PF (7249 6876/www.puppetbarge.com). Warwick Avenue tube. **Available for hire** call for details. **Capacity** 55. **Hire charge** *Party* £50. *Exclusive performance & party* £350. Barge/theatre
For review, *see p108.*

Science Museum
Exhibition Road, SW7 2DD (7942 4460/ booking & information line 0870 870 4868/ www.sciencemuseum.org.uk). South Kensington tube. **Available for parties** *Term-time* 10am-6pm daily. **Capacity** 10-20. **Cost** £50 + £11-£12.50/child. Museum
Got at least 10 children hungry for scientific know-how on your hands? The Science Museum is likely to have the answer. From the IMAX 3D cinema and SimEx Simulator (a motion simulator ride in which kids can be chased by a dinosaur or speed through space) to the Deep Blue café, there's plenty here to entertain a wide variety of ages. The museum does party packages that take full advantage of the rides, and include a co-ordinator to help the day run smoothly. Goody bags (£5.95 each) and cakes (£24) are also available, and free party invitations can be sent via the museum's website: www.sciencemuseum.org.uk. *Catering: in-house. Disabled: lift; toilet.*

Sutton Arena Leisure Centre
Middleton Road, Carshalton, SM5 1SL (8770 4088/www.gll.org). Sutton Common rail. **Available for hire** *Football party* noon-4.45pm Sat, Sun. *Magic Castle* 4.30-5.30pm Mon-Fri; 12.15-5.15pm Sat, Sun. **Capacity** *Football party* 20. *Magic Castle* 25. **Hire charge** *Football party* £75. *Magic Castle* £104.25. Sports centre
With either a football party or Merlin's Magic Castle Adventure Play Land (how much more exciting can it get?) to choose from, you can bet that the almost boundless energy of your average child will be exhausted at the Sutton Arena. And grown-ups will appreciate the free parking. A room for after is provided where you can either consume your own refreshments, or have the café arrange the catering. Beforehand, you can hire out the entire Merlin's Magic Castle for an

hour, with its ball pits, climbing frames and just about everything else you'd expect from a soft play centre. The football party also lasts an hour, and both packages allow you to use the room for 45 minutes afterwards.
Catering: in-house. Disabled: toilet.

PARTIES AT HOME

COOKERY & CREATIVE

Cookie Crumbles
8876 9912/www.cookiecrumbles.net.
Capacity 6-30. **Cost** from £165 + VAT.
Carola Weymouth and her team have taught more than 10,000 children to cook since CC was set up. The well-run cooking workshops offer an enjoyable introduction to food preparation for youngsters from four to 15. During the parties children have a load of fun creating their own celebration tea. Menus are tailored to suit very little chefs and Weymouth has devised some great ideas for sophisticated teen dinner parties for the 11-15 age range too. A two-hour party starts at £165 (plus VAT) for six kids; the price covers everything, including shopping and mopping up all the flour and sugar children have been crunching underfoot. Bonus!

Soap & Bubble Company
0845 430 0130/www.soapandbubble.com.
Capacity 8-20. **Cost** from £175.
Creativity can be a messy business, which makes S&B's parties a piece of clean inspiration. Children make their own soap, bubble and bath treats to take home. Creations include floating duck soap, bath bombs, chocolate lip balm, body glitter and Flower Power bath salt. You can book a photographer to capture all the special moments for an extra fee, so that each party guest will receive a record of the day. The party package costs £175 for up to eight children. Older kids and teens can take part in workshops on skincare and facial scrubs.

MAKEOVERS

Magical Makeovers
01932 244347/07957 681824/www.
magicalmakeovers.com. **Capacity** 5-20.
Cost from £150. **No credit cards.**
Girly girls (aged six to 16) will thoroughly enjoy the services of MM, a friendly beauty therapist with good child skills and a big bag of make-up, nail polishes, hair equipment and endless patience to prettify the celebrants (usually between five and 12 girls). The children are given hair accessories to keep. Prices start at £150 for eight participants for up to two hours. The new spa party package (for 11-18s) offers gentle facials, make-up lessons, manicure and pedicure.

Mini Makeovers
8398 0107/www.minimakeovers.com.
Capacity 4-40. **Cost** from £160.
No credit cards.
Mini Makeovers provides beauty parties with added bells and whistles. With a staff-to-child ratio of one to four, hypo-allergenic cosmetics, disco lights and music as part of the package, and a pink stretch limo an optional extra, girls aged ten to 15 can indulge fairy and princess fantasies, or learn dance routines or preening.

When *we* were kids, little blue men called... **V&A Museum of Childhood**. *See p112.*

VENUES

Guests receive a party bag with hair accessories, bracelet or necklace. Prices start at £160 for eight children. French manicures, a catwalk and a photo shoot are also available.

NOVELTY

Party Bus

07836 605032/www.childrenspartybus.co.uk.
Capacity 24. **Cost** from £350.
A converted coach bedecked with stars is one way of keeping party debris out of the house. It holds up to 24 children (without adults). On-board events, such as games, magic or a disco, are tailored to the age group (from fours to nines). The bus parks outside for two hours and costs from £350, including catering (you provide the cake). Venues within the Low Emission Zone (roughly within the M25) have to pay a surcharge of £200.

PERFORMANCE

Blueberry Playsongs Parties

8677 6871/www.blueberry.clara.co.uk.
Capacity 20. **Cost** from £85.
Guitar-led song and dance for children aged one to five is Blueberry's speciality. Mini-gigs last 45 minutes, and prices start at £85 for up to 20 children. Puppets, balloons and parachute games are included, and there's a gift for the birthday child too.

Club Dramatika!

8883 7110. **Capacity** call for details. **Cost** from £80. **No credit cards**.
If your name's Mrs Worthington, you'll no doubt heed Noel Coward's advice and give Club Dramatika! a wide berth. If not, then Vicky Levy's fun-packed drama parties for birthday kids with thespian leanings could be the start of something big. Parties cost £80 for one hour, £150 for two. Phone for details of after-school sessions in north London for children aged from five.

Dramatic Dreams

8741 1809/www.dramaticdreams.com.
Capacity 20. **Cost** from £350.
No credit cards.
Arwen Burnett and team send out a questionnaire to find out all about the birthday child. On the day, two actors (for up to 20 children) bring round props, face-paints and a script. The children (aged from five) play warm-up games, the actors tell them the plot, then everyone acts it out. This costs from £350 for two hours. DD also offers after-school and holiday drama workshops in south-west London.

Finn Jordan
FIVE-YEAR-OLD AND BOUNCY CASTLE FAN

I've been to three parties in the last month. Bouncy castles are best, but some of my friends have boring parties with too many girls.
The best party I've ever been to was one that had a bouncy castle *and* a slide as well.
I went as Mike (the one-eyed green one) from *Monsters Inc* when I had to dress up for a fancy dress party.
Mike from Monsters Inc is also my ideal party guest.
The best party games are just running around and jumping up and down on bouncy castles.
The party food I like the most is sausages and pizza.
For my 6th birthday party I would like to have a big bouncy castle on a beach. I love bouncy castles.
Adults can come to my party but they can't go on the bouncy castle because they're too big for it.
The best way to impress girls when you're at a party is to stick your tongue out at them.
The best birthday present ever would be a bike.
My coolest party outfit is my Mike from *Monsters Inc* one.
The party music I most like to dance to is Bon Jovi's 'Bad Medicine'.
When it's playing I just love jumping up and down it.
And I never get bored with bouncy castles, of course.

Finn Jordan lives in Hertfordshire and has never been to a party with a bouncy castle that he didn't have a great time at.

VENUES

PARTY SURVIVAL ABC

Ask them what they want
Some children prefer a relaxed game of footie and a few pizzas to the full-on party production.

Be age appropriate
Two year-olds don't get magicians, and will scream at clowns; ten year-olds might sneer at tricks eight year-olds adore.

Chat up other parents
Word of mouth is often the best way to find an entertainer.

Don't try to do too much
A bouncy castle, face painter, arts and crafts, not to mention tea and games – all in the space of a few hours – can over-stimulate the children.

Eject the other parents (nicely)
Too much parental involvement can distract the children (and the entertainer), and you don't want to be topping up wine glasses while you sort out the party bags.

Kate Gielgud Acting Parties
8964 5490/www.tiddleywinks.co.uk.
Capacity call for details. **Cost** from £350.
Re-enactments of kids' classics and action-adventure stories are Kate Gielgud-Killick's forte (acting's in the blood; she's Sir John's great-niece). Costumes and props are provided for plays that may have James Bond or various supermodels in their plots; younger children may prefer *Sleeping Beauty* or *Chitty Chitty Bang Bang*. Whatever you opt for, a good time will be had by all. Prices start at £300 for two hours (four- to seven-year-olds) and from £350 for three hours for eights to 13s.

MovieParty
7387 4341/www.youngfilmacademy. co.uk. **Capacity** 12. **Cost** £1,200.
No credit cards.
Film-making courses at the Young Film Academy are currently the sole provider of movie parties in the capital. The MovieParty concept – planning, shooting, editing and screening a film in a single day – costs £1,200 (includes a DVD per child plus two extra for the host family).

SCIENCE

Mad Science
0845 330 1881/www.madscience.org/ greaterlondon. **Capacity** 20-30. **Cost** from £195.

Bring on the batty professor! Children of all ages have a blast at these excellent science-based parties. Two mad scientists come to you, bearing a portable laboratory. They entertain the troops with bubbling potions, indoor fireworks, rocket launchers and other irresistible tours de force. Choose from Super Cool and Mega parties; prices start from £195. Party bags start at £4.99.

Science Boffins
0800 019 2636/www.scienceboffins.com.
Capacity 5-30. **Cost** from £200.
Pragmatists rest assured: Science Boffins organise parties that are thoroughly empirical in both style and content. A team of boffins (in reality, trained professionals with backgrounds in teaching, science and theatre) arrives at your chosen venue to provide a meticulously conceived party experience with no danger or mess, including exciting demonstrations, and interactive experiments and races. Keeping children from five years to pre-teens entertained with scientific wonders such as self-inflating balloons and light that bends, it's all about educational fun that aims to inform as well as entertain.

SPORT

League One Sports Academy
8446 0891/www.leagueone.co.uk.
Capacity/cost call for details. **No credit cards**.
Warming up for 2012? Coach Danny Grant and his team organise sporty activities for children aged between three and 12, ranging from basketball, football and cricket to a full mini Olympics. Varying skill levels aren't generally a problem, as the coaches will cater for everyone's needs. Prices (phone for details) cover equipment, coaches' fees and a winner's trophy for the birthday child. Venue hire can be arranged for an extra charge.

Pro-Active 4 Parties & Entertainment
0845 257 5005/www.proactive4parties.co.uk.
Capacity call for details. **Cost** from £200.
No credit cards.
Children (aged from two) are kept jumping, shooting and scoring in sports-themed parties organised by hyper-active minders. Prices vary (more children, more dosh), but start at about £200. Activities may include ultimate frisbee and circus skills, depending on the birthday child's proclivities. More sedentary pursuits include makeover and face-painting parties, balloon modelling and discos. Pro-Active can set up parties in homes, but most sports events take place in more spacious venues (booked by parents).

Essentials

Food & Drink

There are few things more important to your average partygoer than good food and booze. Whether you're planning a dazzling dinner party for 12 or a banquet for 200, enticing canapés, cool cocktails or even just a stupendous centrepiece cake can really make a celebration. In this chapter, you'll find innovative catering companies and great cheese shops, drinks suppliers and bakeries, along with bar and hog roast hire, the best delis for dinner-party cheats and plenty of unusual ideas. Raise a glass. Tuck in. Eat, drink and be merry.

Arnold & Henderson

CATERERS

Also take a look at the party planners listed in Organisation & Planning (*see p196*) as many of these also offer catering services.

Amaze in Taste
0844 800 1655/www.amazeintaste.com.
Cost from £10/head (minimum 25). **Delivery** no. **No credit cards**.
For properly hearty food, with excellent booze-soaking potential, try serving Amaze in Taste's imaginative 'bowl food' at your party: mushroom risotto with parmesan and parsley, perhaps, or lamb tagine and couscous. More traditional party food offerings include finger-food buffets, from £10 per head for 25 people.

Ang-Mcguire Catering
115 Ramsden Road, SW12 8RD (07958 478049/www.angmcguirecatering.com).
Balham tube/rail. **Cost** from £14.50/head (drinks party). **Delivery** no. **No credit cards**.
Balham-based Judy Ang-Mcguire is Malaysian, and her company's cuisine combines influences from across Asia, although she can also prepare western food if asked. Presentation is 'oriental' – bamboo baskets and so on – but smart rather than kitsch. Costs tend to average £25 per head plus overheads, depending, of course, on what kind of catering you want. Judy asks for a week's notice at least but says she will be flexible if she can. She can also supply any extras and is happy to staff a bar if you want to provide your own drinks. If you get a taste for her catering, you can always attend one of Judy's cookery courses.

Arnold & Henderson

Rochelle School, Rochelle Canteen, Arnold Circus, E2 7ES (7729 5667/www.arnoldand henderson.com). Liverpool Street tube/rail.
Cost from £90/head. **Delivery** no.
Caterers of the moment Melanie Arnold and Margot Henderson (wife of St John's Fergus) set up their business way back in 1995. Now working out of dedicated kitchens at Rochelle School, they provide simple, seasonal and stylish food to clients including Agent Provocateur, Frieze, Mario Testino, Penguin, Vogue and Volvo. There's a St John (*see p50*) sensibility to the tantalising menus, which include fuss-free, flavour-packed dishes such as langoustines and mayonnaise, spatchcock quails, baked brill and lancashire hotpot. Feasts and weddings (from £140 per head) are a real speciality – think glam oyster bars, imaginative drinks (black velvets, real ales or a spectacular eau de vie, perhaps) and seriously satisfying canapés (welsh rarebit, salt cod cakes, fat radishes served with butter). Arnold & Henderson can also provide event production services and ins to some of the coolest venues in town. A caterer with edge.

Cellar Society

Unit 4, Falcon Park, NW10 1RZ (8453 7141/ www.cellarsociety.com). Neasden tube.
Minimum spend £2,000. **Delivery** no.
No credit cards.
This is top-end catering: Cellar Society has an exclusive contract with Bulgari and Prada, and catered the *Ocean's 13* Monaco cast party. The company doesn't do drop-offs, as all food is made fresh on-site, and has a minimum spend

RECIPE

Fabulously creative and on the ball, David and Simon Wolanski's Recipe provides imaginative catering to clients including the *Guardian* and Marvel Entertainment. We're talking dishes that'll really get your guests talking (think individually served, mini-Christmas dinners, food stations and hearty 'bowl food') with lots of seasonal specials and interesting but unfussy ingredients. You could serve up booze-soaking bowls of slow roast lamb with mash and white balsamic shallots, or offer a 'grab food' menu featuring the likes of cones of root vegetable chips, sesame miso salmon skewers and sun-dried tomato risotto balls. The carefully thought-out sit-down dinners are equally wonderful, with the likes of carpaccio of beef with rocket, gorgonzola and pear among the starters, pan-fried seabass on lemon crushed potatoes for mains and warm chocolate tart with honeycomb and ice cream just one of many indulgent desserts. It's enough to make you book them right now just so you can go to a tasting. Best of all, the owners have a relaxed, easy charm and the sort of encyclopaedic knowledge of food trends that makes it easy to ensure your event has the edge. Businesses in need of inspiring sustenance should check out the company's office catering arm, the Office Diner (www.officediner.co.uk), which supplies fabulous sandwich and salad platters to hip workers around town.
For listings, see p130.

of £2,000. Bookings are taken up to two weeks in advance and party extras are no problem – they have organised tennis competitions, puppeteers and even a visiting animal zoo in the past. 'People give us the concept and we put our creative hats on and come up with the ideas,' says their spokesperson.

Chester Boyd Classic
111 Charterhouse Street, EC1M 6AW (7251 7171/www.chesterboyd.co.uk). Barbican tube. **Cost** *from £41.95/head (3-course dinner).* **Delivery** *yes.*
If you want posh, these are your go-to guys: the company caters Buckingham Palace's garden parties. But CBC is not quite as pricey as you might expect: canapés (prawn cocktail spoons, bang bang chicken) or a finger buffet start at £24 per head. A sit-down dinner, meanwhile, starts at £41.95 per head, with an eight-person minimum. Menus have crowd-pleasing appeal: think smoked tuna niçoise, posh fish and chips, and apple crumble. Next day delivery isn't generally an option, but they always do their best to be accommodating. Anything from furniture to theme ideas can also be supplied. Delivery charges start at £250.

Cooks & Partners
Unit 21, Talina Centre, Bagley's Lane, SW6 2BW (7731 5282/www.cooksandpartners. co.uk). Fulham Broadway tube. **Cost** *from £14.95/head (minimum 10).* **Delivery** *yes.* **No credit cards**.
This company can offer pretty much anything you like from canapés (£15.50 per head) through 'bowl food' (£17.50) to a seated meal (from £34.50; these prices don't include the cost of staff). There is no minimum spend but there's a £70-£100 charge for delivery, depending on where you are and what you want. And a week's notice is the minimum required. Still, they will supply any extras you want, from glasses to the liquid to go in them – drinks menus include classic homemade lemonade and potent mojitos. Canapé menus are imaginative, including bloody mary jellies with celery spears and rare peppered steak on a fat chip, while 'bowl food' spans paneer tossed with shallots, peppers and chilli, and green tea and banana cake with toffee sauce.

El Vergel
8 Lant Street, SE1 1QR (7357 0057/ www.elvergel.co.uk). Borough tube. **Cost** *from £10 (minimum 30).* **Delivery** *yes.*
El Vergel provides catering for weddings, outdoor events, exhibitions and conferences, and also offers a party-planning service. Stella de Garcia and Kiko Sanhueza blend Latin American and Mediterranean influences to create fabulous fusion food. Canapés (from £10 per head) might include Chilean village bread with refried bean spread or smoked salmon and guacamole. Vegetarian finger buffets served on fresh banana leaves cost around £15 per person, dinners from £25.

Fifteen Events
19/21 Nile Street, N1 7LL (7017 0730/ www.fifteen.net). Old Street tube/rail. **Cost** *from £100/head (minimum 20).*
The events and catering arm of Jamie Oliver's Fifteen Foundation caters small dinner parties, huge corporate bashes and everything in between. The team can advise on menus, styling – in fact almost any aspect of your party – and has a great eye for detail. Canapé menus are of the pleasingly hearty variety: soda bread scones with smoked salmon, perhaps, or ash-rolled goat's cheese with fig chutney. Mains, meanwhile, focus on well-sourced, flavoursome ingredients and could include something like pork chop with leeks, potatoes, morels and garlic leaves or chargrilled asparagus and artichoke with poached egg and truffle pecorino. All events are catered for on a bespoke basis so the above is really just a taster of what can be achieved. Fifteen Events also supply fantastic antipasti platters to offices – sure beats the same old M&S sarnie selection.

Gorgeous Gourmets
Gresham Way, SW19 8ED (8944 7771/ www.gorgeousgourmets.co.uk). Wimbledon Park tube. **Cost** *£17/head (minimum 10).* **Delivery** *yes.*
This Wimbledon-based stalwart deals in tried and trusted menus that span the globe – from traditional British cheddar scones to filo tartlets of devilled crab salad – and offers a range of catering options, including a finger-food buffet (menus include the likes of thai fishcakes, mini yorkshire puddings with rare roast beef and toasted brioche with gorgonzola) for ten from £17.00 per head (plus VAT and delivery). Fork buffets, sit-down dinners and canapés can also be catered with aplomb.

Harvey's Catering & Equipment Hire
Unit 4, King James Court, SE1 0DH (7928 3242/www.harveys-catering.co.uk). Borough tube. **Cost** *from £5.70/head (minimum 2).* **Delivery** *yes.*
'We try to work to everybody's budget – we're not out to rob people' say the nice folk at Harvey's, and accordingly they will allow you to

spend just £51.40 (£11.40 plus a £40 delivery charge). The only catch is that they don't supply extras such as flowers, although they can recommend people who will. They do, however, supply glasses, cutlery and crockery, and there is an equipment hire section of the business from which you can rent furniture and linen. Delivery is not charged if you spend over £150, although if you are spending between £100-£150 it is up for negotiation. In a similar vein, while they can supply drinks, they encourage people to buy their own because it will work out cheaper – and if you do so, they will still run the bar without charging corkage. A range of simple but effective finger and fork buffets (cold meats, quiches, salads), as well as sit-down lunch and dinner menus are available.

Jackson Gilmour
8665 1855/www.jacksongilmour.com.
Minimum spend £1,500. **Delivery** yes.
No credit cards.
A very smart firm, with prices to match, but if you've cash to flash this is a company that really knows its onions. Dinner menus are carefully constructed and well-presented with good veggie choices (cannelloni of artichokes, peppers and feta cheese, followed by cobbler pie and iced nugatine with berry parfait, for example). Meat and fish options are equally enticing. The company can also supply information and inspiration on everything from flowers to photography and will happily come to private houses or deal with smaller numbers, although there is a minimum spend of £1,500.

Last Supper
Unit 6, Newington Court Business Centre, Newington Causeway, SE1 6DD (7378 0101/ www.lastsupperltd.co.uk). Elephant & Castle tube/rail. **Cost** from £2,500. **Delivery** yes.
Last Supper has worked for clients including Christian Dior, Fendi, MTV, Rimmel and Sotheby's, and prides itself on a truly bespoke approach. From staff to service, this is a slick operation. Choose from an array of sumptuous canapés and cocktails or impressive dinner menus safe in the knowledge that the team will always manage to come up with an idea or two your guests won't have seen before. A great one to impress with.

Maha's Kitchen
23 Quicks Road, SW19 1EZ (8543 8430/ 07961 440011/www.mahaskitchen.co.uk). Wimbledon tube. **Cost** from £20/head (minimum 40). **Delivery** yes. **No credit cards**.
Maha's Kitchen specialises in last-minute events, 'so it's worth calling even if your party is the next

day.' The company also has lots of experience catering to parties with religious dietary requirements, whether halal or kosher. Being based in Wimbledon, however, venturing too far north can be problematic (they charge a small fee plus congestion charge for delivery to places they will go to). Minimum spend is £20 per head and you'll need at least 40 guests (waiters' fees are calculated on top of this). And once the friendly team has crossed their threshold they'll happily provide any extras you require. Substantial canapés include dishes like bruschetta, baby baked potatoes and skewers of prawns, chicken satay and marinated pork.

Party Ingredients
Kirtling Street, SW8 5BP (7627 3800/ www.partyingredients.co.uk). Vauxhall tube.
Minimum spend £1,500. **Delivery** yes.
This company asks for a minimum spend of £1,500. There's no minimum number of people they expect to cater for, though – so if you want dinner for two it will cost you £750 per head. Menus are carefully tailored to different types of event – cocktail receptions, summery barbecues, dinner parties, weddings and more. Think lobster and langoustine tails with mini herb ravioli, shot glasses of marinated fruit or barbecued swordfish marinated in coriander, lime and chilli. The team will try to manage a booking for the next day, depending on availability. All extras can be supplied, and there's no charge for delivery.

Penni Black
8 Loxley Road, SW18 3LJ (0800 389 6107/ www.penniblack.co.uk). Wandsworth rail.
Minimum spend £500. **Delivery** yes.
Penni Black catered 2007's Black and White Ball at the Porchester Hall so can probably manage a humble home party without too much bother, whatever you're looking for. The company doesn't have a minimum spend; canapés come in at between £7-£15 per head, while a sit-down dinner is £50-£60; catering staff, delivery and so on are extra. There's a very handy price calculator on the website to help with the figures. There is no minimum number of guests and all extras can be supplied; the company will take next-day orders if at all possible too. Delivery is charged at £30 for a simple drop-off, £100 for catering events, plus petrol in both cases.

Peyton Events
National Gallery, Trafalger Square, WC2N 5DN (7747 5925/www.peytonevents.com). Charing Cross tube/rail. **Cost** from £17.50/head (canapés). **Delivery** yes.
For party catering to be proud of, Peyton Events combines imagination, experience and service to

1000 ways to change your life

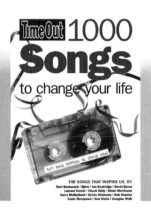

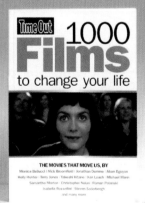

TIME OUT GUIDES
Visit timeout.com/shop

OF COURSE I MADE IT MYSELF

Fabulous delis for dinner-party cheats. We won't tell if you won't.

Atari-ya

20 James Street, W1U 1EH (7491 1178/
www.atariya.co.uk). Bond Street tube.
Open 11am-8pm daily.
Sushi and sashimi platters are made to order
(collection only) at this takeaway branch of
the Japanese grocery chain. An extensive list
of fish and seafood includes eel, squid, surf
clam and, at the pricier end of the spectrum,
sea urchin and snow crab leg meat. There are
three branches in north London (Finchley,
Golders Green and West Acton).

Carluccio's

www.carluccios.com
Always a handy stock-up spot for an
impromtu supper, Carluccio's (20 branches
across London) also provides great quality
party catering in the form of hearty cheese
and meat platters (£24), antipasti (£24) and
canapés (from £6 per person). A simple but
delicious dinner party spread of cheese, meat,
bread and seasonal salads would come in at
around £15 per person. Great for impressing
guests with minimal fuss.

Flavours

10 Campdale Road, N7 0EA (7281 6565/
www.delibelly.com). Tufnell Park tube. **Open**
10am-6pm Tue; 9.30am-6pm Wed-Fri; 10am-
6pm Sat; 10am-2pm Sun.
This fab deli is owned by former *Masterchef*
winner Julie Friend. She creates a great range
of dinner-party friendly dishes, perfect for
cheating your way to domestic goddess status.
Menus often have a Mediterranean slant, but
British grub – such as shepherd's pie followed
by trifle – is popular too. A finger-food buffet
for ten starts at £7.50 per head.

Hand Made Food

40 Tranquil Vale, SE3 0BD (8297 9966/
www.handmadefood.com). Blackheath rail.
Open 9am-5pm Mon, Wed-Fri; 9am-2pm
Tue; 9am-5.30pm Sat; 9am-5pm Sun.
Hand Made Food's Fergus and Vicky Clague
will cater for events of all sizes, rustling up
party food for as few as 25 people if required.
Great canapés are a real speciality, with an
international menu that includes Jamaican
beef patties, spanakopita and parmesan

Flavours

gnocchi (£1.50 each). Ingredients are sourced as locally as possible, and all meat is organic.

Mimosa

16 Half Moon Lane, SE24 9HU (7733 8838/www.mimosafoods.com). Herne Hill rail. **Open** 9am-6pm Mon-Fri; 9am-5.30pm Sat; 9.30am-3.30pm Sun.
Covering Herne Hill and its surrounds, Mimosa offers Moroccan- and French-themed spreads alongside the more usual finger food; you can borrow Moroccan dishes for perfect party presentation too. A buffet for a party of ten costs from £13.75 a head.

Mr Christian's

11 Elgin Crecesent, W11 2JA (7229 0501/ www.mrchristians.co.uk). Notting Hill Gate tube. **Open** 6am-7pm Mon-Fri; 6am-6pm Sat; 7am-5pm Sun.
Always buzzing with activity, pop into this Notting Hill deli at any given moment and you might spot a local A-lister making plans for a dinner party, or planning party catering for up to 200 guests. The enormous menu runs from tempting canapés to à la carte menus, along with sumptuous salads.

Pie Man

16 Cale Street, SW3 3QU (7737 7799/ www.thepieman.co.uk). South Kensington or Sloane Square tube. **Open** 9am-6pm Mon-Fri; 9am-2pm Sat.
A godsend for dinner party novices. If you've ever tasted anything from Murray Tollemache's Chelsea deli, you won't need us to tell you that you're in for a treat with his party catering service. An imaginative canapé selection (minimum 25 guests) starts at £12 per head and ranges from simple shots of gazpacho to the more elaborate likes of seared scallops with pea purée.

Rosslyn Deli

56 Rosslyn Hill, NW3 1ND (7794 9210/ www.rosslyndeli.net). Hampstead tube. **Open** 8.30am-8.30pm Mon-Sat; 8.30am-8pm Sun.
Rosslyn Deli is happy to cater for any event, with a finger-food buffet or an imaginative two-bite canapé list (from £1.35-£1.55 per portion), ranging from *FT*-wrapped mini fish and chips, to lentil balls with spicy apricot sauce. It also offers various enticing dinner party menus.

ESSENTIALS

fine effect. As caterers to the National Gallery, the Wallace Collection (*see p62*) and the ICA (*see p59*), the company has access to endless skilled staff and plenty of ideas and inspiration. Menus are packed with seasonal delights such as carpaccio of beef with rocket and parmesan, line-caught seabass with sweet and sour mushroom broth and Eton mess with strawberries. Advice on wine and cocktails is available too.

Recipe

Unit A, South Studio, Gainsborough Studios, 1 Poole Street, N1 5EE (0845 130 8087/ www.the-recipe.co.uk). Old Street tube/rail. **Cost** from £30/head (minimum 50). **Delivery** yes.
For review, see p124.

Rhubarb

5-25 Burr Road, SW18 4SQ (8812 3200/ www.rhubarb.net). Southfields tube. **Minimum spend** £1,000. **Delivery** no.
Rhubarb is one of London's most fashionable caterers and has great contacts with venues, being one of the preferred caterers at many of the capital's best – Old Billingsgate (*see p98*), Christ Church Spitalfields (*see p79*), the Design Museum (*see p101*). Food is imaginative and creative – the canapés make a real visual impact and taste great too (think slithers of lavender roasted lamb, fat chips with caviar or crispy duck cones). Presentation is a cut above – towering seafood platters, colourful sorbets and platters of mini desserts. If you have cash to splash on party catering, your money will be well spent here.

Seasoned Events

13 Bishopsgate, EC2N 3BA (7236 2149/ www.seasonedevents.co.uk). Liverpool Street tube/rail. **Cost** from £45/head (minimum 100). **Delivery** no.
This is the bespoke catering arm of the Crown Group, which includes an events hire company, so no idea is too grandiose for them to cope with. For home catering the company asks for a minimum of 40 people. The average price for a reception with a buffet menu, wine and champagne is £45 per head (including the price of catering staff) and between £60-£80 per head for dinner with wine. They will try to help on last-minute requests ('We can stretch and pull if it's an emergency') but usually ask for two weeks' notice, or more if the event is for over 400 people.

Scoff

606 Fulham Road, SW6 5RP (8547 0447/ www.scoff.co.uk). Parsons Green tube. **Cost** from £10/head. **Delivery** yes.
'Good food from a good place' is the cheery slogan on Scoff's website, and the company's (local, sustainable) suppliers are listed for those who want to see which good place in particular. 'Our style is informal,' says Scoff's Sarah Rushton, 'hence affordable; we just supply the food hot and leave the party host in peace to organise serving the guests.' So, the minimum order for delivery is just £10. Scoff can tailor menus to all sorts of occasions (the Rushtons are particularly fond of barbecues) and provide any extras. At time of writing the company only covers west and south-west London; however, a

Cakes to impress with. **Primrose Bakery**. *See p134.*

Blistering Barbecues. *See p132.*

second branch is opening in September 2008 in Islington to cater to the north London crowd.

Skye Cooks

The Kitchen, 19 De Beauvoir Road, N1 4EN (07939 592724/www.skyecooks.co.uk). Dalston Kingsland rail. **Cost** from £15/head (minimum 2). **Delivery** yes.

Skye Cooks' imaginative party food is made from fairtrade and organic meat, fish and veg. Vegetarian and vegan menus are a particular speciality: think soba noodle and roast pumpkin salad, aubergine and chickpea curry or burritos with refried borlotti beans. A finger-food buffet for 40 costs from £15 per head. Barbecues (with plenty for veggies once more), weddings, corporate and private events are all catered for. Dinner party cheats might also be interested to know a full meal can be provided for you to pop in the oven just before guests arrive. Oh yes.

Tamarind

20 Queen Street, W1J 5PR (7629 3561/ www.tamarindrestaurant.com). Green Park tube. **Cost** from £52/head (minimum 12). **Delivery** yes (in Mayfair area).

If you fancy offering partygoers used to greasy chicken biryani some really fantastic curry for a change, the Michelin-starred Tamarind restaurant caters parties and events, and can even send a chef to your home to provide three courses of beautiful cuisine from north-west India. Tuck in to everything from aloo tikki (potato cakes with fried lentils, ginger, toasted cumin and spinach stuffing, drizzled with dry ginger chutney) to marinated king prawns and a rogan josh like nothing you've ever had in your local curry house.

Urban Caprice

63-65 Goldney Road, W9 2AR (7286 1700/ www.urbancaprice.co.uk). Maida Vale tube. **Minimum spend** £2,500. **Delivery** yes.

This company has catered everything from Armani events to premières, cocktail parties to sit-down dinners; Urban Caprice is part of Caprice Holdings, which owns Caprice, J Sheekey and The Ivy, so there's certainly no need to worry that the food won't be up to scratch. Unsurprisingly, with this CV, UC isn't cheap: bespoke dinners start from around £2,500 but they are capable of catering for huge amounts of guests (over 1,000). If you're planning something big, you're sorted. Extras, including flowers, staff, marquees and even costumes, can be supplied too.

BARBECUE SPECIALISTS & HOG ROASTS

Barbeque Shop

(01932 868522/01932 866044/www.the bbqshop.co.uk). **Open** 9.30am-5pm Wed-Sat, 10am-4pm Sun. **Delivery** yes.

For that lazy summer afternoon cook-up, this long-established equipment hire firm will rent you a gas or charcoal fired barbecue (also available to buy, if you prefer). If you really want to impress the carnivores in your acquaintance, try the spit roast with heavy-duty motor (capable of turning up to 100lbs of meat) for £139, or the slightly more modest chef might prefer the one-metre wide Master Chef with griddle cooking surface, for £54. Chairs, tables, awnings and patio heaters are also available.

Blistering Barbecues

1-3 Metro Business Centre, Kangley Bridge Road, SE26 5BW (8778 3699/ www.blistering.co.uk). Lower Sydenham rail. **Cost** from £15/head (minimum 40). **Delivery** no. **No credit cards.**

Make sure an alfresco party, wedding or corporate event really hits the spot with a barbecue from open-air cooking fanatics Blistering. Menus are designed to delight carnivores and veggies alike, with dishes such as spicy piri piri chicken, king prawn skewers and chargrilled courgettes. Most importantly, the impeccably professional staff will brave all weathers to ensure your guests get a glorious taste of summer even if the sky is grey. The best in the business.

The Fat Pig

07789 982305/www.thefatpig.co.uk. **Cost** from £500/hog. **Delivery** yes. **No credit cards.**

Straight-talking and super-friendly hog roasters the Fat Pig can provide pigs for up to 600. A fine choice for low-key weddings (or feeding the masses at an evening reception), communal celebrations or even just a break from the weekend barbecue norm – there's nothing quite like the smell of roasting pork and apple sauce to whet the appetite on a sunny day. The company can also supply barbecues, buffets and cool 'keg-in-box' beer kegs.

Flaming Hog Roast Company

01420 476385/www.insidecatering.co.uk. **Cost** from £6.75/head (minimum 100). **Delivery** yes (south-west London only). For review, *see p136*.

Spitting Pig

0800 587 5899/www.spittingpig.co.uk. **Cost** from £450. **Delivery** yes.

This slickly professional outfit provides hearty hog roasts for private parties, weddings, corporate bashes and everything in between. Roasts are served with apple sauce, crackling, stuffing and floured bread rolls (extras like salads and veggie options are available). Barbecues are another speciality – think burgers, gourmet sausages and ribs served with salads and jacket wedges. Why settle for your own burnt banger efforts ever again?

CELEBRATION CAKES

Bea's of Bloomsbury

44 Theobald's Road, WC1X 8NW (7242 8330/www.beasofbloomsbury.com).

Chancery Lane or Holborn tube. **Open** 8am-6pm Mon-Fri; 10.30am-4pm Sat.

This lovely pâtisserie has plenty to offer discerning cake fans. Pastry chef Bea Vo's masterpieces range from pecan-topped cheesecake to rich chocolate concoctions. Better still, 'build-a-cake' allows you to design your dream celebration cake. Gold leaf on top? Passionfruit or praline buttercream? It's entirely up to you. See also the venue review (*see p16*) in the Birthdays chapter.

Cake Boy

Unit 2, Kingfisher House, Juniper Drive, SW18 1TX (7978 5555/www.cake-boy.com). Wandsworth Town rail. **Open** 8am-7pm Mon-Fri; 9am-6pm Sat.

Master pâtissier Eric Lanlard creates the most glamorous gateaux in town: the A-list wouldn't buy their wedding cakes anywhere else. Options range from simple sachertorte or cheesecake (from £24) to elaborate bespoke creations (from £5.50 per serving).

Crumbs & Doilies

www.crumbsanddoilies.co.uk

Whether you opt for a delectable tower of cupcakes, seven or nine tiers high (use the online calculator to work out the cost), or simply a plate of the little fellas, Crumbs and Doilies uses top quality ingredients, 100 different sprinkles and can individually decorate to your taste, so if you fancy sugar flowers… Available by the dozen (£20 for the big ones; £10 the mini versions).

Euphorium Bakery

202 Upper Street, N1 1RQ (7704 6906/ www.euphoriumbakery.com). Highbury & Islington tube/rail. **Open** 7am-11pm Mon-Fri; 8am-10.30pm Sat-Sun.

Last-minute planners take note: with just a few days' notice, Euphorium will create your ideal party centrepiece – a luscious dark chocolate mousse cake, perhaps, or a fraises des bois-soaked vanilla sponge with chantilly cream. Prices start at £13 and a message is free, piped on to the cake or inscribed on a chocolate plaque.

Hummingbird Bakery

133 Portobello Road, W11 2DY (7229 6446/ www.hummingbirdbakery.com). Notting Hill Gate tube. **Open** 10am-5.30pm Tue-Sat; 11am-5pm Sun.

The Hummingbird bakes a mean birthday cake; the Red Velvet (a red-hued vanilla sponge with a hint of chocolate, covered with cream cheese) always goes down a treat. Messages can be iced on to their cakes and their appealing moist and indulgent cupcakes are a winner too.

SMALL IS BEAUTIFUL

London's prettiest party cupcakes.

From £1.55. **Hummingbird Bakery** (www.humming birdbakery.com). *See left*.

From £10 for 20 mini cakes. **Crumbs & Doilies** (www.crumbsanddoilies.co.uk). *See left*.

From £2.25. **Outsider Tart** (www.outsiderstart. com). *See p134*.

From £36 for 48 mini cakes. **Treacle** (www. treacleworld.com). *See p134*.

From £1.15. **Primrose Bakery** (www.primrose bakery.co.uk). *See p134*.

From £1.70. **Lola's Kitchen** (www.lolas-kitchen.co.uk). *See p134*.

ESSENTIALS

Konditor & Cook

*10 Stoney Street, SE1 9AD (7407 5100/
www.konditorandcook.com). Borough tube or
London Bridge tube/rail.* **Open** *7.30am-6pm
Mon-Fri; 8.30am-5pm Sat.*

As well as fabulous traditional birthday cakes
(including the legendary Curly Whirly cake), this
place is famed for its colourful little 'magic
cakes': a letter can be iced on to each fondant-
covered cake, spelling out a birthday message.
Messages can also be iced onto standard sized
birthday cakes too.

Lola's Kitchen

7483 3394/www.lolas-kitchen.co.uk

Lola's hand-crafted cupcakes are freshly baked
daily (with no preservatives) using Madagascar
vanilla, Guittard chocolate, Philadelphia cream
cheese, South African 'Marie Biscuits', and real
butter, eggs and milk. Choose from flavours such
as pistachio, peanut butter and red velvet. For
corporate events, Lola's can add your company
logo to cupcakes too. Order online.

Outsider Tart

*56 Frith Street, W1 DJG (07913 262107/
www.outsidertart.com). Tottenham Court
Road tube.* **Open** *noon-5pm Mon-Sun.*

Chiswick-based Outsider Tart delivers to any
address in London. Cupcakes have names like
PMC (peanut butter, marshmallow and
chocolate), banana split or ginger and lemon, and
you can order them either unfilled or filled (with
chunks of chocolate or lemon and lime curd, for
example; £2.25/£2.50 respectively). There are
tarts, pies and biscuits on offer too. Enthusiasts
can take part in a half-day masterclass and learn
how to bake their favourites at home.

Primrose Bakery

*69 Gloucester Avenue, NW1 8LD (7483
4222/www.primrosebakery.co.uk). Chalk
Farm tube.* **Open** *8.30am-6.00pm Mon-Sat,
10am-5.30pm Sun*

The Primrose Bakery's beautiful cupcakes come
in flavours including vanilla, mocha, carrot and
lime and coconut. The vanilla buttercream looks
particularly pretty in shades of pastel pink, lilac,
mint green and primrose yellow. It's impossible
to list all of the decoration options available, but
there is a wide range of sugar flowers, sprinkles
and sugar letters to suit every occasion.
Cupcakes come in two sizes: regular and mini.
Prices start at £1.15 for a mini cake and £1.75
for a normal-sized cupcake.

Treacle

*110-112 Columbia Road, E2 7RG (7729
5657/www.treacleworld.com). Liverpool
Street or Old Street tube/rail.* **Open** *9.30am-
3.30pm Sun.*

Mini cupcakes (48 for £36, minimum order 24
per flavour, thereafter £9 per dozen) are the
signature cake here and Treacle can 'custom-ice'
names, messages or doodles as you like. We
love the glittery ones (and suspect your little
princesses will too). Layer cakes (lemony,
chocolatey, vanilla-ey and jammy) are also
available and Treacle stocks an eclectic mix of
vintage china tea sets for you to display them on.

CHEESE SHOPS

La Fromagerie

*2-6 Moxon Street, W1U 4EW (7935 0341/
www.lafromagerie.co.uk). Baker Street or
Bond Street tube.* **Open** *10.30am-7.30pm
Mon; 8am-7.30pm Tue-Fri; 9am-7pm Sat;
10am-6pm Sun.*

Delicious cheeses are hand-selected from small
artisan makers for sale in this chic deli-café's
refrigerated cheese room. Buffalo ricotta,
mascares (fresh herb-coated cheese made with
a mixture of goat's and ewe's milk), and
sottocenere al tartufo (a brine-washed cheese
flavoured with truffle and coated in ash and
spices) are among the unusual varieties on offer.

Hamish Johnson

*48 Northcote Road, SW11 1PA (7738 0741).
Clapham Common tube/Clapham Junction
rail.* **Open** *9am-6pm Mon-Sat. 11am-4pm Sun.*

For a varied party cheeseboard this is definitely
the place to come. Three large chiller cabinets
aren't enough to contain the huge selection of
cheeses available at this popular shop – varieties
such as feta and halloumi spill into a fourth.
British artisan-made options include lord of the
hundreds and lincolnshire poacher – though the
rest of Europe is well represented too. Keeping
the emphasis on British suppliers, Hamish
Johnson also stocks good chocolates from
Browne's in the West Country, coffee from Paddy
and Scott's in Suffolk, and jams from Rosebud
Preserves in North Yorkshire.

Jeroboams

*96 Holland Park Avenue, W11 3RB (7727
9359/www.jeroboams.co.uk). Holland Park
tube.* **Open** *8am-8pm Mon-Fri; 8.30am-7pm
Sat; 10am-6pm Sun.*

The fabulous Jeroboams supplies cheese to more
Michelin-starred restaurants than any other British
retailer. And if it's good enough for them, we're
sure it'll suffice for your next party cheeseboard.
French varieties are a speciality – particularly the
carefully matured version of pave d'affinois. You'll

THE PERFECT CHEESEBOARD

No foodie party is truly complete without a tremendous platter of cheese to round off a meal. The current vogue in dairy matters is to think small scale, think artisan and, definitely, think British. With over 500 types to choose from and at least 100 artisan dairies making raw-milk varieties, today's British cheese can definitely hold its own. The British Cheese Awards' (www.thecheeseweb.com) Juliet Harbutt couldn't agree more: 'Cheese here is as good as anywhere else in Europe – there's no way that a British focus could leave you with a poor man's board. In fact, it's quite the opposite.'

Ready to compile the cheeseboard to end all cheeseboards? We picked the brains of Harbutt and Rhuaridh Buchanan of Paxton & Whitfield (www.paxtonandwhitfield.co.uk) for tips on creating the perfect selection. Both were firmly agreed on three key points: a) keep it simple, b) keep it local and c) keep it interesting with a combination of flavours, shapes and textures.

There are six main types of cheese: fresh (unripened, curd-style cheeses such as ricotta); soft (brie, camembert); semi-soft (edam, rind-washed cheeses); hard (cheddar, parmesan); blue (stilton, gorgonzola);

flavour-added (smoked cheeses, cornish yarg). Then, of course, there are different sources of milk: goat, cow, sheep and mixtures of the three. For maximum interest and flavour Harbutt suggests choosing a cheese from each category for your board and including cheeses made from a variety of milks. Though she also notes that it is 'better to just have one fantastic cheese than lots of little bits and pieces'.

Buchanan agrees: 'More isn't necessarily better – stick with a well-chosen three or four. Your taste buds can't take much more than that at a time.' The 'keep it simple' rule applies to what you serve with your choices too. Buchanan prefers to accompany his cheese with just a knife, while Harbutt suggests dried fruit, nuts, apples or quince paste.

As for the main event, well, there's certainly no shortage of cheese that makes the grade. Harbutt suggests kicking things off with a touch of celebrity. She chooses little wallop (available from Paxton & Whitfield), the fresh goat's cheese washed in cider brandy and wrapped in vine leaves that she helped Alex James (of Blur) create. Made by Pete Humphries of White Lake Cheese in Somerset, it's an unusual, punchy cheese that lives up to the rock star hype and is a great start to a board. She also suggests old winchester (www.lyburnfarm.co.uk), a hard, cow's milk cheese made in Wiltshire, and Scottish highland blue (widely available) made by Rhuaridh Stone of Highland Fine Cheeses in Tain.

Stone's Paxton & Whitfield namesake Rhuaridh Buchanan also opts for a highland blue for his ideal board, along with a spicy, crumbly hard sheep's milk cheese from Kent called crockhamdale and a creamy, rind-washed (in honey mead) oxford isis.

Raring to get your mouth round a few of these? Check out the cheese shops listed in this chapter (*see left*) for a party board to be proud of.

also find a fine selection of olive oils, Poilâne bread, syrups in fig, lychee and lotus blossom flavours, organic muesli and foodie gift lines.

Neal's Yard Dairy
17 Shorts Gardens, WC2H 9UP (7240 5700/ www.nealsyarddairy.co.uk). Leicester Square tube. **Open** 11am-7pm Mon-Sat.

A great place to come for inspiration and ideas, Neal's Yard Dairy's staff are always ready to advise on interesting cheeseboard combinations. The shop specialises in British cheeses but has traditional French attitude to retailing in that, like an affineur, it buys from small farms and creameries and matures the cheeses in its own cellars until ready to sell in peak condition. It's

Oyster Boys

ESSENTIALS

Choc Star

No party is complete without a shed-load – or in this case, a van-load – of chocolate and Petra Barran's Choc Star van is undoubtedly the coolest way to ensure your do gets its dose. Chocolate can be offered molten, frozen, baked or iced, so it's suitable for all seasons. Why not add hot chocolate floats to your party's dessert menu or serve ice cream, millionaires' shortbread and shakes after dinner? Whatever you opt for, we doubt there's been an unsatisfied client yet.
Best for Chocoholics.
Must do Prepare for a throng round the van.
Inside tip Book early during the summer.
For listings, see right.

Flaming Hog Roast Company

Inside Catering's Flaming Hog Roast Company serves up fabulous hog roasts with all the trimmings (apple sauce, crackling) at parties, weddings and events in London, Hampshire, Surrey and Berkshire. For £15.50 per person (min 100) you could serve guests a veritable feast of spit roast, whole baked salmon, potato salad, tomato and basil salad, green salad, fruit salad and coffee; for £6.75 per person (min 100) you could just go all out for hog. Inside Catering also offers barbecues, canapés and buffets, and is also able to roast you an entire cow or buffalo should appetites desire.

Best for Hearty tucker for informal parties.
Must do Recommend the crackling.
Inside tip Cows and buffalos might have novelty appeal but it's the hogs that get the crowd going.
For listings, see p132.

Human Canapés

Balti Boy, Anti Pasti Man or Savoury Sophia won't add much class to your party but will certainly raise a few smiles. Once the preserve of swingers' parties and sex clubs, human canapés are now adding a bit of extra sauce to the menu at mainstream parties and events, from stag dos to charity balls. Playtime Platters has more than 20 themed hunks and honeys on its books who will arrive at your party, wash, strip down to their underwear and cover themselves in mouth-watering treats for your guests to nibble at under the watchful eye of a supplied 'host' (on hand to replenish supplies and make sure nothing untoward happens with the chopsticks).
Best for Novelty factor.
Must do Keep your hands to yourself.
Inside tip You may need to lead the way…
For listings, see right.

Lola's on Ice

Lola's purple-painted van dispenses gloriously grown-up ice-creams and sorbets at some of

London's coolest parties and events, and will add real wow factor to your bash. Tuck into flavours such as burnt orange, caramel or crisp, gin and tonic sorbet (a finer dessert option we can't imagine?) – all made from fresh, organic ingredients. Hire within London costs £200 for two hours, then £3 per double scoop of ice-cream. You get to choose six flavours for your event, so pick wisely.
Best for An alternative dessert at weddings.
Must do Go for a balance between unusual and classic flavours.
Inside tip The mango sorbet is delicious.
For listings, see right.

Oyster Boys

Colin Thwaites and Robin Dunlop set up the Oyster Boys in 2005 and have been a rousing success at hip parties across the UK since. Totally charming, flexible and very easy on they eye, they'll turn up clad in tartan ready to work the room and shuck spankingly fresh oysters before your guests' eyes. Great for making an impact at a glam do, wedding or corporate bash – watch as even oyster virgins and sworn seafood enemies tuck in with glee.
Best for Injecting some energy into a bash.
Must do Down in one.
Inside tip Don't accept any imitations, these boys are the best.
For listings, see right.

best to walk in and ask what's good today – you'll be given various tasters too. The company also has a sizeable shop just off Borough Market.

Paxton & Whitfield
93 Jermyn Street, SW1Y 6JE (7930 0259/ www.paxtonandwhitfield.co.uk). Piccadilly Circus or Green Park tube. **Open** 9.30am-6pm Mon-Sat.
In business for over 200 years, the last 100 of those on this site, wonderfully traditional Paxton & Whitfield sells a wide range of British and continental European cheeses, plus excellent hams, biscuits and real ale. Service is exemplary and delightfully unstuffy. Among the unusual English varieties to look out for are oxford isis (washed in mead), caradon blue from Cornwall and cave-aged cheddar from Somerset. A small area at the back of the shop stocks gift items such as cheese knives and boards.

FOODIE FINISHING TOUCHES

Choc Star
07748 073848/www.chocstar.co.uk. **Cost** from £250. **Delivery** yes. **No credit cards.** For review, *see left.*

Lola's on Ice
07871 797260/www.lolasonice.co.uk. **Cost** £200/2hrs plus £3/head (London); £300/2hrs plus £3/head (40 miles outside London). **Delivery** no. For review, *see left.*

Oysters Boys
07792 868502/www.oysterboys.co.uk. **Cost** from £1,600. **Delivery** no. **No credit cards.** For review, *see left.*

NOVELTY FOOD

Human Canapés
7622 5952/www.playtimeplatters.com. **Cost** from £450. For review, *see left.*

Incredible Ice Cream Company
0844 800 9004/www.incredibleice cream.co.uk. **Cost** from £700 plus £2/ice cream. **Delivery** yes. **No credit cards.** Add squeals of childish joy (from all ages) to your party's soundtrack by hiring in one of the Incredible Ice Cream Company's *Charlie and the Chocolate Factory*-esque machines. Subtlety is

Elbows at the ready – the **Choc Star** van's arrived. *See p137.*

not on the menu – we're talking swirly bright colours, whirls of strawberry, vanilla, chocolate and mint choc chip, and an array of brightly coloured sprinkles and sauces. It's all DIY for maximum interactive fun – and shameless greed with the hot fudge sauce – and is guaranteed to slap a huge smile on the face of even the most jaded party guest.

DRINKS SUPPLIERS

BBR
3 St James's Street, SW1A 1EG (0870 900 4300/www.bbr.com). Green Park tube. **Open** 10am-6pm Mon-Fri; 10am-5pm Sat. **Delivery** yes.

This venerable wood-lined Mayfair wine merchant is happy to provide party refreshment – and to advise if you're not sure what you're after. The wine selection is wide-ranging and there's also a great range of spirits; sale or return applies to a maximum of 20% of your order, with a £10 charge applied for collection. Minimum spend is £100, with delivery free on orders over £200, otherwise it costs £10; this will get your order to you within six working days. Shorter delivery times or Saturday delivery is pricier, but the website has a cost calculator. Glassware can be hired.

Beers of Europe
01553 812000/www.beersofeurope.co.uk. **Open** 9am-6pm Mon-Sat; 10am-4pm Sun. **Delivery** yes.

The Beer Academy (www.beeracademy.co.uk) swears by this website and you can't ask for a better recommendation than that. Beers of Europe stocks 300 different British ales and an impressive selection from elsewhere – and not just Europe. In fact, the name is rather misleading – this is also the place to come for Chinese wine or schnapps as well as more ordinary party lubricants. There's no minimum spend, which means you can order one bottle of beer if you want to, although with the £7.49 delivery charge that'll be an expensive shot of ale. Next day delivery is the same cost but you must call before midday and they don't do weekends. Glass hire is also available.

TheDrinkShop.com
0800 169 6760/www.thedrinkshop.com. **Open** 9am-5.30pm Mon-Fri. **Delivery** yes.
No shops means no overheads and this company does its best to pass those savings on to customers. There is no minimum spend and the sliding scale of delivery charges starts at £5.49 for deliveries up to three kilos taking up to three working days to arrive and goes up to £8.99 for next day delivery of up to three kilos; above these weights there's a 26p per kilo surcharge. If you want Saturday before noon, there's an extra charge of £5.49. The site sells an impressive range of liquor: over 2,900 drinks from pisco to poteen as well as the usual suspects; cocktail shakers and other accessories are also available and there's a glass hire service.

Fortnum & Mason
181 Piccadilly W1A 1ER (7734 8040/ www.fortnumandmason.com). Green Park or Piccadilly Circus tube. **Open** 10am-8pm Mon-Sat; noon-6pm Sun. **Delivery** yes.
Lovely Fortnum's with its 15-year pedigree, mint green bags, fine produce and now, a delightful basement wine bar, is a fine (though pricey) place to shop for party booze. The wine selection is stupendous and you can, of course, also get anything from a pot of caviar to a full hamper to keep drinkers' stomachs lined. There is no minimum spend but delivery costs £7 and takes a week (deliveries over £50 are free for account card holders). If that's too long a wait, pay £12 for a two-three day wait instead. Hampers start at £200 for two people and need to be ordered four working days in advance.

Gerry's Wines and Spirits
74 Old Compton Street, W1D 4UW (7734 2053/7734 4215/www.gerrys.uk.com) Piccadilly Circus tube. **Open** 9am-6.30pm Mon-Thur; 9am-8pm Fri; 9am-10pm Sat. **Delivery** yes.

The owner of Gerry's – Michael Kyprianou – started his first off licence on Old Compton Street almost 50 years ago by buying seized goods from British Customs; his stock is less haphazard these days but the interior still reeks of another era. Order online – there's no minimum spend and delivery starts at £6.49 for anything up to three kilos, which takes four working days to arrive. There's no next day delivery and no glass hire or food – despite the website ordering, this is a gloriously old-fashioned joint. Great selection though – check out the enormous absinthe range, just for starters.

Jeroboams
50-52 Elizabeth Street, SW1W 9PB (7288 8850/www.jeroboams.co.uk). Sloane Square tube/Victoria tube/rail. **Open** 9am-7pm Mon-Sat. **Delivery** yes.
This independent wine merchant has a fantastic selection of vintages and offers lots of expertise to help out dithering party planners. There's no delivery charge on online orders in excess of £200 and there's also a glass hire service. You can also order fantastic cheese platters from the website. For a fuller menu, call the delicatessen on 7229 0501.

Majestic
201-207 Shoreditch High Street, E1 6LG. (7247 9381/www.majestic.co.uk). Liverpool Street tube/rail. **Open** 9am-7pm Mon-Fri; 9am-7pm Sat; 10am-4pm Sun. **Delivery** yes.
Majestic offers a glass and chiller bin loan service, free delivery if you organise your order far enough in advance, a sale or return service (12 bottles minimum, any mix of wine or spirits) and even a downloadable party planner on the website. In addition, the company offers a superb range of reasonably priced wines, particularly sparkling (champagne and more mundane fizz) and lots of deals and offers. The only downside is that you have to order at least a case, but then it won't be much of a party with less will it?

NOTE

BOOZE SOS

It happens all too easily. An enthusiastic cry of 'all back to mine' as you leave the pub, the draining of the drinks cabinet... the delving in the back of cupboards for foul dessert wine and that weird stuff you brought back from Turkey. Put it away and call The Lock-In (7350 2424, www.latelondon.co.uk) instead. They'll replenish supplies in no time.

DRINKING SESSIONS

Nina Caplan gets the experts in for a drinks party with a difference.

Theatre of Wine

It is a truth universally acknowledged that the narrowing of the class divide is a Good Thing, except when it comes to parties. Most of us would gladly shoulder the responsibilities of *noblesse oblige* and the threat of revolution in return for a little – no, a great deal of – home help. Short of becoming a millionaire or marrying one, the best option is to invite an expert into your home to talk your guests through the differences between a caipirinha and a caipiroska, and make them one of each at the same time. We tested the waters…

Wine-tasting

Daniel Illsley, owner of independent wine merchant Theatre of Wine, turns up for my wine-tasting party in a whirl of fine wine, decanters, glasses, branded bags ('for your guests to take leftovers home!'), an impressive copper cauldron to serve as an ice bucket and an equally impressive assistant, who whisks glasses away and washes them while his boss talks. 'We do anything,' Daniel says cheerily as he lays out groups of wines and snacks to match them, 'corporate dos, hen nights and parties for people who just really like good wine. And each event is totally bespoke.'

How much instruction you get is up to you: I have invited some very clueless girlfriends and ask Daniel to tutor us. Fizz-lovers all, they are fascinated when he breaks down

champagne into its three component grapes – pinot meunier, chardonnay and pinot noir – then drives the point home by serving an example of each, only the first of which (Les Vignes de Vrigny 1er Cru, Egly-Ouriet NV) is champagne. Daniel serves it with petit langres, a rich, creamy cheese. 'You wouldn't think to have champagne with cheese,' he says, 'but often it goes better than red wine because there aren't the tannins to contend with.' And, he points out, Champagne is a cheese-producing region, and matching local wines and foods tends to make sense.

To demonstrate the (much-maligned) chardonnay grape, he has a Chablis 1er Cru: Vaillons 2005, from Dauvissat. 'Lie it on your tongue, see what flavours you can pick out,' he tells us, which is no hardship. Claebitou, a Burgundy goat's cheese, is the match (Chablis is in northern Burgundy).

The third wine, Collection Réservée 2002 from Vignoble Guillaume in the Franche Comté region, brings out the poet in Daniel. 'Pinot noir is the gypsy grape, it will climb everywhere, it's thin-skinned, mercurial, fleeting,' he says, sounding like Paul Giammatti in *Sideways*. His enthusiasm prompts a slew of imaginative descriptions.

Next up is a Cremant du Jura Rose NV by A&M Tissot, a biodynamic fizz from Jura ('a really neglected area') which demonstrates that there's good wine with bubbles outside Champagne. The information and the new tastes that we're given are fascinating, but it's Daniel's enthusiasm that really makes this a party. He's a wine buff but no wine bore and, unlike so many party guests, he knows when to be quiet and when to go home. *Theatre of Wine, 75 Trafalgar Road, SE10 9TS (8858 6363/www.theatreofwine.com). Prices start at £25 per head without food (minimum £250); a full dinner with their chef Jane Rawson starts at £75 per head.*

Cocktail-mixing

'Don't knock Thunderbird,' says Nick Wykes of IPBartenders, laying out martini glasses, 'it got me through college.' Despite the premium spirits and the mixing kit complete with giant syringe he has brought to my living room, my friends and I gaze at him fearfully. What the hell will this champion of bottom-end fortified wine try and make us drink?

He starts with the best moscow mule I've ever tasted. 'I prefer dry cocktails,' he says, which explains the predominance of lime and the use of diet ginger beer. It's fantastic.

Next up is a mixed berry caipirinha, made with cachaça ('the Brazilians get very upset if you call it rum – it's made with sugar cane juice, not molasses') and puréed fresh berries. Nick chats easily while performing his complicated tasks: 'that's part of what we do – talk guests through the drinks, make up recipes if asked. If you just want someone who'll bring out the drinks and get everyone drunk, you can find it for half the price.' IPBartenders is a drinks training and events company; its best-known member is Ben Reed, formerly the man at the Met Bar. Nick got into this by 'phoning Ben up and asking for a job', but there was probably more to it than that since his drinks are incredible – even the experiments, like the Quantum Theory (Elements 8 rum, Galliano and apple juice), which has a weird jelly thing floating in it and isn't, Nick says, quite there yet.

If you decide to get Nick or his colleagues in for your party, it'd be wise to get them in early: setting up and preparing the first drink took nearly an hour. And note that they don't really do food. But frankly, when the drinks are this interesting, and their creator such an expert party facilitator, any snacks really just need to line the stomach.

IPBartenders, Unit 114, Buspace Studios, Conlan Street W10 5AP (8962 2752/ www.ipbartenders.com). All events are bespoke, but start at £65 not including drinks; with drinks from £300. This would cater for 25 to 30 people. No credit cards.

Beer and food-matching

Jane is here but the beer isn't. No problem, she says, hopping back on her bike, and returning with a Waitrose bag full of unusual beers. This glitch means we don't get to taste Raspberry Grand Cru from Meantime, the Greenwich-based brewery, but never mind – it's an impressive save. And when I ring up the Beer Academy to point out that I can't really recommend a beer company whose beers don't arrive, they tell me they have already changed their courier company as a result of our no-show. Jane Peyton, a former TV producer, is one of the Academy's roster of beeromaniacs, and if she is hardly what I was expecting, her enthusiasm matches that of any bearded CAMRA stereotype. She launches into the story of beer ('the oldest known alcoholic beverage'), sings its praises ('it's just milled cereal such as barley or wheat and water, yeast and hops, so very healthy') and distributes snacks to match.

First up is White Shield from UK beer mecca Burton-on-Trent, an India Pale Ale. 'It's so great with curry!' says Jane, dishing out samosas. 'I always tell people, "if your local curry house doesn't have an IPA, tell them to get one in!"' And certainly, the bitterness of the beer slices through the samosa's grease a treat.

'I do all kinds of events,' says Jane, handing out Innis & Gunn, a fabulous oak-aged beer, which goes particularly well with apple pie. She has just done a stag night for 25 lads, which sounds like a no-brainer to me, but next week she's doing a romantic tasting à deux. In between the Fuller's Honey Dew beer (which really does taste of honey) and the Kriek, a raspberry beer from Belgium, Jane imparts endless beer-related facts and insights. It's fascinating – and several of the beers even convert my anti-ale pals. Jane may not look the part, but she's one highly competent beer monster. *Beer Academy, 33 Clarges Street, W1J 7EE (0777 193 8471/beeracademy.co.uk). Tastings start at £300 + VAT for five guests.*

Planet of the Grapes

9 New Oxford Street, WC1A 1BA (7405 4912/www.planetofthegrapes.co.uk). Holborn or Tottenham Court Road tube. **Open** 10am-6pm Mon; 10am-8pm Tue-Fri. **Delivery** yes.

Although the entertainingly named Planet of the Grapes is a wine merchant, it can provide spirits and mixers for parties if requested (although they point out that the latter would be cheaper from a supermarket). And if it's fine wine you want, you'll find yourself in very good hands. There's a minimum spend of one case (12 bottles) or £100, but delivery is free in central London (up to Zone 3). Glasses can be provided and they'll also happily direct you to caterers if required. Next day delivery depends on van availability, but they'll do their best if it's an emergency.

Rent a Keg

Unit 9, Latimer Road, W10 69Q (0800 977 5113/www.rent-a-keg.com). Latimer Road tube. **Open** 9am-5pm Mon-Fri. **Delivery** yes.

Ditch the dustbin filled with slush and lukewarm Stella in favour of a keg of beer at your next bash. A technician will deliver the keg and show you how to use it (it only takes about ten minutes), then you can kick back with a damned fine pint and feel pleased with yourself. Great for barbecues, weddings at home and all manner of other occasions.

Sampler

266 Upper Street, N1 2UQ (7226 9500/ www.thesampler.co.uk). Highbury & Islington tube/rail. **Open** 11.30am-9pm Mon-Sat; 1-8pm Sun. **Delivery** yes.

Sampler employs the ingenious Enomatic system which is able to preserve open wines for weeks, allowing visitors to the shop to try really incredible wines in affordable dribbles. Jamie Hutchinson and his team can deliver a case or more of wine locally (N1 or N5) for nothing, and usually within 24 hours. Delivery elsewhere in London costs £10 per case – unless you order lots, in which case that's free too. They don't sell soft drinks or beer and the

NUMBERS GAME

How to make sure you don't run out of booze before midnight.

When planning how much booze (or food) you'll need for a party, a certain amount of common sense is required: you won't go far wrong if you err on the side of generosity. Most drinks suppliers will do sale or return on unopened bottles and if you do end up ordering too much from one that doesn't, an excessively enhanced drinks cabinet is surely preferable to a reputation as a mean host. That said, you don't want to go totally overboard. A bottle of champagne contains six glasses and Nazia Hassan, sales and events manager for Browns Bar & Brasserie on St Martin's Lane, calculates that most people have a glass and a half (the half is a top-up) to kick off a smart party. So, if you have 20 guests drinking a glass and a half each, you'll need to allow for approximately five bottles. With wine, it's sensible to allow at least half a bottle per person over dinner. Beer is slightly more difficult to calculate, but a crate (24 bottles) should do for three or four people for an evening, according to Daniele Cannas of the Beer Academy.

Hassan advises starting guests off with a drinks menu of wine and beer, before moving on to offer a dark and light spirit option as the evening progresses.

As for canapés, the rule of thumb is six to eight per person (a mixture of hot and cold is usually best), and don't forget at least one vegetarian option.

range of spirits is limited, apart from a good selection of cognacs, armagnacs and whisky. Glass hire is available too. Sale or return is available on bulk orders: they'll also take up to 30% of purchases back.

Soho Wine Supply

18 Percy Street W1T 1DX (7636 8490/ www.sohowine.co.uk) Tottenham Court Road tube. **Open** 9am-7pm Mon-Fri; 9am-6.30pm Sat. **Delivery** yes.
If it's Estonian Herb and Rum Vodka you're seeking, this Fitzrovia wine merchant is the place to come, although they also sell a good selection of wines from all over the world, including some surprisingly well-priced clarets and burgundies. Minimum spend is £200 for delivery, which costs £17 for the next working day, and there's no glass hire. But if it's novelty liquor you're after, this place is hard to beat.

Stone, Vine & Sun

01962 712351/www.stonevine.co.uk. **Open** 9am-6pm Mon-Fri; 9.30am-4pm Sat. **Delivery** yes.
Stone, Vine & Sun was set up by Simon Taylor, a picture expert bored with middle management at Sotheby's. The shop specialises in French wine: 'why go anywhere else?' asks their website, but they do, with unusual offerings from all over the world. Delivery is £5 for the first case, sliding to £1.50 per case for three or more; orders of less than a case cost £6.95 while those over £250 are free. SV&S will try to deliver within 48 hours. For party animals, they offer discount on larger volumes, sale or return and are happy to supply advice if asked; glass hire is unfortunately not available to Londoners.

Swig

(8995 7060/www.swig.co.uk). **Open** 9am-5.30pm Mon-Fri. **Delivery** yes.
Swig just sells wine, but very good wine, and although the minimum purchase is 12 bottles, delivery is a flat rate of £9.50 no matter how much you order. Sale or return is offered and the company will deliver on some evenings to accommodate those who work. Most importantly, the selection is really unusual, so you'll be offering your guests something special. And the trio who run Swig are very approachable for those wanting advice on what to choose.

Vintage House

42 Old Compton Street, W1D 4LR (7437 5112/www.vintagehouse.co.uk). Leicester Square tube. **Open** 9am-11pm Mon-Fri; 10am-11pm Sat; noon-10pm Sun. **Delivery** yes.

Salvatore Calabrese
COCKTAIL EXPERT AND BAR SUPREMO

All you need to make cocktails is a chopping board, a good sharp knife, a large spoon and a jar with a good seal on it for shaking the drinks. There's no need to spend money on a flashy cocktail shaker. My tip for great party cocktails is keep them simple. The more complicated they are, the less likely they are to be a success, so choose drinks with no more than three or four ingredients.

A cosmopolitan is a great one for the ladies – it's just vodka, lime, Cointreau and cranberry juice. Or try making a champagne cocktail – a lump of white sugar, some Angostura bitters and a little cognac, topped up with champagne.

In summer, go for a daiquiri, with a little bit of strawberry thrown in. It's very easy – light rum, syrup, fresh lime juice and a good shake. Perfect.

Remember to try out the drinks you're planning to make before a party. If you know you're having a bash next week, come up with two or three that you're comfortable making and practice them. Not five or six – you'll only confuse yourself.

If it's a big party, make a classic punch. Punch is always fun, because you can put anything in it. My favourite is toledo punch – with dark rum, dry sherry, a little bit of camomile syrup, mandarin liquor, fresh lime juice, nutmeg and citrus fruits. Let it infuse and then throw in some soda water.

A great cocktail should be like a beautiful woman. It looks sexy, it smells great and the taste – I'll leave that up to your imagination.

Salvatore Calabrese can be found behind the bar at members' club Fifty London (www.fiftylondon.com).

Squeeze. *See p147.*

There can't be many wine and spirit merchants who can offer you 18 different kinds of Japanese whisky – and enough rums and tequilas to make your eyes blur before you've even touched a drop. Vintage House has no minimum spend and, if you shell out over £50, no delivery charges either (it's £5 if spending under £50); the downside is that its vans don't like to venture too far outside central London. Wine and champagne glasses are available for hire.

Whisky Exchange

Unit 7, Space Business Park, Abbey Road, NW10 7SU (8838 9388/www.the whiskyexchange.com). North Acton or Park Royal tube. **Open** 9am-6pm Mon-Fri. **Delivery** yes.
Not really an exchange, except in the sense that you exchange your money for their whisky – or champagne, sherry or spirits. Don't come to WE if it's fine wines you're after but spirit lovers will find they can order as little as they wish, with a delivery charge of just £7.50. Delivery takes three-four days, but next day is possible if you order before noon. There's a limited range of glasses for hire and cocktail making equipment is sold on the website.

Wine Society

(01438 737700/thewinesociety.com). **Open** 8.30am-9pm Mon-Fri; 9am-5pm Sat. **Delivery** yes.
You have to join the Wine Society to order from them, but at £40 for life (and you can bequeath your membership) it's well worth it, since the Society is all about great wine at the best prices, pouring any profits back in to the business. Delivery is free if you're ordering at least a case or spending £75 (dangerously easy to do), otherwise it's £5; next day delivery is £11.50. They can provide glasses, and despite their name they do sell spirits and soft drinks as well.

MIXOLOGISTS & MOBILE BARS

Create Cocktails

(8548 4022/www.createcocktails.com). **Cost** from £195.
A cocktail company with sterling credentials: not only have Saatchi & Saatchi used them but über-party girl Kate Moss has too. They ask for a minimum spend of £1,000 but will manage your entire event if asked, from lighting to food to marquees. Even cloakroom attendants and DJs can be provided if you have the space. Minimum notice is two weeks but may be more depending on what you want.

Inflatable Pub

(01793 431406/www.inflatablepubs.com). **Cost** from £500.
Forget lone kegs, dusty beer tents and fancy cocktails served on silver trays, what your guests really want is a night down the pub – an inflatable one (it holds up 50 people)! As well as the blow-up boozer itself, the Inflatable Pub Co can provide drinks and trained staff to man the pumps. Prices start at £500. Bear in mind that if you want your guests to pay for their own drinks you may need to apply for a temporary alcohol licence. The company can advise on all of the above.

London's Mobile Bar

(07757 025470/www.eventcocktails.com). **Cost** from £95/mixologist.
London's Mobile Bar does what it says on the tin – provides mobile bars for thirsty but homebody Londoners. The company's mixologists can create a drinks menu especially for your event or you can stick with their classic concoctions. There's no minimum spend (your bill will start from £30, which includes delivery, depending on where you are in the capital you are) but early booking is advisable as they are much in demand, especially in summer. Keg hire can also be arranged.

Mobile Bar Hire

(08454 686888/07951 822015/ mobilebarhire.co.uk). **Cost** from £900.
Whether it's a smooth black bar you require or one lit up in tic tac orange, Mobile Bar Hire can help. Alternatively, the company will set up on a table if you don't fancy shelling out for bar hire. A month's notice is required, as is a minimum spend of £900, but they are happy to do either a pre-paid bar or handle the requisite cash if you want guests to pay (you may need a licence for this, however). The company can provide any brands you ask for and can organise food through a catering company too.

Mobile Mixology

97a Westbourne Park Villas, W2 5ED (7221 2544/mobilemixology.co.uk). Notting Hill Gate or Royal Oak or Westbourne Park tube. **Cost** from £500.
Mobile Mixology is pretty flexible: they say they can manage on a week's notice, depending on availability, and prices start at £500 for bar service only. They can also offer catering, marquees and so on, and will supply any spirit brands, wine or draught beer that you ask for. Delivery starts at £50, depending on where you are, but it's included in your quote. Oh, and they claim to have the 'best looking bartenders around' too – which would give a lift to any party.

SHAKER MAKER

Nina Caplan goes on the hunt for the ingredients for the perfect cocktail.

You've invited your guests, sorted the food and nailed down anything that might get broken in the debauchery – but we all know it's the drinks that really get the party started. Where should a novice mixologist start in the quest for cocktail-shaking perfection?

'Ice is more important than anything else,' says drinks writer Victoria Moore, whose as yet untitled cocktail book will be published in spring 2009. 'You do need a cocktail shaker, of course, but people always overlook ice. Make lots, in batches, a few days in advance – really fill your freezer. Think how quickly one or two cubes melt in a gin and tonic, and how tragic that is.'

Don't buy off-licence ice, though. It's too hollow and the indents increase the surface area so it melts faster than it should. 'It smashes into the wrong kind of shards entirely,' says Moore.

In addition, you'll require a good selection of spirits. In his book *The Art of the Cocktail*, Ben Reed, former bartender at the Met Bar, recommends choosing at least four of gin, vodka, light rum, aged rum, tequila, bourbon, whisky and cognac, and points out that premium spirits always result in better cocktails. It's also a good idea to have a few bottles of fizz on hand (not necessarily champagne: cava or some of the better New World sparklers are much cheaper and just as good for mixing purposes; prosecco can be too, if you like your drinks dry).

Fruit juices, particularly orange, cranberry and pineapple are essential (and great for keeping any non-drinkers at your party happy too), as is soda water, Angostura bitters and at least one type of liqueur (Cointreau is a great bet as it can be used in cosmopolitans, margaritas and many other drinks; it really makes a cocktail sing).

Then there's the fruit itself – oranges, limes and the all-important lemon – and herbs such as mint or lemon thyme, plus syrup (you can either buy this ready-made or make your own by heating caster sugar in an equivalent amount of water until it dissolves, then letting the mixture cool). For kit, an ice crusher is a great gadget to have on hand and a shaker is totally essential, as

is a good, sharp knife and a chopping board – for when you've mastered the impressive-looking knack of peeling a tiny piece of citrus skin for its oil.

Reed's first principle of cocktail-making is that the base spirit should provide most of the taste while sweetening and souring ingredients provide the balance. 'When actually making your drinks,' says Jamie Forbes, ambassador for Monkey Shoulder whisky, 'it's all in the shake. Go at it hard and fast, but only for about ten seconds. Otherwise you dilute the drink too much.' He too is obsessed with the chill factor: 'If you are making a cold drink, keep all the ingredients as cold as possible, including glassware and spirits,' he advises.

DO TRY THIS AT HOME

The simple one
King Solomon's Cooler
40ml Whitley Neill gin
50ml pressed English apple juice
Traditional lemonade
Squeeze one wedge of lemon and one wedge of lime into a tall glass. Then simply add ice, good-quality gin and apple juice. Top it off with lemonade.

The colourful one
Watermelon Martiki
50ml Elements 8 Platinum rum
15ml elderflower cordial
Flesh of a big slice of watermelon
Muddle the watermelon. Add the rum, elderflower cordial and ice. Shake hard in cocktail shaker. Double strain into a martini glass. Garnish with a slice of watermelon or a raspberry. This drink was designed by Richard Hunt of Mahiki.

The exotic one
Kappa Saketini
50ml Tokiwa shochu
25ml Akashi Tai Honjozo Genshu saké
Mix the chilled shochu and saké in a shaker and pour into a martini glass. Garnish with a strip of cucumber. Saké has very delicate flavours so if used in a cocktail it should be a simple recipe. Shochu or other spirits like vodka and gin can be also added to reinforce the body of this one.

Orbit Bar
145-157 St John Street, EC1V 4PY (3239 9779/www.theorbitbar.com). Farringdon tube/rail. **Cost** from £250.
If you want Tom Cruise circa *Cocktail* behind the bar, this is probably the closest you'll get: mixology experts who juggle bottles with finesse and can serve up to 10,000 guests. There's no minimum number of people required, although you must spend at least £250. That done, you can save money however you choose, including supplying booze yourself, providing a table instead of hiring the full mobile bar or finding someone to help collect and clean the glasses. Orbit requires at least a week's notice and, if you are buying your drink from them and plan to charge your guests, remember you may need a licence.

Peppermint
19 Pensbury Street, SW8 4TL (0845 226 7845/www.peppermintbars.co.uk). Vauxhall tube. **Cost** from £500.
This south London company claims to require a mere two days' warning; they can usually quote you a price the same day you call. Minimum spend is £500, including delivery and one bartender. They can, of course, supply any drink you need, as well as glasses. The company doesn't do food but is happy to put you in touch with others who do. And they do their best to be green too.

Shaker Events
75 East Road, N1 6AH (0870 720 2877/www.shaker-events.co.uk). Old Street tube/rail. **Cost** from £49.
If you quite fancy the idea of showing off your culinary skills at your bash but have no idea where to start on the booze side of things, give Shaker Events a buzz. The company can create wonderful cocktails for private or corporate dos and can create a special bespoke drink just for your event. Beats boxes of cheapo wine and vodka and cherryade anyway.

Squeeze
Unit 9, Latimer Road, W10 6RQ (8969 6606/www.squeezeuk.com). Latimer Road tube. **Cost** from £250.
Squeeze provides mobile bars and professional bartenders for all manner of parties and events. Mobile bar sizes range from six to 60 ft and can be lit up in all manner of complementary colours. Drinks are impeccably prepared and packed with quality ingredients: think pineapple and ginger martinis, pink grapefruit collins and jamaican mules. Bespoke cocktails can also be created. The company offers team-building events too.

Music & Entertainment

Whether a subtle accompaniment to cocktails and chatter or a dancefloor-filling riot of chart cheese, music is always an essential party ingredient. In this chapter, you'll find ideas, inspiration and suggestions for great musicians (mariachi bands to harpists), party-friendly DJs and crowd-pleasing jukeboxes for hire. You'll also find reviews of London's finest and most unusual performers, be they burlesque stars, stiltwalkers or dance troupes. Children's entertainment and booking agencies are also covered. Some acts are not based in London but all are very happy to work at events in the capital.

MUSICIANS & BANDS

To offer an idea of potential costs, we asked the musicians and bands listed below how much they'd charge for two 45-minute sets in central London on a Saturday. Bear in mind, however, that most prices are negotiable depending on factors such as time of year. Smaller acts (booking a soloist rather than a full band, for example) may also work out cheaper than the prices quoted. It's always worth calling to discuss your requirements and budget.

Abba Revival
07957 443804/www.abbarevival.co.uk.
Cost from £1,450. **No credit cards**.
One sure-fire way to make sure your DJ isn't badgered with requests for 'Dancing Queen' the whole night is to hire the Swedish superstars themselves – or, rather, their accomplished British tribute band, which is close enough. Justin, John, Vicki and Lisa do a convincing Björn, Benny, Agnetha and Anni-Frid respectively, storming stages and filling dancefloors with their fully-choreographed compilation of the classics, which features live guitars and an authentic white baby grand piano (drums, bass and strings are backing tracked), plus audience participation and no less than six costume changes over the course of one hour-long or two 45-minute sets. They also do a '90-minute epic' that they consider to be their best show.

Backflash
0871 890 1015/www.backflash.co.uk.
Cost from £1,200. **No credit cards**.

Bollywood Pandits

Eminently professional and justifiably proud of their ability to rock parties of all shapes, sizes and inclinations, Backflash is a five-piece covers band specialising in crowd-pleasers from the '60s right up to the present day. The band are all music graduates with a combined record of working alongside the likes of Jamie Cullum and Jamiroquai, and all look, as well as sound, the part – frontwoman Phillipa Cookman is especially easy on the eye, and boy can she sing (or, as their website puts it: 'gob like a fog horn on a freight train'). The band has its own 2kW PA system and lighting rig to help give parties a proper gig feel.

Bagpipers for Hire

7735 1864/07876 403711/www.bagpipersfor hire.co.uk. **Cost** from £175. **No credit cards**.
Bagpipers for Hire's experienced and professional pipers can appear – in full regalia naturally – solo, as a quartet or even a full band to add a touch of Scottish Highland flair to a celebration. Particularly popular for weddings, piper repertoires include renditions of 'Highland Cathedral', 'Silver Threads among the Gold', 'Lara's Theme' (*Dr Zhivago*) and 'Ave Maria'. Just remember, where bagpipes are concerned, less is often more. Think entrances, exits and cocktail hour rather than three-hour sets and dancing.

Bollywood Pandits

07957 190680/07956 579391/ www.bollywoodpandits.com. **Cost** from £1,200. **No credit cards**.
The multi-award-winning Bollywood Pandits (formerly known as Strings) have been performing a range of Indian music since their inauguration in 1994. Founding member Kiran Thakrar is an accomplished producer and Bollywood collaborator who has performed with some of the biggest names in world music (he backed Bebel Gilberto at a recent MOBO Awards ceremony), and the band has played everything from international festivals and royal receptions

EBONY STEELBAND

More than just a steel band, Ebony is also a charitable organisation offering free musical workshops to disadvantaged youths, most of them from London's Afro-Caribbean community. As such, it recently became the first voluntary organisation in the borough of Kensington and Chelsea to receive a royal charter – something that will probably get lost in an award cabinet already bursting with accolades picked up since the band's foundation in 1968, including two European Championships at the French Steel Band Music Festival. The band has also toured internationally and played to enormous audiences – including at stages around Europe during the FIFA World Cup and in Delhi at the opening of the International Cricket World Cup – but they're just as happy playing at private parties around London. Hiring the band couldn't be easier, with variations from solo performances (£350; £400 including workshop) up to five-piece shows (£700; £900 including workshop). As a cheaper but no less cheerful alternative, it's also possible to hire a five-piece Millennium Volunteers band (£450; £550 including workshop), comprised of 16- to 24-year-olds still learning the drums but deemed capable of performing in public by their elders. Performances take place over four hours and constitute either two 45-minute or four 30-minute sets. (The volunteer band performs two 30-minute sets).
For listings, see right.

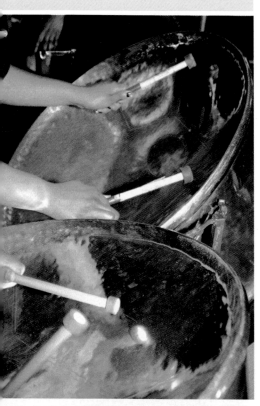

to *Never Mind The Buzzcocks* (where they did a rousing version of 'Cotton Eye Joe') – even a two-night stint performing alongside Bill Bailey in front of 20,000 people at the O2 Arena. With vocals by the lovely Anuradha – who is also an Indian television and radio presenter – BP offers Indian music in a range of styles, from Hindi pop and soul-shaking Bollywood classics to bhangra, folk and disco. For smaller events and receptions, the band can organise a soothing sitar player to pick away gently in the background; for larger events, Bollywood dancers can be brought in to add an exotic kick. The band is even happy taking requests to play Western pop songs, although admittedly this may be akin to ordering an omelette in an Indian restaurant.

Ebony Steelband

7792 1418/www.ebony.org.uk. **Cost** from £350. **No credit cards**.
For review, *see left*.

Fleurs de Paris

0845 838 3514/www.silverdogmusic.co.uk/ fleursdeparis.htm. **Cost** from £1,000.
Singer Lo may be the only certifiably French member of the band – otherwise composed of fiddle, guitar and accordion players, all English – but Fleurs de Paris does a roaring trade in reviving the soulful chanson music that filled Parisian cafés and music halls between the 1930s and '50s. The band's repertoire features better-known songs by the likes of Edith Piaf and Charles Aznavour alongside a number of obscure little gems dug up and dusted off during the band's own research into the era, and all will make perfect accompaniments to more conversational gatherings, from cocktail parties to wedding receptions.

Freespirit

07930 415185/www.aliveband.co.uk. **Cost** from £950.
An infectiously funky five- to seven-piece band fronted by charismatic female lead singer Val Kelly, and with a range of material from soul and swing jazz to disco and more dance-oriented pop. Despite having toured internationally – from cruise ship residencies and new year celebrations at the Hilton in Addis Ababa to a gig for the late James Brown in Beirut – the band are still best known for filling dancefloors at weddings and for private parties of all shapes and sizes, from intimate in-house celebrations to major corporate events.

Hula Groove

8341 1223/07966 229490/www.hulagroove. co.uk. **Cost** from £1,950.

ESSENTIALS

A considerable cut above the average covers band, Hula Groove has garnered a reputation for being among the most professional party outfits in the capital after rocking more weddings than they care to remember and kick-starting corporate events for everyone from Alliance & Leicester to Hilton International. Four gorgeous female singers backed by a five-piece band belt out a range of infectious soul, funk and disco hits shot through with sunshine – from Al Green to Alicia Keyes and from Aretha Franklin to Amy Winehouse. A male duo horn section is also available for an additional charge.

Hullabaloo

0871 890 1015/www.hullabaloo-uk.com.
Cost from £1,200. **No credit cards**.
You're probably thinking that any band that's played at Jamie Oliver's wedding is good enough to play at yours – and you're probably right. A swing and jazz four piece featuring drums, double bass, guitar and saxophone, Hullabaloo combine creative vocal harmonies with an eclectic take on classics from the slow and soulful to the blisteringly upbeat. The band is as comfortable contributing a laid-back ambience to cocktail receptions with songs like 'Autumn Leaves' and 'Moon River' as they are setting the dancefloor on fire with their outlandish versions of tracks such as 'Mack The Knife'. The band also deal in instrumentals and covers of pop songs from 'Brown Eyed Girl' to 'Baggy Trousers'.

Left of the Dial

01843 581607/www.left-of-the-dial.co.uk.
Cost from £800. **No credit cards**.
The funk and soul canon gets treated with the respect it deserves by Kentish five-piece Left of the Dial, featuring accomplished vocals from Katie Bradley – resident in London blues bar Ain't Nothin' But..., and erstwhile collaborator of Suzanne Vega, Caravan and the Crazy World of Arthur Brown – and drumming from Steve Wye, formerly of prog rock outfit Gizmo and, er, Sooty the glove puppet's backing band. A wide repertoire includes everything from James Brown and Bonnie Raitt to Santana to Steely Dan – there's even a cover of Portishead's 'Glory Box' in there if you want it.

Licence to Ceilidh

07792 390334/www.licencetoceilidh.co.uk.
Cost from £1,000. **No credit cards**.
Turn even the most ostensibly civilised London gathering into a spirited barn dance with Licence to Ceilidh, purveyors of upbeat folk music from England, Ireland and Scotland. The group specialises in rallying even complete beginners to take part in a range of traditional ceilidh dances, starting out with simple numbers like the 'Gay Gordons' before moving on to more elaborate affairs such as 'Strip the Willow' and the 'Virginia Reel', with competent instructions from the callers allowing all but the most inebriated of partygoers to get involved.

Mexteca

8570 7163/www.mariachimexteca.com.
Cost from £320 (for trio). **No credit cards**.
Mexico's reputation as a nation with the party spirit flowing in its veins is well-founded, and there's no better way to import a piece of the action to your own gathering than by hiring Mexteca, a traditional mariachi band available either as a full sextet, quintet, quartet, trio, duo or solo. Formed in 2002 by Salvador Jimenez Hernandez – who began his musical training aged eight in his native city of Guadalajara – Mexteca use horns, guitars and vocal harmonies to variously add a ray of sunshine or simply rock the dancefloor at parties of all sizes.

Ronnie Scott's Rejects

01732 479979/07976 877358/www.ronnie scottsrejects.com. **Cost** from £1,400.
No credit cards.
The band with one of the most likeable names in the business comes either as a five- or six-piece ensemble (the latter featuring a two-piece horn section), and performs some of the most memorable show tunes from the '30s and '40s, as well as the century's finest swing jazz and a range of '60s pop covers with a soulful twist. Singer Hazel Holder has a voice more than capable of doing justice to the Billies, Ninas, Sarahs and Ellas of this world, and the band's repertoire has a set for everything from sedate cocktail receptions to raucous, rip-roaring dancefloor shakedowns.

Royal College of Music

7591 4367/www.rcm.ac.uk. **Cost** from £120 (for solo pianist). **No credit cards**.
Those looking to host an event with musical accompaniment more refined than your average covers band would do well to investigate the musicians for hire at the Royal College of Music. All are either current students or graduates of the college, and as such are guaranteed to perform with a pedigree befitting so internationally renowned an institution (they're also expected to present themselves with the proper deportment). All manner of classical and jazz musicians are available – from solo pianists to string quartets, wind trios and swing bands. It's a nice little earner while studying – beats pulling pints, anyway – and is all good practice, at the end of the day.

ESSENTIALS

Rubber Soul

07884 075739/www.tonhauser.com/
rubbersoul. **Cost** from £1,500.
Formed in 1998 at the University of Surrey's School of Performing Arts and fuelled by a profound technical ability as well as a passion for playing, Rubber Soul is a nine-piece ensemble that can – if pushed – break down into composite elements to suit the situation: from a lone piano player at cocktail parties to a jazz quintet for wedding receptions. Needless to say, it's also possible to hire the full shebang, which includes male and female vocals, a horn section, keys, guitars and drums. The band's repertoire runs the gamut from Stevie Wonder and Marvin Gaye classics to more contemporary crowd pleasers like Robbie Williams's 'Angels'.

Shebeen

01962 760986/www.shebeen.biz. **Cost** from £600. **No credit cards.**
Hampshire's favourite Irish rabble-rousers have been recording and performing since 1989, in that time becoming a regular fixture on the pub and festival circuit and a firm favourite for parties with a Gaelic flavour – since being featured in *Wedding Ideas* magazine they're also increasingly in demand for marriage ceremonies. Plus there's the luck of the Irish to take into consideration – London Irish RFC has apparently never lost a game when the four-piece has played at their home ground. Their repertoire of Irish folk music can be given a more dance-oriented kick with traditional ceilidh instruments and calling if requested in advance.

Soul System

07825 817355/www.soulsystem.co.uk. **Cost** from £1,600.
Soul System performs either as a seven- or five-piece ensemble (with or without horns, respectively), or as a jazz duo, trio or quintet depending on the size and nature of the event. The lion's share of licks are soul classics, with a song list covering danceable numbers by everyone from Bill Withers and James Brown to the Commitments and the Commodores, plus a dash of '70s disco to help build up a sweat. They work with a wide range of vocalists (frontman Dan's voice is a real show stealer), and the band is a big hit at weddings thanks to their professional attitude.

Straight No Chaser

07941 971411/www.big-band-jazz.co.uk. **Cost** from £2,000. **No credit cards.**
For a celebration with real swing, the 18-piece Straight No Chaser big band takes some beating. Needless to say only larger venues will accommodate the entire group, but they can arrange smaller denominations for more intimate events, and play anything from soul, funk and covers bands to jazz or swing quartets – even a soprano accompanied by a harp. Those able to hire the full band will find a repertoire of over 300 songs broken down into programmes suiting all manner of parties, plus a range of themed performances based around the Rat Pack, Latin American music or the work of Glenn Miller (the latter played in military uniform). Choose from Sinatra-style male crooning or sultry female vocals, or go the whole hog and hire both.

Three Waiters

7436 4484/www.thethreewaiters.com. **Cost** call for details. **No credit cards.**
In a hoax to rival the Hitler Diaries, the Three Waiters appear to be exactly that – three marvellously turned out waiters who are well informed about the food they're serving and meticulously organised in serving it. All that changes once the meal is finished, however, when one of the waiters takes to the stage to nervously inform the audience that he's been dared by one of his colleagues to sing a little song. Needless to say there's much awkward shifting in seats and concerned whispering among the audience… until the waiter begins, and it turns out that he's a fabulously well-trained opera singer. Before long the other two have joined in and the whole thing has dissolved into a gleeful showcase of operatic crowd-pleasers complete with plenty of audience participation and a hearty dash of highbrow theatrical humour. The concept was originally conceived in Sydney in 1998, and in ten short years its unprecedented success has led to the opening of offices in New York and London, won various entertainment awards and astonished guests at countless functions – from intimate dinners to enormous gala balls. The show has been adapted to include requests, such as special songs. Get in and book them before their big secret is a secret no more.

NOTE

PARTY KILLERS
Attempt at your peril:
- *Awkward match-making*
- *Conversations about fantasy dinner parties*
- *Ice-breaking games, especially those that involve oranges under chins*
- *Playlists containing anything by Black Lace*
- *The restriction of alcohol*

ESSENTIALS

Would you like a canapé with your Puccini? **Three Waiters**. *See p155.*

Transilvania Band
07791 871752/www.transilvaniaband.co.uk.
Cost from £450. **No credit cards**.
Under no circumstances to be confused with late
'80s chart botherers Transvision Vamp, the
Transilvania Band is an enigmatic five piece with
a globe-trotting repertoire belted out on
accordion, double bass, cimbalom and guitar.
The band specialises in Eastern European and
gypsy music – with great gusto and in a way that
can't help but fill a dancefloor – but they're just
as comfortable playing Latin swing, traditional
Jewish music and a range of western jazz
standards.

Wedding Harpist
www.theweddingharpist.co.uk. **Cost** from £300.
There are few sounds more soothing than a harp
being strummed, and few better suited to adding
an air of luxurious refinement to a wedding
celebration. It's little wonder, then, that Vicki Kirk
has found such success offering her services as
a professional wedding harpist. She's performed
at over 300 such events since 1999, from
restrained civil ceremonies to full-blown church
affairs and receptions. Kirk, who was trained at
the Royal College of Music and has toured with
the Berkshire Symphony Orchestra, has also
been featured on ITV1's *This Morning* and was
voted one of the five best wedding harpists in the
country by *Brides* magazine.

Yul Emirali
07814 330128. **Cost** from £150. **No credit
cards.**
Emirali has played piano at the Ivy, for Gordon
Brown and is a regular tinkler at the Grosvenor
House Hotel. With a repertoire including jazz
standards, classic pop and bebop, Emirali is an
expert at creating background mood for quiet
cocktails, guiding the bride down the aisle or
providing centrepiece entertainment. Easy on the
eye as well as the ear, you can hire him solo or
with a sax player or singer.

DJS

Where possible below we have listed
a starting price for each act. Prices may
be higher depending on the night you want
to book and the time of year; it may also
be possible to negotiate a lower price.

INDIE MASH-UPS
& DANCE

Durrr DJs
www.myspace.com/durrrclub. **Cost** email
for details.
When only the super cool will do, try the Durrr
DJs. Comprising the Lovely Jonjo and Rory

Phillips, Durr is spot-on for a party oozing with guitar anthems (Bloc Party, the Mystery Jets) and 1980s crunk-electro (Duke Dumont's 'Hoy'). Ten minutes in and it'll be perfectly clear why Durrr is one of London's leading Monday night party pumpathons.

Girlcore

www.myspace.com/girlcorerules. **Cost** email for details.
This east London collective of girl DJs can turn any party into a riotous affair as each and every one of them exudes as much credibility, style and excitement as their sound-of-the-moment playlist. Think baile funk, fidget house, old school rave and singalong gems. You'll most likely find them at music industry parties, magazine launches and cool house parties.

Jodie Harsh

7927 6222/www.jodieharsh.com. **Cost** call for prices.
As London's drag queen du jour, it's a rare party that doesn't have Jodie Harsh on the guest list, never mind behind the decks. With records as big as her towering blonde hair, the flamboyant Harsh sparkles with accessible throw-your-hands-in-the-air party anthems and rocking guitar-fuelled hits. Think Stardust's 'Music Sounds Better With You' alongside AC/DC. Bookable through Insanity Artist Agency (*see p161*).

Nathan Gregory Wilkins

www.myspace.com/historyclock/nathan. gregory.wilkins@gmail.com. **Cost** email for details. **No credit cards**.
London based DJ and co-promoter of the Tropical Hot Dog parties, Nathan Gregory Wilkins is the fashionista's DJ of choice, joining the dots between modern pop, kooky techno and '80s disco, making the three sound like natural bedfellows whether at a village fête or paparazzi-filled stadium. With a quiff as cool and stylish as his record collection (Santogold, Das Pop, Klaxons) he'll have you striking a pose in no time.

Queens of Noize

07919 055675/www.queensofnoize.com. **Cost** from £2,500. **No credit cards**.
Glamorous party promoters and radio presenters, the notorious Queens of Noize could turn popping down the shops for a pint of milk into a rock 'n' roll affair. Complete with lashings of infectious enthusiasm and a cheeky bag of tricks (a kissing booth, dressing-up box and karaoke machine), they'll have the most jaded partygoer spinning around to indie pop treats and '80s acid house before you can say 'Ooh look, it's Kate Moss'.

INTERACTIVE PARTY DJS

Actionettes

www.actionettes.com. **Cost** from £300 (to DJ only). **No credit cards**.
Clad in matching mod outfits, this 12-strong group of girls perform synchronised go-go routines to 1960s girl bands. Book them to DJ, and they'll also teach a few hot moves to the crowd too.

Cuban Brothers

www.thecubanbrothers.com. **Cost** from £6,000 (four-piece). **No credit cards**.
Insane in the membrane, this quartet of costume-wearing DJs also sing and do a little bit of (optional) naked break-dancing. Russ Cuban dishes out the party hip hop, while lead vocalist Miguel fires up your guests with close-to-the-bone Havana-themed rapping and Archerio and Kengo destroy the dancefloor with wicked break-dance routines. Definitely a winner for any party, just make sure the kids are in bed.

Laundrettas

www.myspace.com/laundrettas. **Cost** call for prices.
We heart the Laundrettas! Popular at festivals, Guilty Pleasures nights and off-kilter cabaret parties, this collective of girls spring-clean any event they're at. Dressed as 1950s housewives, they tickle with dusters, rearrange sloppy outfits and spin American diner rock 'n' roll. Bookable through Guilty Pleasures (*see p161*).

Shellac Sisters

07976 407927/www.shellacsisters.co.uk. **Cost** from £600/3hr set.
Decked out in vintage prom dresses and perfect hair dos, the Shellac Sisters have a vast collection of '78s they play on a 1920s gramophone. Perfect for starting the party – gramophones only go so loud – they can tailor playlists to fit a Christmas party, afternoon tea, wedding, whatever. Wiggle along to '40s swing, big band numbers and more.

Swap-a-rama

07919 055675/www.kirstiinternational.com. **Cost** from £2,000. **No credit cards**.
Why not get someone else to arrange the games at your party? Swap-a-rama Razzmatazz will certainly make sure that the photographs are keepers. Partygoers help themselves to second-hand clothing strung around the room on washing lines. At the sound of the klaxon, everyone swaps one item of clothing with the person next to them while DJs Mister Frew and Jimmy Jeans spin vintage hits, rock 'n' roll and party numbers.

ESSENTIALS

TIPS FOR DIY DJS

Crucial dos and don'ts to get your party started.

Do think about the best music to start your party off with. Old crooners such as Dean Martin and Frank Sinatra at Christmas, for instance, or try some rock 'n' roll at a birthday party.

Don't waste the first couple of hours with your finest playlists. Chances are folk will be late and won't get to hear what you spent six days whittling down.

Do clear the area around your stereo and put all your CDs out of eye's reach. If people can't see them, they can't rifle through them.

Don't lose your temper if someone tries to 'have a go'. Yes, it's incredibly rude to take over someone else's stereo, but they're still a guest. Firmly explain that you've got the music sorted, thank you very much, and promise to grab them when your playlists are over.

Do keep a few faithful hits somewhere on your iPod. You may think Diplo's baile funk 'Rhythm' is the coolest thing since sliced bread, but it might not work for grandma over in the corner.

Don't be afraid of playing the cheesiest record even if your audience is predominantly male. Gay or straight, blokes really dig singalong pop music, especially after a couple of beers.

Do put 'Happy Birthday' on a playlist if you're playing one; Stevie Wonder's version always goes down a treat.

Don't underestimate the power of pop. Even if you're playing a mostly male crowd, after a few drinks everyone loves a good power ballad. Just don't play 'Power Ballads – the Extended Compilation' all the way through.

Do allow for the natural ebb and flow of a good party. You might want your dancefloor jumping until 5am, but it's a house party, not a techno club, so cool things down every hour or so and let folk naturally take a breather.

Do make sure you've got the right equipment before you start (*see p160*) and take a peek at the tips that Kevin Durham (Kill the DJ) suggests. *See p159.*

Don't ignore our 'Party Killers' advice. *See p155.*

Tayo's Tracksuit Party
07919 055675/www.myspace.com/ tayostracksuitparty. **Cost** from £1,000. **No credit cards**.
Much in demand as a breaks producer and DJ, Tayo also hosts regular party homages to the tracksuit. Jump around to block party hip hop, reggae, disco and house party anthems.

CHEESY CROWD-PLEASERS

Charlotte Hotham
7684 5228/www.buggedout.net. **Cost** from £250. **No credit cards**.
With her mind-the-gaps backroom pub DJ skills, east London girl about town Charlotte Hotham creates a poptastic affair every time. Heart, Madonna and even Angry Anderson will all receive airtime.

Feeling Gloomy
07757 855 138/www.feelinggloomy.com. **Cost** from £500/DJ set. **No credit cards**.
Promoters of club nights such as Sniff The Glove (big hair, bigger early '80s riffs) and Feeling Gloomy ('the club that brings a tear to your eye'), Leonard and Cliff are fond of turning up to bookings wearing questionable 1970s charity shop suits. They can organise the whole shebang or just DJ for a few hours.

Johnno Burgess
07919 055 675/www.kirstiinternational.com. **Cost** from £500 (personal appearance); £1,000 (Erection Section). **No credit cards**.
Leader of the power ballad pack, Johnno's party piece is the Erection Section, a session of love songs, ballads and soft rock. Complete with bubble machines and request forms, hold your lighters aloft and get ready to sing your heart out to Bonnie Tyler and Foreigner.

Sean Rowley
07919 055 675/www.guiltypleasures.co.uk. **Cost** from £3,500 (Guilty Pleasures). **No credit cards**.
There's many a musical feather in Sean Rowley's cap. Not only is he Mr Guilty Pleasures (think School Disco but with bags of credibility and style), peddling hits from days gone by (anyone for 'Video Killed the Radio Star' by Buggles?) and current faves (Girls Aloud's 'Biology'), but he also runs not one but two radio shows (one on BBC London and the other on 6 Music) where he gets to push the more obscure, psychedelic side of music that he loves. With a genuine love for pop, rockabilly, northern soul and more (Rowley also runs a night called Pop Odyssey with fellow Guilty

ESSENTIALS

Pleasures pal Johnno Burgess), it's easy to see why Guilty Pleasures has turned into such a phenomenon. Rowley a fine bet for weddings, parties and festivals because wherever he lays his decks and his tracks down, that's his home.

VINTAGE & ROCK 'N' ROLL

El Nino
www.ladyluckclub.co.uk/ladyluckhq@yahoo. co.uk. **Cost** from £100/hr. **No credit cards**. Promoter of Lady Luck, London's long-running sleazy vintage happening, El Nino is also a much in demand DJ. Often appearing with his gorgeous wife and fellow record spinner Lady Kamikaze, the suavely turned out El Nino spins floor-filling, underground sounds of the 1920s to 1960s, taking in swing, gypsy jazz and blues.

Healer Selecta
07949 161002/www.healerselecta.co.uk. **Cost** from £400/set. **No credit cards**. London-based Parisian Healer Selecta heads the acclaimed Raison D'Etre collective and is a talent surf guitarist and internationally admired DJ. His record collection is high-quality vintage and a guaranteed dancefloor-filler.

Hula Boogie
8672 5972/www.hulaboogie.co.uk. **Cost** from £50/hr. **No credit cards**. DJs Miss Aloha and Reverend Boogie organise regular vintage dance nights across London, with a winning combination of bopping swing, 1950's and 1960's records, hula and jive classes, and burlesque performances (if you book them for the works).

Wheelie Bag
7690 8498/www.djwheeliebag.co.uk. **Cost** from £50/hr. Well into his sixties, DJ Wheelie Bag plays out rockin' vintage hits, scorchin' ska and retro doo-wop numbers from his specially created decks-on-shopping trolley on wheels. Yes, you read that right. He's like a one-man band with his own sound system that's constantly on the move. It's the future, man.

BOOKING AGENCIES

Also worth checking out are Live Music Management (www.lmmuk.com) and British Arts (www.britisharts.co.uk).

Decked Out
7400 4500/www.primary.uk.com

Kevin Durham
DIRECTOR OF KILL THE DJ

The most bizarre party I've DJ'd at is the National Parking Awards ceremony. I wasn't expecting parking attendants to be easy customers, but they surprised me. They were really wild once the lights went down – you couldn't get them off the dancefloor. Those people are party animals in disguise. **If you want to clear the dancefloor**, play 'The Music Man' or 'Agadoo'. Black Lace is definitely a dancefloor killer. **If you're playing to a mixed crowd**, anything that's hardcore in any way is a bad idea – so no Metallica. **The worst DJ-ing experience I've ever had** was at a party on HMS *Belfast*. One drunk guest wanted me to play nothing but funk music, but I didn't have my funk CDs with me and he started getting agitated. It got to the point where he was threatening to chuck me overboard if I didn't play more James Brown, so I had to play 'I Feel Good' on loop until he got bored and left me alone. **Hosts should never be** selfish about music. I did a gig last year for a client who loved his '80s music, and kept complaining any time I tried to play other people's requests. Everyone else was standing there with a glum look wondering why we were listening to Duran Duran over and over. You've got to know your audience. **My proudest moment** was when I saved the day at a charity fancy dress ball by auctioning off the guests. It wasn't the plan, but their own auction had gone really badly, so I raised a bit of extra cash by getting the guests on stage. I sold Bananaman and a nun with hairy knees for £130.

Kevin Durham is a director of, and one of the ten DJs who provide DJ services at, Kill the DJ (www.killthedj.co.uk).

ESSENTIALS

LAST NIGHT A DJ SAVED MY LIFE

Let **Cyrus Shahrad**'s handy guide to the technical stuff save yours.

An inherent fear of electronic equipment should be no barrier to hiring a PA system and setting up a DJ rig of your own. Just be sure you've hired the correct size system: an 800W rig will work fine for small house parties, but will be drowned out at a larger gathering; a 3.5kW system will be loud enough to power a small club, but will lead to police intervention if operated in a residential area.

Once you've picked a suitable system, run a quick checklist on the equipment. You should be looking at a pair of turntables or 'decks'– most likely industry-standard Technics 1210s for vinyl or Pioneer CDJ1000s for digital DJs (note that vinyl decks will skip if set up on anything other than a solid surface, especially if dancing is involved). These will be connected to what will most likely be a three- or four-channel cross-fade mixer via red and white phono leads (usually protruding from the turntables themselves); the left deck should be linked up to channel one; the right deck to the last channel, usually three or four (it's easier to flip the cross-fader between them with intervening channels muted).

The mixer can then be connected to your amplifier, again with red and white phono leads; most amps are all-inclusive, self-mixing units, although some larger systems come with a separate mixing desk for modulating levels manually (best done by a professional sound engineer; *see below*).

The amp will then be connected to your speakers via either three-pin XLR cables or, if you're using a large PA, Speakon cables. Positioning of the speakers is important: most small setups tend to include a pair of all-in-one Mackie PA speakers plus stands, which should be placed behind the DJ (although not so close as to be deafening), otherwise the sound of what's bouncing back off the walls will make beat-matching records impossible. Larger systems will feature separate bass bins – to evenly distribute the sound – and possibly monitors (small speakers) placed in front of the DJ to avoid bounce back. You should also be provided with a pair of headphones for mixing, and you may want to hire a microphone, which will be connected to and controlled by the mixer.

With everything connected, you should be ready to plug in and play – but don't just turn everything up and switch it all on. For the safety of both equipment and ears, it's best to turn all the mixer channels down, raise the amp volume to around 20 per cent, and with a tune playing on either the right or left turntable, slowly raise the gain on the corresponding mixer channel. Only when you're happy with what's coming out of the speaker should you raise the volume on the amp to a more party-hearty level. If there's no sound emerging, double-check all connections (with the amp turned down) and then try again. If there's still no sound, check that the turntables are working, either by monitoring the LED on the mixer or with the headphones – vinyl turntables are particularly prone to bouts of silence easily sorted out with an adjustment of the needle arm. If they work fine – and they should, provided the leads are in the right sockets (vinyl decks also have ground leads for eliminating feedback) – then have a play around with the switches and faders on the mixer to make sure that nothing is muted and that no effects are overriding the output.

The PA hire places listed on pages 162-163 can often offer a helping hand in setting up (usually around £35), advisable for larger systems, although those utilising on-board mixing desks are best operated by a professional sound engineer, whose services for the evening will set you back around £150.

One of the largest DJ agencies in the world, this is the place to call if you want to book the hottest international record spinners for your big event. Think Basement Jaxx, Erol Alkan, Justice, LCD Soundsystem DJs, Tiga, Justin Robertson, Jon Carter and the like.

Guilty Pleasures

www.guiltypleasures.co.uk
Here you'll find DJs, live acts and all the components of the Guilty Pleasures phenomenon. There's DJ Sean Rowley (*see p158*), as well as the other GP DJs (check the website for more details), the Laundrettas and even the Priest with his confessional booth. And whether your event is a corporate affair or a small shindig put together by friends, as far as they are concerned, 'it's your event and you can have as much cake as you want'.

Insanity Artist Agency

www.insanitygroup.com
For a party with a celebrity edge, this agency can help with a number of actors/models/bands-turned-DJs to get your guests talking (Jodie Harsh, the Mighty Boosh, Alexa Chung and the like). Expect mind-the-gaps party DJing and a crowded dancefloor. Plus, you get to pretend to your mates that you're friends with some really famous peeps.

Kirsti International

07919 055675/www.kirstiinternational.com
A 'one-stop party shop' with its emphasis firmly on light-hearted fun, Kirsti International is home to the likes of Johnno Burgess and party concepts such as Tayo's Tracksuit Party and Swap-a-rama. Equally at ease organising corporate parties as smaller birthday shindigs, Kirsti International can supply you with just a DJ or live act or produce the whole shebang.

Morris Agency Ltd

0871 890 1015/07776 202708/www.the morrisagency.co.uk. **No credit cards.**
This agency can provide everything from soloists to full bands, covering genres from classical to pop. Weddings are a speciality but suitable acts can be sourced for any type of event. On the books are soul and funk band Love Train, Ben Mills from the *X Factor*, four-piece jazz, jive and swing band Hullabaloo (*see p153*), Backflash (*see p148*) and Ronnie Scott's Rejects (*see p153*). Magicians can also be supplied.

Whoopee Agency

7012 1077/www.thewhoopeeagency.com
One of London's biggest burlesque promoters, the Whoopee Club also have an agency crammed with performers, musicians and DJs. It's difficult to get on the books of this agency, so quality is very high, and DJs tend to be of the jump-jiving and retro variety such as Hitman Hearn and Titty Titty Bang Bang. Costs for performers start at around £500 but the sky's really the limit with Whoopee.

JUKEBOX HIRE

Jukebox45s

01604 473101/www.jukebox45s.co.uk
You'll struggle to find a wider range of models for hire than at Jukebox45s, with compact disc versions of more conventional styles like the Americana and the Manhattan (both with colourful lights and hypnotic bubbles galore) alongside digital variations (the Digital Nostalgia, featuring over half a century of Top 40 hits). There are also a few modern oddities: the Spaceman (£445), for example, is a digital jukebox built inside a six-foot plastic astronaut, or the ultra-modern Silversmith Touchscreen Digital, a minimal installation for parties with a more futuristic feel. There's also the Jukebox in a Box (£155), a space-saving touch-screen number that plugs into your existing music system. A daunting list of CDs with which more traditional models are stocked can be browsed on the website, which also offers advice and instructions for customising playlists with personal favourites. The company isn't based in London, but delivers to the capital on a weekly basis.

Jukebox One Night Hire

8894 4463/www.jukeboxonenighthire.co.uk. **No credit cards.**
Turn your dining room into Al's Diner from *Happy Days*, with a compact disc version of the classic 1950s Wurlitzer 1015. The model comes loaded with 1,200 tracks covering classics from the '50s onwards – from Elvis to the Verve, from Rod Stewart to Robbie Williams – and with plenty of 'best of' albums covering both genres (Motown, reggae) and decades. More selective swingers also have the option of customising playlists with CDs of their own (installed upon delivery; no more than 25 tracks per CD). In-built speakers should power any house party, but more can be delivered for larger events (and a volume control helps avoid neighbourly disputes during smaller ones). Prices vary depending on the delivery area but start at £220. Disco lights and mirror balls can be provided for a small extra charge.

London Jukeboxes

8318 2852/www.london-jukeboxes.com. **No credit cards.**

ESSENTIALS

CD jukeboxes are all well and good, but those seeking an authentic crackle to their pop can hire a more enigmatic model from London Jukeboxes, which complements the conventional, Wurlitzer-shaped Rockola Bubbler (£245), which takes 50 CDs, with the McKenna (£200), a combination creation that plays ten CDs and 80 seven-inch records, and the all-vinyl Jakovich (£165); both models are decidedly boxier than the Rockola and more '80s than '50s in terms of aesthetics. Choose your weapon and you'll be sent sheets on which you can mark the records you want loaded for your party – everything from '50s barbershop pop to the latest chart-toppers courtesy of those nice people at *Now That's What I Call Music*. Delivery is charged outside south-east London postcodes.

SM Jukeboxes

42 Harfield Gardens, Grove Lane, SE5 8DB (7771 2464/www.jukeboxhire.co.uk). Denmark Hill rail. **Open** by appointment only.
CD jukeboxes here come in the form of either the Manhattan or the Royale (from £295): the former is a traditional Wurlitzer design, the Royale more streamlined and better suited to smaller celebrations and house parties, but both models have retro features aplenty (bubbles, coloured panels and chunky buttons for flipping through the decades) and powerful built-in speakers. They offer 1,500 and 1,000 tracks respectively – mostly classic pop and rock from the '50s to the present day, with contemporary chart and alternative hits added on a monthly basis. Those

seeking a more behemoth back catalogue can plump for the Digital Nostalgia (£385), a digital jukebox housed in a classic Wurlitzer-style body and boasting every Top 40 hit from 1952 onwards – over 35,000 tracks in total – plus 10,000 gems that never made the charts.

SOUND EQUIPMENT

Alive & Sound

Unit 21, Pensbury Industrial Estate, Pensbury Street, SW8 4TL (7993 9769/www.aliveandsound.co.uk). Wandsworth Road rail. **Open** by appointment only.
Alive & Sound rents out equipment capable of meeting the exacting demands of some of the capital's top turntablists, but is equally happy kitting out a London residence for a more informal night's entertainment. Complete PA systems including a mixer and either vinyl or CD turntables start from £250 per day (for a 50-100 person party) and go all the way up to professional club systems and outdoor rigs. Lighting rigs, meanwhile, start at £146 for a basic party kit for small, personal events such as weddings and anniversary bashes (scanners, lasers and a smoke machine) and go up to complex clubbing rigs (from £310) that are best operated by a sound engineer (£150).

Audiohire

Old Dairy, 133-137 Kilburn Lane, W10 4AN (8960 4466/www.audiohire.co.uk).

HOW TO GET THE BEST OUT OF PERFORMERS

A happy performer is a good performer – make sure your party runs smoothly with a read through the below.

When you book a performer, be sure to find out what technical equipment they'll be expecting. Be as specific as you can and find out how big a stage they'll require and how much vertical space they'll need. If they're musical, are they bringing a CD or iPod for their routine, in which case, does your venue have the correct sound equipment and cables? Most performers will require a green room, somewhere to get changed and retire to following the routine. Make sure it's easily accessible from the performance space – a half-naked burlesque performer won't appreciate being pawed after her routine if she has to elbow her way through a drunken crowd of stockbrokers, for instance. You'll be

expected to provide water, alcoholic drinks will be appreciated, and transport might be requested as part of their rider. Ensure that someone remains sober enough to get them into their transport at the end of the show; they won't like being dumped to look after themselves. If in doubt, be clear that you're not sure what they'll require and ask them to email you a specific breakdown of all their requirements. Finally, work out payment before the show – if they're expecting cash on the night, it's embarrassing if you haven't arranged it. Performers can work around nearly every issue except sound – be triple sure that you know every cable, speaker and CD player is working.

Kensal Green tube/rail. **Open** by appointment only.
Audiohire rents out complete party packages by way of a colourful website that allows visitors to view technical details and prices on a sliding bar that goes from 'smallest' (200W, up to 50 people; from £100 per day) to 'largest' (20kW, over 1,000 people; from £500). All packages come with a mixer and either Technics 1210 or Pioneer CDJ-1000 turntables, and the bigger rigs have the additional option of a helping hand with the setting up (from £35 per hour, per person) or even a personal sound engineer for the night (£150). DJ separates are also for hire (although you'll need to look elsewhere for lighting and effects units), and the company also rents out equipment for bands and microphone systems for corporate events.

Capital Hire
3 Stean Street, E8 4ED (7249 6000/ www.capitalhire.com). London Fields rail. **Open** 10am-6pm Mon-Sat.
'Keeping London entertained' is quite a claim, but it's one that the folk at Capital Hire take seriously. Prices are low and equipment is presented with a refreshing absence of technical jargon and in easy-to-use bundles for the uninitiated: two direct drive vinyl turntables and a three-channel mixer will set you back £55 per day; two CD turntables and a four channel mixer will cost £55 (there's also a basic one-piece unit with two CD drives and a mixer built in for £55). PA systems are handily broken down by the number of people they can play to: from a 500W system (up to 120 people; £65) to a 7,500W system (up to 900 people; £495), plus everything in between. Packages combining PAs and either vinyl or CD turntables start from £99 and £135 respectively (both catering to 40 people), and there's all manner of effects machines and lighting units – from single spots to digital laser shows – for more hardcore parties. A star cloth can be hung on a wall to create a lovely, twinkling effect (from £40), or for something more dramatic try an 'inferno projector' which creates a wall of towering flames (£30). Dancefloors can also be hired (per week), from 50p per square foot.

Peter Webber Hire
110-112 Disraeli Road, SW15 2DX (8870 1335/www.peterwebberhire.com). East Putney tube/Putney rail. **Open** 10am-6pm Mon-Fri.
As well as providing musical instruments (guitars and drum kits), Peter Webber Hire will supply pretty much anything you need in the PA system department. They also stock all sizes of lighting

and staging rigs, and will transport gear to you. Needless to say, depending on what equipment is required, size and length of hire, prices can vary massively, but PWH claim that they are 'always up for a deal'.

Sound Division
7609 3999/www.sounddivision.co.uk
A number of framed messages of thanks from big-name radio and club DJs helps highlight the professionalism of Sound Division, which since 1990 has been renting out all the necessaries for throwing everything from small house parties to major mash-ups. Gear leans towards the higher end of the performance spectrum: complete 2.5kW PAs start from £180 per day; mixers are from £35 and turntables go from £45 each for vinyl (Technics 1210) or £50 for CD (Pioneer CDJ-1000). Those looking to stage something more clubby than cosy will also find everything from spot- and floodlights (from £20) to strobes (from £25) and smoke machines (from £45) – even complete parquet dancefloors (3.5 x 3.5 metres from £350).

Stargazer Discos
8594 1320/www.stargazerdiscos.co.uk
As well as DJs themselves, Stargazer hires out equipment for home-grown spinners and scratchers, including sound systems (an amp, mixer, two speakers, microphone, headphones and leads) from £90. Add a pair of top-quality Technics turntables and the cost rises to £110. The lighting effects available to hire here are also good – try an 'Abstract Hypermoon' for just £20 for multi-coloured rotating light beam.

PERFORMERS

Most performers' prices vary depending on the size and type of event in question. Artists love doing small, underground performance parties, but these don't pay well (if at all), so they tend to supplement their income with more corporate work.

Where possible we've listed a starting price below. Generally, you might expect to pay anything from £50 an hour for a very new burlesque performer at a small midweek party, through to £10,000 and above for the international stars. Private parties could spend around £500 for a compère and one act, while a full line-up at a branded corporate show could easily hit the £5,000 mark. Many of the agencies listed will tell you what you can expect for your budget and work incrementally from there.

Bourgeois & Maurice. *See p166.*

BURLESQUE

Bearlesque

7012 1077/www.thewhoopeeagency.com/ www.bearlesque.com. **Cost** from £250/bear. **No credit cards**.

Hairy men probably don't spring to mind when you're thinking about burlesque. So audiences usually find it hilarious to discover Bearlesque, the bear burlesque troupe ('bear' being gay-speak for, well, a hairy fuller-figured gentleman). Bearlesque are branching out into more cabaret-styled routines – as well as their comedic take on burlesque – however their signature routine will forever be Fred Bear's version of 'Maniac' from *Flashdance*, complete with bucket of water. Book the whole troupe for bigger parties, or just one or two bears for a special birthday.

The Devil

7012 1077/www.thewhoopeeagency.com

Winner of the Whoopee Club's inaugural Male Tournament of Tease in 2007 – where wannabe male burlesque strippers get a chance to strut their new stuff in front of industry leaders – the Devil is, quite simply, sex on hetero legs. He wears pimp-daddy outfits, mixed with just-out-of-bed hair, and an air of sleaze. Since his real job is as a talented funk and soul singer, he can also perform with his band. A sure-fire screaming hit with the ladies. For prices contact the Whoopee Agency (*see p161*).

Fancy Chance

7012 1077/www.thewhoopeeagency.com

London's burlesque terrorist, Fancy Chance lives very much in 'Alice in Wonderland' territory. In fact, accidental acid-taking occasionally features in the storylines of her comedic burlesque routines. Small in stature but big in stage presence, this founding member of acclaimed 'queer cabaret' collective BurlyQ is popular with cool nightlife folk who appreciate her cutting-edge talents and she regularly appears at the most interesting industry events in London. For prices contact Whoopee Agency (*see p161*).

Gwendoline Lamour

7012 1077/www.thewhoopeeagency.com

With milky skin and ravishing auburn hair, Miss Lamour is nothing short of stunning. One of the country's leading performers of quality, glamorous burlesque, she's also a dedicated burlesque promoter in her own right, has written a master's on burlesque and given numerous talks on the subject. Back to performing, though – her gimmicks include a decadent rose petal bath and a giant crystal shoe. For prices contact the Whoopee Agency (*see p161*).

Immodesty Blaize

7012 1077/www.thewhoopeeagency.com
Got money to burn? Then you'll be putting in a call to the UK's queen of burlesque, Miss Immodesty Blaize. She's been at the forefront of the country's burlesque revival since it began some eight years ago, and constantly performs internationally. Fond of the Las Vegas showgirl-style of burlesque, she is, quite simply, one of the best performers of her generation. Blaize spends small fortunes on extravagant, high camp costumes and giant props, including her signature giant rocking horse. For prices contact the Whoopee Agency (*see p161*).

Ruby Blues

8509 3353/www.continentaldrifts.co.uk. **Cost** from £360/personal appearance. **No credit cards**.
One of the more glamorous performers to inhabit the edgy alternative burlesque scene, Ruby Blues travels the world with edgy art party promoters Mutoid Waste (they helped produce Trash City 'fields' at Glastonbury and Burning Man in 2008). Also being a creative producer really shows in her theatrical, goth fairy tale costumes and props. An all-rounder – she fronts an electro band and is a sublime aerial artist and circus performer.

Ziegfeld Girl

www.mariannecheesecake.com. **Cost** from £150 (for private shows). **No credit cards**.
Marianne Cheesecake is a show-stopping Ziegfeld siren adorned with crystals and feathers. When she invites you to peek beneath the luxurious folds of her fantasy robe, she reveals a feast of feathers that inspires the most feverish dance. She performs a highly captivating and stylised fan dance influenced by the 1920s surrealist movement, which makes this masterpiece both beautiful and bizarre.

CABARET, VARIETY & MCS

Bourgeois & Maurice

07739 802750/www.bourgeoisandmaurice. co.uk. **Cost** from £200. **No credit cards**.
Young, post modern and terribly camp, Georgeois Bourgeois and Liv Maurice make up one of the most exciting pop culture cabaret pairings since, oh, forever. Bourgeois might wear a sequinned disco top stolen from Donna Summer's cupboard, Maurice will sit behind a keyboard straying, for brief moments, into unhinged and deranged territory, but from there, anything might happen. The classically trained pair sing bitingly original songs about living in east London, going to art school, and stalking people on the internet.

Dusty Limits

www.dustylimits.com/dusty@dustylimits.com. **Cost** from £1,500 (for private shows). **No credit cards**.
Don't waste this London-based Australian drunken raconteur on just anybody – he's very much for a sophisticated, liberal-minded audience. Leader of Britain's neo-Weimar scene, Mr Limits is beautiful to look at and usually heartbreaking to listen to. Often working as an MC for variety shows and burlesque parties, Limits' scope covers much ground – from the best damn drunk impression we've seen (during which he sings Sondheim's 'Losing My Mind' to a gin bottle) to gently ribbing the audience and always, always getting away with it. An exceptional and very special talent.

Frank Sanazi

8650 0411/07956 316 881/www.iraq pack.co.uk. **Cost** from £250 (personal appearance). **No credit cards**.
Frank Sanazi and his Iraq Pack are one of the best cabaret acts on the circuit. Strangely like the bastard lovechild of Adolf Hitler and Frank Sinatra – funnier than it sounds, trust us – Sanazi's rich, crooning tones run over his latest album 'Songs For Swingin' Leaders'. It's his bar room banter that's won him so many fans, although his push to dub the movement 'Fatherlounge' is a little bit dubious. Hilarious stuff.

Mat Fraser

7025 0618/www.matfraser.co.uk. **Cost** from £350 (for private shows). **No credit cards**.
It's telling that Mat Fraser's Sealboy routine is no longer considered taboo. Based on Sealo the Sealboy, a 1930s American freakshow performer who was born with very small arms similar to Fraser's, the routine sees Sealboy wow the audience by (gasp!) drinking whiskey and even (double gasp!) shaving with a cut-throat razor. It's rare that this popular routine is the most shocking thing on the bill nowadays, although Fraser is usually the best looking bloke on the bill. He is also an exceptional burlesque stripper and popular MC on the cabaret and burlesque circuits.

Millionth Muse Productions

7739 5300/www.millionthmuse.com. **Cost** from £500/act. **No credit cards**.
London's cabaret scene owes much to Paul L Martin who, through his cabaret agency Millionth Muse, has worked tirelessly to give the capital's performers nights at which to shine. Book Martin – who is, first and foremost, a cabaret singer in his own right – or Sarah-Louise Young, or indeed any number of musical theatre and cabaret performers they've discovered along the way.

Pustra/Vile-een

07875 683169/www.pustraandvile-een.com.
Cost from £300. **No credit cards**.
One of the most colourful and original performers around, this vaudeville duo look as though they've stepped off the set of a silent era film and taken a wrong turn at Seriously Strange-ville. With exquisite sets and props – their puppets are eerily similar to themselves, for a start – they bring quality clowning to the show.

CIRCUS ACTS

Bryony Black

8509 3353/www.continentaldrifts.co.uk.
Cost from £360/set. **No credit cards**.
There are quite a few hula-hoop performers, but few are able to spin 40 hoops… all at the same time. To be fair, Bryony Black needs half a dozen people to help her with this particular routine – and they need to be skilled in the timing of their hoop throwing – but it's one of the most impressive circus routines you'll ever see. She's also an expert whip-cracker and rope thrower, and is popular on the burlesque circuit.

Captain Frodo

www.myspace.com/captainfrodo. **Cost** email for details.
Captain Frodo, the Incredible Rubberman, is an eye-watering sideshow performer – that's if you can bear to look at his routines at all, of course. Originally from Norway and currently based in Australia, he's nonetheless in the UK regularly and Frodo does things with tennis rackets that will make you rub at your shoulders in sympathy.

Circus Whiz

01827 715011/www.circuswhiz.co.uk.
Cost call for details.
For review, *see p172*.

Empress Stah

www.empressstah.com/twinkle@empress stah.com. **Cost** email for details.
It's impossible to put this London-based performance artist into a box but hell, we're going to try. Stah sprang out of the fetish and festival circuits – so there's an edgy level to her work – but this neo-burlesque, trapeze, and cabaret performer is, literally, in a league of her own; she won the coveted Jerwood Circus award for her breathtaking 'Swinging from the Chandelier' piece. Although Stah does walk-around routines – covering herself with needles and speared strawberries usually proves a bit of a talking point at parties – it's her aerial work for which she is most held in awe.

Hui Ling Zhu

01255 860175/www.ling-chinese-ents.co.uk.
Cost from £250. **No credit cards**.
As she's a former member of the Chinese State Circus, it's a good idea to set aside some time to work out what exactly you would like Hui Ling Zhu to do. A little foot juggling with blankets, paper umbrellas and massive wooden blocks, perhaps, or a breathtaking lion dance? What about some close-up Chinese-style magic? Equally at home at children's parties as at adult-only soirées.

Miss Behave

7637 2994/www.stillmissbehaving.com.
Cost from £1,000/performance.
A big believer in connecting with her crowd – as opposed to merely performing as though she's the only one in the room – Miss Behave is one of the best in the business. A talented street performer as well as a regular on the fetish circuits, she may dress in a red latex heart-stopping dress and killer stacked heels, but she's cheeky and comedic rather than intimidating. Putting swords, fire sticks and roses where she shouldn't, she's also a great MC and comedian.

Missing Link Productions

Circus Space, Coronet Street, N1 6HD (7739 7713/www.circusperformers.com).
Old Street tube. **Cost** call for details.
For review, *see p168*.

NOTE

PARTY THEMES
Stuck for something to base your bash around? Try one of these on for size:
• Beach Party
• Big Band
• Bingo
• Cabaret
• Camp Fire Singalong
• Circus
• Country + Western
• East Enders
• Eurovision
• Hollywood
• Marching Bands
• Mardi Gras
• Mini Festival
• Pirates
• Punk
• Pyjama Party
• Roaring Twenties
• Treasure Hunt
• Tube Stop Fancy Dress

ESSENTIALS

MISSING LINK PRODUCTIONS

Based at the Circus Space in Hoxton, the UK's premier circus school, Missing Link (www.circusperformers.com) provide the most comprehensive roster of circus performers in the country. While they won't represent anyone who works with animals, they can arrange pretty much everything else – from sorting out a single clown for an hour to costumes and design to the organising of the most complicated of events. Admittedly, when you're looking through hundreds of performers on their site, it can seem a bit overwhelming, so they're quick to point out that you can call with a budget and they'll make suggestions. Also, they have ideas and themes on their website. Looking for something for your glamorous party? Try An Act Above, an elegant contortionist who, dressed as flapper, works with burlesque fans. Something for Christmas? Try a Santa from Electric Cabaret stuck up a chimney.

But what if you find yourself in a real, last-minute pickle? They provide a 'what if' helpline, 24-hours a day.
For listings, see p167.

COMEDY

Most comedians will do practically any gig they're offered – provided the price is right – with many of the larger comedians making thousands of pounds from a single corporate event.

One of the biggest agents for corporate work is Bound and Gagged (www.boundandgagged.com); it has an extensive roster of comedians such as Lucy Porter, Omid Djalili and Tim Vine.

Amused Moose
7287 3727/www.amusedmoose.com.
Cost from £1,000/night.
Hils Jago seems to knows pretty much everyone and, more importantly, exactly how to throw a party. She'll happily welcome a group of you to one of her clubs or will be equally pleased to throw a party for you and sort out all your entertainment needs in the process.

Comedy Club Limited
0870 0425 656/www.hahaheehee.com.
Cost from £400/30min set.
These guys can organise everything from comedians for parties to regular comedy nights. They can book a huge range of comics for you from Andy Parsons to Frank Skinner, Frankie Boyle to Jack Dee.

Comedy Store Management
7930 2967/www.comedystoremanagement.com. **Cost** from £2,500/25-min set.
The world famous Comedy Store is not only the world's greatest comedy club, its management department can also organise an unforgettable night of comedy to suit whatever you have in mind, from large corporate schmooze-fest to office Christmas party. Prices are on the high side but it's always worth calling with your budget to see what they can do. They have all the best talent at their fingertips and after years and years of experience know how to throw together a great evening of laughter.

Jongleurs
08700 111960/www.jongleurs.com.
Cost from £5,500.
The One Stop Entertainment Shop. The other legendary chain of comedy clubs also offers a bespoke service for every kind of occasion. You can even hire out their venues for the party itself There are clubs all over the UK, and in London there's a Jongleurs in Battersea, Bow and Camden. They can also organise music, cabaret and speakers specific to your requirements and budget.

DANCE TROUPES

CanBootyCan
07812 456852/07967 331673/www.can bootycan.co.uk. **Cost** call for details.
Can-can dancers put through a post-punk blender, this gaggle of up to ten gorgeous girls cat-call, squeal and high kick their way through long production pieces or short routines, depending on the size of your party. They've shared a stage with bands at festivals, provided welcome diversions at corporate gigs and have run riot at bigger birthday parties.

Glitterbanditz
07985 074600/www.glitterbanditz.com.
Cost from £2,000.
This troupe of three blokes won the World Disco Dancing Competition back in 1983, or so they say, and are still doing the same moves. Wearing eye-watering hot pants, big mullets and decked head to toe in glitter, beer bellies never looked so wrong. They've supported George Michael at Wembley, disco-ed their way through music festivals in the snow and appeared on the *Charlotte Church Show*, but they'll just as easily turn a small office party into a disco-tastic affair.

Lady Greys
7288 7291/www.ladygreys.com. **Cost** call for details. **No credit cards**.
With a repertoire that includes a 1920's chorus line, a sweeping skirt dance, a decadent tea party and a 1930's aerial take on 'Swan Lake', the talented Lady Greys are firm faves on the variety show scene. Depending on the event, the exquisite troupe ranges from three to eight feather-clad girls, all professionally trained as dancers and actresses.

DRAG QUEENS

Big Wigs
07921 621273. **Cost** from £70/hr.
No credit cards.
When only the biggest wigs on your drag queens will do, this duo wear some of the most sizeable blonde numbers in the business. Popular as door whores, Dotty and Kevina also host corporate parties and meet 'n' mingle.

Jonny Woo
www.myspace.com/jonnywoouk. **Cost** email for details.
Cast aside any notions of *Priscilla, Queen of the Desert* right now. Jonny Woo is the post-modern drag queen whose original work puts him right at

the top of the alternative performance tree. An excellent compère for events, and sure-fire highlight of any performance bill.

Ryan Styles
07791 456115/www.ryanstyles.com.
Cost from £350. **No credit cards**.
Exquisitely beautiful, Ryan Styles performs breathtaking mime pieces and surreal cabaret as well as frocking up as one of the famous Lipsinkers – the drag collective who perform at Hackney's Bistrotheque. He can tailor his performances to the event, but we're enormous fans of his 'Suicide Blonde' routine during which he comically lip-synchs to INXS.

FORTUNE-TELLERS

Calmer Karma
7401 9745/www.calmerkarma.org.uk.
Cost from £195. **No credit cards**.
When crystal ball and tarot card readers just won't cut it, this agency also offers psychics who can read handbags, lipstick, mobile phones… you name it, they claim that they can do a reading from it. Their clairvoyants will also dress according to your theme – whether Hollywood, Thai, pirates or Roaring Twenties – and they promise to meet any budget.

Knights Templar Events
8508 1530/www.knightstemplarevents.co.uk.
Cost call for details.
In addition to providing a gun-shaped ice sculpture, spoof paparazzi and medieval minstrels, this 'total event management' company also offers fortune-tellers. They're happy to do tea leaf readings, handwriting analysis or tarot readings, but won't do readings that 'are in any way disturbing or upsetting'.

INTERACTIVE ENTERTAINMENT

Boothnation
7613 5576/www.boothnation.com.
Cost from £1,545 (for 4 hours).
For review, *see p172*.

Entents
01989 563783/www.entents.co.uk
For review, *see p173*.

Magic Lamp Events
8300 3994/www.magiclampevents.co.uk.
A one-stop shop for hiring out a whole host of inflatables and games, as well as catering equipment, marquees, sound systems including karaoke, and pretty much everything else.

Miniracing.com
01628 675805/www.miniracing.com.
Cost from £480. **No credit cards**.
For review, *see p173*.

Sasaquads
01923 802744/07842 448695/www.sasaquads.com. **Cost** from £175. **No credit cards**.
The place to come if you're after something a bit unusual to make that party go with a bang. As well as a range of bouncy castles, there are also sumo suits, rodeo bulls (complete with inflatable safety bed) and quad bikes up for grabs. The rodeo package includes supervisory staff and a certificate for the best rider; a supervised quad package has all safety equipment included.

Sidestalls.net
07973 429663/www.sidestalls.net.
Cost from £480. **No credit cards**.
For review, *see p173*.

MAGICIANS

Christian Lee
7737 5300/www.betterchemistry.co.uk.
Cost from £350/hr. **No credit cards**.
A talented magician and comedian and a popular compère too, Christian Lee's skills run the full variety show gamut – diabolo juggling through to unicycle. It's as a comic magician, however, that he's best known. He's as adept at working in small spaces as large theatres.

Kieron Kirkland
07828 780829/www.kieronkirkland.com.
Cost from £75/hr. **No credit cards**.
A very popular close-up and walk-around magician who does a mix of coin, card and found object tricks together with some pretty spooky mind-reading. With a background in street performance, Kieron Kirkland can handle any audience with skill and style.

Magicians Directory
www.magician-directory.com
The online international directory of magicians features plenty of London performers. A good starting point as they cover everything from street magicians and 'pick pockets' through to bigger corporate performers.

Marc Spelmann
8341 7988/www.marcspelmann.co.uk. **Cost** from £575/hr; £650/2-3hrs. **No credit cards**.

ESSENTIALS

Circus Skills

Midlands-based **Circus Whiz** has developed an ingenious inflatable circus ring that can be quickly erected in any garden or outdoor space with up to eight metres to spare. The ring comes complete with a three-metre canopy, colourful flags and signage, and 50 pieces of equipment, including juggling balls, diabolos, spinning ropes and pedal-gos. Rather than watching the professionals do their thing, the idea is to have a go yourself – by jumping in the ring and grabbing the nearest pair of stilts – or, for the less fearless, by taking a lesson from one of two enthusiastic entertainers. Children of all ages can take part; a six hour 'workshop' costs £550 and the Whiz can be hired anywhere in the UK.

Best for Kids' parties and team-building fun.
Must do Hire Pamela, the fabulous face painter.
Inside info Measure up carefully to make sure you can fit the gear in.
For listings, see p167.

Photo Booths

Always forget to take party pictures in the heat of the moment? Then hire a **Boothnation** mobile photo booth for the evening and watch as your guests squeeze in to strike a pose. Even the most camera-shy partygoer won't be able to resist a touch of comedy retro photo fun – seriously, wait till the first round of cocktails kick in and instead of queues for the bar there'll be queues for the booth. The Classic Booth is a 1950s US import, but for sheer glamour it's hard to beat the sparkly, silver-clad Glitterbox, complete with silver lamé curtains. Prices include on-the-day prints, and start at £1,545 for four hours. Whatever you choose it makes for a perfect, quirky record of your event.
Best for Weddings where you want to capture every guest.
Must do Grab a mate and recreate the kind of comedy shots last posed in a suburban Woolies circa 1989.
Inside info Be brave and get in there before the masses do.
For listings, see p171.

Boothnation

ESSENTIALS

Race Nights

Bring Ascot into your living room (fancy hats optional) with one of **Entents**' race nights. A basic £80 package includes a DVD of eight real-life races filmed at Newmarket, Aintree and Chepstow, among others, complete with race previews, professional running commentaries, on-screen leaders displays, results boards and final announcements – plus tote tickets, calculators and instructions for organising the betting. All you need is a good-sized TV screen and DVD player. Alternatively, hire one of the company's own compères, who can organise things for you and set up a giant screen and sound system. The more expensive packages include dog, camel and even sheep racing – surprisingly popular apparently.

Best for Competitive banter all round.
Must do Insist on sporting a full-on John McCririck get-up – as host it's your prerogative.
Inside info Book a venue with good acoustics so the cheering doesn't drown out the race.
For listings, see p171.

Slot Cars

If you can't indulge your inner child at a party, then when can you? And there's nothing like a little bit of Scalextric-style slot car racing to reduce men to excitable little boys. Unlike other operators, **Miniracing.com** is run by an engineer and manufactures its own equipment, making its tracks super slick and reliable. The company provides compères who use a specially-designed computerised scoring system to give a running commentary on both the race and individual players' performances – making things a bit more interesting for spectators, too. Track sizes range from four by two metres to six by three metres and can incorporate eight or more lanes. Prices start from £500 for three hours.

Best for Corporate events requiring an injection of fun.
Must do Book a radio-controlled flying saucer for added fun.
Inside info Don't worry about turning the girls off – they tend to love it almost as much as men do.
For listings, see p171.

Victorian stalls

If it's good, old-fashioned fun you're after, **Sidestalls.net** can turn your garden into a Victorian fairground, with vintage-style stalls featuring favourites such as hook a duck, tin can alley, hoopla and coconut shies (£200 per two x two metres stall for four hours). Stall 'owners' come dressed in 19th-century attire – waistcoats, cloth caps and the like – and the canopies themselves are beautifully designed, with striped overhangings, scalloped edges and traditional fairground artwork. For a real ride back in time, you can also hire authentic Victorian carousels (£2,200).

Best for Musing about the good ol' days.
Must do Hire a candy floss barrow.
Inside info Staff can wear your 'uniform' if required.
For listings, see p171.

ESSENTIALS

One of the most talented magicians you'll see, Spelmann's act includes feats of mental psychology, mind-reading and freaky physical stuff. He can perform 'mix and mingle' tricks, a 40-minute close-up show (for a large dinner party, say) or a cabaret on stage. He'll perform at any party, he says – other than children's dos and heavy metal concerts.

Piff the Magic Dragon

07802 770966/07810 407724/ www.piffthemagicdragon.com. **Cost** from £200/performance. **No credit cards.**

Not all magicians wear a tuxedo, you know. You'll have heard of his rather more famous elder brother, but the younger Piff is carving out a name for himself as a magician. Dressed in bright green dragon costume, the slightly morose comedic magician has a very sweet and funny act.

Romany the Diva of Magic

07801 341066/www.romanymagic.com. **Cost** £750/cabaret performance. **No credit cards.**

A flamboyant hybrid of Bette Midler and Mary Poppins, and 'Magic Circle Stage Magician of the Year' (2007/8), Romany brings a razzle dazzle riot of feathers, magic, original comedy and glamour to any event. Popular on the variety show circuit, she also regularly hosts corporate events.

QUIZMASTERS

Elliot Eastwick's World Famous Pub Quiz

www.myspace.com/worldfamouspubquiz

Although based in Manchester, Elliot Eastwick has taken his legendary music trivia pub quiz right around the world, and his client list includes Xfm, Fabric, Emap and Glastonbury Festival.

Quiz Quiz Quiz

07017 497849/07774 525 473/ www.quizquizquiz.co.uk. **Cost** from £300/set.

Offering nothing other than quizzes, Quiz Quiz Quiz claims to be the top quiz company in London. They can run a regular pub night or put together newspaper challenges as well as train wannabe quizmasters. As for events, they'll arrange a Christmas quiz for your office, team-building quizzes, sports quizzes and more.

Toffs Quiz

8301 2509/www.toffsquiz.co.uk. **Cost** from £350/hr. **No credit cards.**

A London-based mobile quiz company, Toffs Quiz will tailor the questions for the company or people booking them. Expect to pay around

£325 for a quiz of up to 50 people or £500 for the quiz and disco, for parties of up to £200, it rises to £400 for the quiz only, or £575 for the quiz and disco.

SPEAKERS

Now You're Talking

0189 582 7818/www.nyt.co.uk. **Cost** from £1,000/evening. **No credit cards.**

'Unaccustomed as I am…'. Then why not get someone who knows what they're talking about to, er, do the talking. NYT has some of the funniest, most inspirational, educational speakers in the business on it's books. Whatever the occasion, choose from the likes of Ant and Dec, Sir Ranulph Fiennes, Tracey Edwards, Jonathan Ross or Malcolm McGrath – the disabled businessman who went on to conquer North and South poles.

Toastmasters

www.toastmastersguild.org.uk. **Cost** call for details. **No credit cards.**

Contact the guild for members' details if you want a man in a red ('hunting pink') tailcoat to perform Master of Ceremonies functions at a wedding (of all religions), bar mitzvah, dinner or any celebration that needs a bit of added gravitas.

WALKABOUT

Big Hand People

01737 844044/www.bighandpeople.co.uk. **Cost** from £250. **No credit cards.**

This is one of the bigger agencies and can provide just about any type of performer you could ask for. A cheerleading team to tumble through your party? Contortionists? Stiltwalkers dressed as explorers on camels? Cocktail barmen? Town criers? Victorian chimney sweeps? Spend a little time on their website and you realise just how many entertainers are working in the capital. They've got a long list of Christmas-themed entertainment, too.

Impact Artists

01179 555456/www.impactartists.co.uk. **Cost** from £300. **No credit cards.**

Impact Artists is a performance artist agency with a good selection of stiltwalkers. Foxtrot Oscar sweeps around the floor ballroom dancing with his puppet, while crusty old waiters Dithering, Doddering and Waiter present strange wriggling canapés and dripping trays of champagne. The agency also has a wide selection of aerialists, circus performers, look-alikes and jugglers.

Snakey Sue
8989 2560/www.snakeysue.com. **Cost** from
£300. **No credit cards**.
A belly dancer and snake charmer, Snakey Sue
walks around small or large parties showing off
one of her 50 reptiles. She also does original
snake dance routines.

Spanner in the Works
01905 353551/www.spanner.co.uk.
Cost from £200/performer. **No credit cards**.
Providing staff that have been wreaking havoc for
more than 20 years, Spanner in the Works
'waiters' work alongside the real deal at cocktail
parties and sit down meals. Doing what, exactly?
Losing contact lenses, nibbling on food, changing
light bulbs mid-course… Their 'In-Security' will set
up at the entrance to your event with bleepy tools
and a metal detector (you never know when
someone might be trying to smuggle through a
rocket launcher, they warn), while the Spanner
Band, the Cheasy Listening Band, and wandering
busker Mr Coconut & Friends add comedy
musical turns. British service at its very best.

Ultimate Chaos
0800 118 2747/www.ultimatechaos.info.
Cost from £550. **No credit cards**.
If it's light-hearted mix and mingle chaos your
event needs, this company offers Loud Aussie
Waiters – dirty, unhygienic and loud – plus
security staff who will show guests to their tables
using a none-too-subtle seven million candle-
powered lamp. With Condiments is their frankly
awful lounge singer duo that was, they say,
thrown out of Las Vegas.

CHILDREN'S ENTERTAINMENT

More information on the entertainers
listed can be found on their websites.
Check that the entertainment you want to
book is suitable for your target age group.

Ali Do Lali
01494 774300/www.alidolali.com.
Cost call for details. **No credit cards**.
The celebrated Do Lali has routines to suit from
three years and up, and all situations. He lives
in a magic lamp, as would be expected.

Amigo's Magic
8480 8176/www.amigosmagic.co.uk.
Cost from £125/hr; £185/2 hrs.
Simple Simon, Magic Circle member and all-
round top joker and balloon modeller, is the child-
friendly face of Amigo's.

NOTE

CLASSIC KIDS PARTY GAMES
Go retro with a few of these:
• Apple bobbing
• Limbo
• Memory game
• Musical bumps
• Musical chairs
• Musical statues
• Pass the parcel
• Pin the tail on the donkey
• Sardines
• Simon says…
• Sleeping lions
• What's the time Mr Wolf?

Billy the Disco DJ
*8471 8616/07949 936864/www.billy
thediscodj.co.uk*. **Cost** £195/2 hrs.
No credit cards.
These popular disco parties for ages five to 11
may include limbo contests, temporary tattoos,
bubble machines, pop quizzes, dancing
competitions and karaoke. Billy can even take
care of those pesky party bag needs too, for a
little bit extra.

Boo Boo
7727 3817/www.mr-booboo.co.uk.
Cost call for details.
Sean Hampson dons spectacular trousers, steps
out of the dry ice and is Boo Boo at parties for
threes to eights. His shows include music,
balloon-modelling, bubbles, smoke, dancing and
lots of comedy.

Christopher Howell
7993 4544/www.christopherhowell.net.
Cost from £150/hr. **No credit cards**.
A member of the Magic Circle, Howell uses
magic, music and storytelling, in which the
children play a part. The story is followed by a
balloon-model game. £5 of the fee is donated to
the Roald Dahl Foundation.

Foxy the Funky Genie
7692 5666/www.foxythefunkygenie.com.
Cost from £95/45 mins. **No credit cards**.
Foxy is an accomplished magician and balloon
modeller and his show gets everyone dancing
with balloon limbo, disco and karaoke. He also
puts on a puppet show for the under-fives.

Jenty the Gentle Clown
*8527 4855/07957 121764/www.jentythe
gentleclown.com*. **Cost** £145/hr; £195/2 hrs.
No credit cards.

ESSENTIALS

Little Blisters

Parties for children aged one to 11 include singing, banjo, guitar, magic, storytelling, face-painting, balloon-modelling and limbo dancing. Choose activities to suit your child's tastes.

Circus skills (including plenty of juggling), action-packed storytelling and all sorts of other fun stuff are included in Juggling John's one- or two-hour shows with ages starting at one year.

John Styles
8300 3579/www.johnstylesentertainer.co.uk. **Cost** from £125/hr. **No credit cards**.
Kids are enthusiastic devotees of the antique art of ventriloquism as practised by Mr Styles and his team; he also does a Punch and Judy show, balloon modelling and magic for children aged three years and above.

Juggling John
8938 3218/0845 644 6659/www.juggling john.com. **Cost** from £125/hr.

Just George
07944 863961. **Cost** £180/2hrs.
No credit cards.
George McAllister's two-hour parties include parachute games, music, magic and balloon models. All this goes down well with three- to eight-year-olds.

Laurie Temple the Party Wizard
8951 9469/07951 596240/www.theparty wizard.co.uk. **Cost** from £130/hr; £180/2hrs.
No credit cards.

Well known on the London party circuit, Laurie Temple can wave his magic wand and make the party happen. He and his team of conjurers, jugglers, balloonologists, DJs, puppeteers and magical storytellers can entertain children from as young as two for one or two hours. He can also provide catering and decorations.

Lee Warren

8670 2729/07973 337575/www.sorcery. org.uk. **Cost** from £130/hr. **No credit cards**.
Magician Lee combines sorcery with audience participation. The hour-long shows – for four- to eight-year olds – cost from £130 for a performance in your own home or £140 in a hired hall (that you have booked) and Lee says he's able to deal with nearly any size of audience (minimum eight).

Little Blisters

8392 9093/www.childrensentertainment-surrey.co.uk. **Cost** from £100/hr. **No credit cards**.
Ava de Souza has created the characters of Flossie Bella the Fairy, Sea Lily the Mermaid and Kitty Willow the Magical Cat for her shows with stories, music and optional face-painting. Her productions are for three- to seven-year-olds.

Lydie's Children's Parties

7622 2540/www.lydieparties.com. **Cost** from £400/party. **No credit cards**.
Lydie has a vast repertoire of themes for boys and girls (from *High School Musical* to *Batman*) and promises to turn your home into a magical, musical world. She turns up five hours in advance to set up for the two-hour show, then, pleasingly, stays another two hours to dismantle her set and clear up the house.

Magic Mikey

0808 100 2140/www.magicmikey.co.uk. **Cost** call for details.
Disco, magic, balloon modelling, games and the hyperactive Rocky the Super Racoon make up the two-hour Magic Mikey bash for children up to 12 years old. A seasoned professional, with lots of cruise ship experience, Magic Mikey is strong on slapstick and high-energy discos.

Merlin Entertainments

8866 6327/01494 479027/www.merlin ents.co.uk. **Cost** from £135/hr; £155/2hrs. **No credit cards**.
If you're not sure what kind of party you want, talk to Merlin, a one-stop shop for entertainers of all types, from mad scientists to sane clowns, as well as an animal encounters show, Punch and Judy theatres, face-painters and makeover artists.

Mr Squash

8808 1415/07939 252241/www.mr-squash.co.uk. **Cost** £150-£180/hr. **No credit cards**.
Mr Squash travels all over London with his musical puppet show, balloon tricks, singalongs and funny stories. Well known on the playgroup circuit, he's experienced in engaging the very young (two- and three-year-olds), but his parties are suitable for children aged up to six. His puppets, performing in a booth, invite audience participation, especially from the birthday child.

Pekko's Puppets

8575 2311/www.pekkospuppets.co.uk. **Cost** from £150/hr. **No credit cards**.
Stephen Novy's puppet plays are aimed at children aged three to 12, with shows for under-fives packing in two shorter tales presented by Pekko, a lively and cheerful bird; there's plenty of singing and audience participation. The repertoire for older children includes Celtic folk tales, popular classics, humorous verse and chillers like Dracula, all enacted from one of Mr Novy's two mobile booths.

PK Entertainments

01344 626789/07771 546676/www.fair andfete.co.uk. **Cost** call for details. **No credit cards**.
All the fun of the fair (well, village fête) can be hired from PK. If you have the room, this outfit can provide the hoopla, swingboats, bouncy castles, candy floss and popcorn – even a bucking bronco. PK can also provide clowns, magicians and face-painters. There's plenty of child-friendly entertainment here and lots that adults will love too. Check out the price list online.

Professor Fumble

01395 579523/www.professorfumble.co.uk. **Cost** call for details.
The Professor can put on a 30-minute balloon modelling party for tinies (aged two to four), an hour-long clowning, slapstick, balloon modelling and circus workshop party, or the two-hour Super Dooper Wizzo with added workshops, prizes and party games galore (and exhausted children guaranteed) for three- to eight-year-olds.

Silly Millie the Clown

7823 8329/www.sillymillietheclown.co.uk. **Cost** from £85/hr. **No credit cards**.
Purple-haired Silly Millie was born in 2001, when Faith Tingle started her training as a special clown working in hospitals with sick children. Cuddly, crazy parties for three- to nine-year-olds include magic, balloon animals, singalongs and puppets – all wrapped up in general daftness.

Party Shops & Decorations

Regardless of the type of bash you're throwing, you'll want to make an impact with the finishing touches. Look no further. We've scoured the capital's finest party shops for balloons, blooms and Batman outfits, and uncovered the best places to buy everything from children's party bags to fireworks online. You'll also find lighting ideas galore, tips on buying Christmas trees and places to hire furniture, beanbags, vintage teacups and more. For marquees and tents, check out Weddings (see *p214*).

PARTY SHOPS & FANCY DRESS

Angels
119 Shaftesbury Avenue, WC2H 8AE (7836 5678/www.fancydress.com). Leicester Square or Tottenham Court Road tube.
Open 9.30am-5.30pm Mon, Tue, Thur, Fri; 10.30am-7pm Wed.
Angels is the undisputed doyenne of fancy dress hire for adults and children in the capital. The enormous range is unparalleled and the quality is excellent; some of the costumes have even found their way to the six-floor hire shop from the massive collection of handmade costumes Angels have created for films over the years. The ever-increasing range of packet costumes, sold

via the website, are also very good, with Playboy bunnies, sumo wrestlers and Marie Antoinette-alikes new for 2008. Dogs get a look-in too – the Superman Dog is £14.99. Outfits for hire from the shop start at £80 plus VAT and include suitable accessories, plus £100 deposit.

Balloon & Kite
613 Garratt Lane, SW18 4SU (8946 5962/ www.balloonandkite.com). Earlsfield rail.
Open 9am-6pm Mon-Fri; 9am-5.30pm Sat.
Despite looking like a balloon-themed grotto where you might expect to be served by two kerrazy clowns with hooters, Balloon & Kite takes business seriously. Professional and calm, with masses of experience, this is the place to turn to if you need a balloon drop for your office

VV Rouleaux. *See p193.*

party finale, a loved one's name printed on a thousand bright pink balloons or an awesome pyrotechnics display to accompany a balloon-model of your gran. Party accessories are also stocked, as are beautiful kites of all shapes and sizes – why not fill the sky with a colourful flotilla at your next big bash?

Circus Circus

176 Wandsworth Bridge Road, SW6 2UQ (7731 4128/www.circuscircus.co.uk). Fulham Broadway tube. **Open** *10am-6pm Mon-Sat; 10am-2pm Sun.*
Pretty cheap and most definitely cheerful, Circus Circus sells everything you could ever need for a straightforward party, from bags to balloons to boobs (of the fake plastic variety). On the

costume front, there is a great selection to buy for around the £11 mark, whether you fancy being Queen Cleopatra or Al Capone for the evening. Accessories are more fun than convincing, with thick stick-on beards and plastic cowboy guns. Kids can also get in on the act, with a fine selection to choose from of their own.

Contemporary Wardrobe

The Horse Hospital, Colonnade, WC1N 1HX (7713 7370/www.contemporary wardrobe.com). Russell Square tube. **Open** *viewings noon-6pm Mon-Sat (hire by appointment).*
Established in 1978 by stylist and costume designer Roger Burton, there are some serious treasures in this 15,000 plus collection of

garments, including vintage Dior, Biba and Yves Saint Laurent and a huge collection of European street fashion and couture. Pop and rock outfits also abound, some of them worn by names as famous as the Beatles. Hire prices for a complete outfit are around £75 plus VAT for a week's hire.

Costume Studio

Montgomery House, 159-161 Balls Pond Road, N1 4BG (7923 9472/www.costume studio.co.uk). Highbury & Islington tube/rail/ 30, 38, 56, 277 bus. **Open** 9.30am-6pm Mon-Fri; 10am-5pm Sat.

Supplying costumes to the media, theatre and film worlds since 1987, Costume Studio has a huge range of good quality dressing-up gear available for hire. Saucy nurses, pearly kings, sharp-suited disco kids, dandies, punk rockers and Egyptian pharoahs are just some of the looks you can adopt and prices for a full outfit (accessories included) start around £80 for a week's hire. Space suits and suits of armour fall into the unusual and therefore pricier category and cost £150-£200. Bespoke outfits can also be made up.

Escapade

150 Camden High Street, NW1 0NE (7485 7384/www.escapade.co.uk). Camden Town tube. **Open** 10am-7pm Mon-Fri; 10am-6pm Sat; noon-5pm Sun.

The emphasis here is on fun, brightly-coloured costumes to get you noticed. A great range of costumes, masks, wigs and other accessories can be purchased (online as well as in person), but the hiring side is where the best quality, most detailed attire can be found. The website helps narrow down the choices, with handily clear subheadings. Animal costumes incorporate bats, beagles and bumble bees, while the more sophisticated hirer will love the 1920s-style flapper dresses (£40 plus refundable deposit for three days' hire).

Hopscotch Dressing-Up Clothes

8696 1313/www.hopscotchdressingup.co.uk
From Roman soldiers to disco dollies, online mail order company Hopscotch can cater for most children's dressing-up requirements, and provides all the accessories (crowns, fezzes and wands). We adore the dinosaur at £24.95, but serviceable outfits sell from just £7. For parents who want to avoid that nightmare-before-nativity needlework, your Mary, Joseph, kings and shepherds can be tricked out by Hopscotch too.

J&M Toys

01274 599314/www.jandmtoys.co.uk
Firefighters, lollipop men and ladies, fairies, witches, pirates, cowgirls, Vikings, dragons, police officers, nurses – Jim and Melanie's stock includes more than 150 children's dressing-up

PARTY PARTY

An essential fixture on the Ridley Road scene for nearly 30 years, Party Party is a three-floored extravaganza of a shop. The selection of costumes (to buy only) is wide-ranging but if there is something you can't see on the rails, it's worth asking for a look in the catalogue – anything can be ordered and in the shop within three to four working days. Otherwise, a basic costume with top, bottoms and a hat or a gown and a belt will set you back just £9.99. Those going all out to impress can blow up to £100 on a fantastic chicken outfit or gorilla suit but most costumes fall in the £10-£30 range.

Also worth noting is the excellent, extremely extensive and slightly unexpected selection of cake-baking and decorating equipment on the top floor – you can also order iced cakes from the shop which start at £20 and go up to £600 for multi-tiered wedding jobs. Meanwhile, the ground floor is crammed full of balloons, glitter, coloured hairspray and just about every other party essential.
For listings, see p182.

costumes, available in age ranges three to five and five to eight. J&M are medieval enthusiasts, so regal robes, Robin Hoods and knights' armour, with wooden swords and shields, are also here. It's all surprisingly cheap; most costumes cost no more than £15, with discounts on group purchases.

Non-Stop Party Shop

214-216 Kensington High Street, W8 7RJ (7937 7200/www.nonstopparty.co.uk). High Street Kensington tube. **Open** 9am-6.30pm Mon, Tue, Thur-Sat; 10am-6pm Wed; 11am-5pm Sun.

This emporium seems out of place on Kensington High Street – from the outside it looks like a pound shop – but it's what's on the inside that counts. All the fancy dress staples are covered with plenty of options for wannabe nurses, pirates and cowboys. A selection of latex celebrity masks has comedy appeal at £17.99 a pop – though the current range featuring Tony Blair, Hillary Clinton and Posh Spice may need updating. The shop next door specialises in balloons and provides a personalised decorating and printing service as well as creative four-foot balloon arch displays and bouquets. The shops are linked by a huge downstairs department stocking everything from spyglasses to confetti, themed party cutlery and sombreros. Staff are full of suggestions for the uninspired party planner.

Oscar's Den

127-129 Abbey Road, NW6 4SL (7328 6683/www.oscarsden.com). Swiss Cottage tube/West Hampstead tube/rail. **Open** 9.30am-5.30pm Mon-Sat; 10am-2pm Sun.

Despite the St George flag display in the window, this party shop caters for all types of party – bar mitzvahs, Diwali, hen nights and more. Besides all the usual party staples, Oscar's stocks a particularly good range of eye masks and an inspired piñata (a gaudily-coloured paper vessel hung on a rope which is filled with sweets and treats) selection encompassing everything from mermaids to the Loch Ness monster. Most impressively, they have a huge range of helium-filled animal balloons (the cult festival accessory of the moment) featuring everything from ducks to pandas – the dalmation, dachshund and terrier balloons get most of the admiring glances though (£10 per balloon, helium-filled in the shop). Fireworks, smoke and bubble machines, bouncy castles and entertainers can also be supplied.

Pantaloons

119 Lupus Street, SW1V 3EN (7630 8330/ www.pantaloons.co.uk). Pimlico tube. **Open** 11am-5pm Mon, Tue; 11am-6pm Wed; 11am-7pm Thur; 11am-8pm Fri; 10am-6pm Sat.

Based in Pimlico, Pantaloons offer a 'haute couture' service, where your party costume is designed and fitted to your individual

requirements – thus ensuring you'll never turn up in the same gorilla costume as someone else ever again. The standard hire costumes (vicars, priests and nuns, horror and halloween, Christmas, superheroes) number over 2,000 and include Ali G's yellow tracksuit and Buzz Lightyear's spacesuit. A week's hiring starts at a very affordable £35. A range of children's costumes is also available.

Party Party

9-13 Ridley Road, E8 2NP (7254 5168/ www.ppshop.co.uk). Dalston Kingsland rail/ 67, 76, 149 bus. **Open** 9am-5.30pm Mon-Thur; 9am-6.30pm Fri, Sat.
For review, *see p180.*

Party Pieces

01635 201844/www.partypieces.co.uk
You'll find myriad party games and accessories aimed at kids on this clearly laid-out website. There are as many as 24 different types of piñata. The kids whack it with sticks to release the goodies. Aside from football- and monkey-shaped piñatas (from £12.99), there's an extensive balloons section and a small amount of stuff for 'grown-ups'.

Party Plus

4 Acton Lane, W4 5NB (8987 8404/ www.partyplus.co.uk). Chiswick Park tube.
Open 9.30am-5pm Mon-Fri; 9am-5pm Sat.
If money's a bit tight, you can't say fairer than the prices here – not to mention the enormous choice of partyware, including helium balloons, ribbons, neon signage and those all-important party bag fillers. Great for parents with kids demanding themed parties: the 'licensed' party section is comprehensive, with all the latest Pixar and Disney releases represented.

Party Superstore

268 Lavender Hill, SW11 1LJ (7924 3210/ www.partysuperstores.co.uk). Clapham Junction rail. **Open** 9am-6pm Mon-Wed, Sat; 9am-7pm Thur, Fri; 10.30am-4.30pm Sun.
Conveniently located near Clapham Junction station should the need for a foil wig, 20 decorated paper cups and a nurse's uniform arise while you're dashing for the 18.43 to Dorking, the Party Superstore is exactly what you'd expect. It's packed to the rafters with all manner of party essentials; come on down for tableware and banners, balloons and streamers, party bags and fillers, and the obligatory gorilla outfit. The costume choice is huge – ideal for the more competitive fancy dresser – and it's a great place to stock up on fireworks. Be prepared to queue during the silly seasons though.

Prangsta Costumiers

304 New Cross Road, SE14 6AF (8694 9869/www.prangsta.com). New Cross Gate rail. **Open** 11am-7pm Mon-Sat.
Close to Goldsmith's College (though proprietor Melanie Wilson is a St Martin's grad), you'll often find unconventionally dressed types perusing the rails at Prangsta. Specialising in the theatrical and the bizarre – all beautifully handmade – Prangsta is best known for its burlesque ensembles, often made from vintage fabrics. Hiring costs from £30 up to £100, depending on how ornate the costume is. Included in this price is the costume being styled on you, plus relevant accessories. If you want to buy, Prangsta offer a made-to-measure service so it fits like a glove.

Preposterous Presents

262 Upper Street, N1 2UQ (7226 4166). Highbury & Islington tube/rail. **Open** 10am-6pm Mon-Sat.
An old-school jape player's dream shop, you'll find fake blood, fake moustaches and eye patches-a-plenty at this treasure trove, not to mention whoopee cushions and fake cigarettes. Costumes for adults and children were once available to hire but now they're only to buy. Nevertheless, the prices are reasonable and start at £10, for which you can transform yourself into a nun, monk, priest or surgeon. Romantics can splurge £45 on a medieval knight's outfit; tragic types will prefer the Mark Antony (£35); wannabe urban gangsters should opt for the 'deluxe pimp' (£45).

So High Soho

96 Berwick Street, W1F 0QQ (7287 1295/ www.sohighsoho.co.uk). Oxford Circus tube.
Open 10am-6pm Mon-Wed; 11am-7pm Thur-Sat.
During 12 years in the heart of Soho, friendly So High have sourced an extensive collection of very reasonably priced costumes available to buy, including vampires, superheroes and belly dancers. Every budget is catered for – from a pirate's eye-patch costing just £1.50 to a Victorian frock coat priced at £75. Wigs, make-up, jewellery, shoes and other paraphernalia are also in huge supply, including a 'mother of all afros' wig for £20 and shiny platform boots for £45. Both men's and women's sizes available.

Wood 'n' Things

57 Brushfield Street, E1 6AA (7247 6275/ www.woodnthings.uk.com). Liverpool Street tube/rail. **Open** 10am-7pm Mon-Sat; 10am-6.30pm Sun.
As well as selling children's traditional wooden toys, competitively priced adult costumes and

THE PARTY'S OVER

Pack 'em off happy with one of these fantastic bags of loot.

Empty bags from 20p; gifts from 35p. **Happy Green Earth** (www.happy greenearth. com). *See p185.*

Wrapping & sweets £1.50; gifts from £1.25. **Semmalina Starbags** (www. starbags.info). *See p185.*

Empty bags from £2.50; pre-filled bags from £2.75. **Frog in the Field** (www.froginthe field.co.uk). *See p185.*

Empty bags from 45p; gifts from 25p; pre-filled bags from £4. **Little Cherry** (www.littlecherry.co.uk). *See p185.*

Empty bags £1.50; gifts from 99p. **Ethical Party Bags** (www.ethical partybags.co.uk). *See p184.*

ESSENTIALS

MCQUEENS

Since opening in 1991, McQueens has garnered a well-deserved reputation for flair, imagination and sophistication while never going overboard. In the intervening years, founder Kally Ellis has expanded the business beyond the large warehouse-like space in Old Street to open a smaller flower shop on St John Street. With around 100 stems to choose from, McQueens' florists are just as adept at pulling together a glamorous statement arrangement as they are a more traditional bouquet. Similarly, when it comes to wedding flowers, they are accustomed to designing the blooms for both large-scale nuptials for several hundred guests, or a simple bridal bouquet of roses (£80).

During the initial consultation, you will be shown details of past weddings to inspire ideas, whether for button holes, pew ends or elegant flower arches. Importantly, no 'house style' is ever imposed on the client, so whether you prefer country garden peonies and hydrangeas in pastel shades, or a stark monochrome look using white roses and kitty grass, it can be done. And for those who like the idea of creating their own arrangements, the Old Street-based floristry school is a thriving enterprise, attracting students – both professionals honing their skills and enthusiastic beginners – from all over the globe. *For listings, see p187.*

Venetian masks are available to buy at this friendly Spitalfields stalwart. The costumes (also available online) run along the usual superhero and historical period lines and start at £17.99 for a doctor's white coat or a saucy French maid's outfit. You can get an accessory kit for £6.50, kids' costumes from £9.50, and a dracula cape for £12.50, with the top price of £99.99 for a gorilla. The Venetian masks start at £45, though there are plenty of cheaper options for masked ball attendees on a budget. Staff are helpful and friendly.

CHILDREN'S PARTY BAGS

Most of the below are available by mail order. If you prefer to shop for fortune-telling fish and whistles in person, **Party Party** (*see p180*) has a good selection of fillers for all budgets.

Bumble Bags
01380 831134/www.bumblebags.co.uk

Fabulous themed party bags (dinosaurs, pirates, princesses, ballerinas – all the classics are covered) with boys', girls' and unisex options. Bags are also grouped by price with lots of choices under £6 and £10 – and some over £10 bags for the flush. For £4.95 you can buy a jungle-themed bag filled with plastic wild animals, an animal pencil, punch balloon and a wooden whistle.

Ethical Party Bags
07948 343653/www.ethicalpartybags.com
Recycled, fairly traded party bags available empty (options include bags made from recycled paper and old juice cartons) or pre-filled. Fillers include mini footballs (£6.50), ring boxes (£2.50), magnets (£1.25) and animal whizzers (£1.50).

Frog in the Field
0845 170 2010/www.froginthefield.co.uk
Frog in the Field's excellent website makes party bag purchasing a total doddle with a search function that sorts the options by age and gender. Either pick and mix items yourself or choose from a range of great pre-filled bags.

A £4.99 cupcake bag filled with bubbles, a spinning top, key ring and bouncy ball needs only a wedge of cake to make any kid's day. Special bags for weddings (from £5.99) and the insanely rich are also available.

Happy Green Earth

0845 388 0931/www.happygreenearth.com
HGH's eco-friendly bags start at 20p, and gifts at 35p (a cardboard mask or a colour-in bookmark) making this is a very cheap option for DIY party bags. Animal slide whistles cost £1.45.

Little Cherry

01753 857003/www.littlecherry.co.uk
The bags (available empty at £1.50) themselves are particularly lovely at Little Cherry, featuring bright, fabric designs themed with monsters, robots, jungle animals and diggers. Fill them with fabulous eco-friendly toys such as frog rattles (£1.50), skipping ropes (£4.49) and clown pencils (99p). Pre-filled bags are also available. Little Cherry also supplies party decorations, tableware, gift wrap and invites.

Party Bag Boutique

01761 436876/www.partybagboutique.co.uk
Lovely take-home bags either pre-filled or to fill yourself. Girly girls will love the princess themed bag (£3.95) which includes a veiled tiara and glittery flower hairbands. Boy-focused footie (£3.95) and racing car (£3.95) bags are also on offer, as are unisex bags. Fillers include finger puppets (95p), bead sets (£2.25) and bouncy balls (12 for £3.49). Fairly traded bags are also available and sweets can be added to any bag at your discretion.

Semmalina Starbags

225 Ebury Street, SW1W 8UT (7730 9333/ www.starbags.info). Sloane Square tube.
Open 9.30am-5.30pm Mon-Sat.
Semmalina's glitzy party bags (versions for adults are also available) start with a cost of £2.50 for the wrapping and sweets, after which the rest of the contents are entirely up to you. Options include trad favourites such as stickers (£1.50), bubbles (£1.25) and spiky balls (£3) but the sky is the limit.

THE SHORTLIST

WHAT'S NEW | WHAT'S ON | WHAT'S BEST

 **Amsterdam** 2009

 Barcelona 2009

 Berlin

 Cyprus

 Dubai

 **Dublin**

 **Dubrovnik**

 Edinburgh

 Florence

 Las Vegas

 London 2009

 **Malta**

 **Manchester**

 **Marrakech**

 Mexico City

 New York 2009

 **Nice & Cannes**

 Paris

 **Prague** 2009

 Rome 2009

 San Francisco

 **Sydney**

 **Tokyo**

 Venice

- **Pocket-sized guides**
- **What's on, month by month**
- **Full colour fold-out maps**

TIME OUT GUIDES WRITTEN BY LOCAL EXPERTS

timeout.com/shop

Time Out Guides

FLOWERS

Angel Flowers

60 Upper Street, N1 0NY (7704 6312/
www.angel-flowers.co.uk). Angel tube.
Open 9am-7pm Mon-Sat; 11am-5pm Sun.
This much-loved local flower shop overlooking
Islington Green styles itself as the ideal
compromise between a friendly local and a top-
rung corporate florist. The arrangements can be
dramatic – studded with hothouse orchids and
other structural beauties – or rather more simple
and country garden-like, it's up to you. Either way,
the quality of the blooms you choose for your
party as well as the arranging itself will be second
to none. Bouquets start from £30. You can also
buy Angel blooms online.

Bloomsbury Flowers

29 Great Queen Street, WC2B 5BB (7242
2840/www.bloomsburyflowers.co.uk). Covent
Garden tube. **Open** 9.30am-5pm Mon; 9.30am-
5.30pm Tue-Thur; 9.30am-6pm Fri.
Combining a sense of fashion with friendliness
sums up Bloomsbury Flower's approach to flower
arranging. The choice of blooms changes with the
seasons, so there will always be something new
to see (and to sniff): a seasonal bridal bouquet
starts at £85; a buttonhole £6. Unconventional
bouquets are a hallmark here and may include
glossy evergreens and fragrant herbs along with
more traditional flowers. And if you want to learn
to create your own floral displays for those special
events, why not try one of the evening and one-
day design courses that are held at the Highbury
branch (21A Highbury Park, N5 1QJ, 7704 0480).

Chivers Flowers

43-45 Charlotte Street, W1T 1RS (7580
7595/1761/www.chiversflowers.co.uk).
Goodge Street tube. **Open** 8.30am-6pm
Mon-Fri; 9am-5pm Sat.
Surrounded by trendy Fitzrovian restaurants on
Charlotte Street, Chivers' flowers always look
sumptuous but contemporary in their classy
metal pots – it's hard to believe the company has
been operating out of this street for over 40
years. Corporate orders, wedding and funeral
flowers are all areas of experience – ring up to
speak to an adviser. As for style, Chivers is happy
to veer from the modern and sculptural to the
more traditional and pretty.

Chocolate Cosmos

07966 022918/www.chocolatecosmos.co.uk
Hackney-based Sam Selby specialises in floral
displays for parties, events and weddings using
seasonal blooms. Designs are simple and natural
emphasising the beauty of the flowers – no gaudy
tropical displays in the middle of winter here.
Selby has worked with the likes of MTV but has
plenty of private clients too. Her service is totally
bespoke so feel free to let your imagination run
wild in the planning stages. Prices for a seasonal
but stylish table centre start from £25.

In Water

70-76 Bell Street, NW1 6SP (7724 9985/
www.inwater.uk.com). Edgware Road tube.
Open daily by appointment for party
arrangements.
In Water's innovative and contemporary displays
(it's a flower 'studio', don't you know?) are about
as far away as you can get from a bunch of
forecourt carnations; instead, you get avant-
garde blooms as you've never seen them before.
The roll call of prestigious events and high-profile
weddings the company has catered to is
impressive (from Blenheim Palace to Tate
Modern) and yet the results are never overblown;
'deceptively simple, seriously stylish' being part
of the mission statement here. Contact the
studio to chat with a creative consultant. Dining
table arrangements start at around £50, but the
sky's the limit.

Louise Taylor Flowers

135 Dulwich Road, SE24 0NG (7737 6565/
www.louisetaylor-flowers.co.uk). Herne Hill rail.
Open 9am-6pm Mon-Fri; 10am-6pm Sat.
Opposite Brockwell Park, between Dulwich and
Brixton, you'll find this reliable and stylish florist
where the arrangements come with unusual
touches; greenery, fruit and seed heads along
with the blooms themselves. Thanks to the open-
plan layout of the shop, you can also see the
florists working their magic – great for
prospective party hosts who want to check out
the talent first. Prices are very reasonable – a
simple bouquet starts at £15 – and a local
delivery service is also available.

McQueens

70-72 Old Street, EC1V 9AN (7251 5505/
www.mcqueens.co.uk). Old Street tube/rail.
Open 8.30am-6pm Mon-Fri; 9am-3pm Sat.
For review, *see p184.*

Rebel Rebel

5 Broadway Market, E8 4PH (7254 4487/
www.rebelrebel.co.uk). Bethnal Green tube/
London Fields rail. **Open** 10am-6pm Tue-Fri;
10am-5pm Sat.
Hackney's popular Broadway street market has
helped the permanent businesses thrive too. One
is friendly, stylish and quirky florist Rebel Rebel,
owned by Mairead Curtin and Athena Duncan.
Despite the slightly anarchic name, the emphasis

ESSENTIALS

here is on pretty blooms and the specifically English flowers the proprietors love so much. Bouquets cost from £30 and the owners are always happy to discuss specific plans for special party arrangements.

Scarlet & Violet

76 Chamberlayne Road, NW10 3JJ (8969 9446/www.scarletandviolet.co.uk). Kensal Green tube/Kensal Rise rail. **Open** 8.30am-6.30pm Mon-Sat.

Established on Kensal Rise's popular shopping street for 14 years, Scarlet & Violet is as colourful as its name implies, with vessels full of gorgeous, mostly traditional blooms. Vic Brotherson's arrangements manage to be both stylishly up-to-date and old-world pretty, with pastel-hued bridal bouquets or striking floral displays in bolder colours while keeping the lines soft and natural. Weddings and parties requiring a personal touch are a strong point here; they're happy to provide just a buttonhole or deck out the church, reception and bridal party too.

Wild at Heart

54 Pimlico Road, SW1W 8LP (7229 1174/ www.wildatheart.com). Sloane Square tube. **Open** call for details.

Established by Nikki Tibbles in 1993, Wild at Heart started life in the well-known Turquoise Island on Westbourne Grove (No.222, 7727 3095) which was once a public loo. Today her newly opened (September 2008) flagship store is here in Pimlico where beautiful products (textiles, candles, toiletries and ceramics) can be found alongside the spectacular blooms. Alternatively, log on to the website, which sells a selection of five lovely rose-dominated bouquets in varying sizes depending on your budget but starting at £45. Popular for weddings and events, whether intimate or larger-scale, the resulting displays can be girlishly traditional (scores of pink roses) or sophisticated chic (cream roses in metallic bowls). There is a branch at the Great Eastern Hotel, Liverpool Street.

Woodhams

45 Elizabeth Street, SW1W 9PP (7730 3353/ www.woodhams.co.uk). Sloane Square tube/ Victoria tube/rail. **Open** 9am-6pm Mon-Sat.

In addition to the flowers here, you'll also find plenty of more unusual architectural plants and orchids, as well as garden design and maintenance services – which could be useful for the urban gardener wanting to spruce up their space in time for an al fresco party. Those looking for flowers are not neglected, with an array of impressive and unusual floral displays that give you a taste of what they can create for events.

Hand-tied bouquets start at £25; a romantic bridal bouquet or dramatic centrepiece for a table cost upwards of £80.

You Don't Bring Me Flowers

15 Staplehurst Road, SE13 5ND (8297 2333/www.youdontbringmeflowers.co.uk). Hither Green rail. **Open** 8am-6pm Tue-Fri; 9am-6pm Sat; 10am-5pm Sun.

At Lynne Norledge's lovely shop, the florists are happy to create whatever look you want for your wedding or party, whether it's bold and imaginative, using shape and texture as much as colour, or something much more traditional, such as a tight knot of exquisite blush-coloured roses. Whichever you choose, the flowers tend to be traditional with plenty of perfume, rather than hothouse-exotic.

LIGHTING

Also worth a look are **Alive & Sound** (*see p162*) and **Capital Hire** (*see p163*).

Diptyque

195 Westbourne Grove, W11 2SB (7727 8673/www.diptyqueparis.com). Notting Hill Gate tube. **Open** 10am-6pm Mon-Sat; noon-5pm Sun.

Cast a glamorously flickering glow over party proceedings and a fantastic aroma to boot with a trip to Diptyque. The brand pioneered the trend for scented candles, producing its first line over four decades ago. Scents range from fruity and floral to woody and spicy – fans can sniff out the trademark Tuberose (£32) at 50 paces. Unlike many other perfumed candle brands these really do fill a room with fabulous (and totally non-cloying) scent and are tremendously long-lasting. Well worth the investment if you want to add a touch of class to an intimate dinner, engagement do or other special occasion.

Ealing Lighting Design

8932 3557/www.ealinglightingdesign.co.uk

Specialising in lighting for stage and theatre (including 'am-dram' and school productions), Ealing Lighting Design also has an off-shoot business dedicated solely to weddings, particularly those on a restricted budget (www.lightmywedding.co.uk). This is a bespoke service where you consult with a lighting designer who will also work in conjunction with other services employed on the day. Alternatively, a cheaper option is to choose a fixed price package, where the designer takes a more ad-hoc approach on the day. From £800 plus delivery according to mileage from Ealing.

Caravan. See p192.

Fireworks Crazy

0845 226 0797/www.fireworkscrazy.co.uk
As well as offering an array of rockets, fountains and roman candles to buy online, this Chelmsford-based company can also provide professional displays at your party – they're becoming very popular to celebrate divorces apparently. Prices start at around £495 plus VAT. If budgets are tight there's a varied selection of DIY display packs for keen followers of the Fireworks Code to make their mark with. Particularly cheap 'n' cheerful are the glow/sky lanterns – £29.99 for ten, including postage and packing.

Fireworks London

102 East Barnet Road, EN4 8RE (8361 1943/www.fireworks-london.co.uk). New Barnet rail. **Open** *9.30am-5pm Mon-Fri; by appointment Sat.* **No credit cards**.
Established for 25 years, Fireworks London can produce fireworks shows for any size of event, from large fundraisers to weddings to indoor pyrotechnic displays. Wedding firework displays tend to last for two to five minutes and the helpful, clearly laid-out packages start at £950 for two or three 'short, sharp and spectacular' minutes of comets, dancing golden pearls and palm shell

Hang the expense. Go for retro cool with **Zigzag Bunting**. *See p194.*

bursts. For a cheaper, but still magical outdoor light display, you can also buy customised sky lanterns from the website and shop.

Fisher Productions
8871 1978/www.fisherproductions.co.uk
Fisher Productions now take a multi-disciplinary approach but when the company started out in 1985, it provided specialist lighting for the events industry. The client list is about as long and distinguished as it gets and includes Claridges, Harvey Nichols and Buckingham Palace for starters. For smaller scale events, dry hire is available for private parties and includes a whole plethora of lighting options from £40 for a scoop light, as well as mirror balls (£20), smoke machines (£35) and confetti cannons (£25).

Flowerglow
www.flowerglow.com
A small mail order company which sells high quality and highly detailed ropes of fairy lights at very reasonable prices. Blooms are obviously the overriding theme, and the roses, carnations, frangipani and ordinary 'flower' designs all come complete with pollen detail and are available in seven different colours. In addition to the blooms are striking leaf and branch designs, as well as strings of rattan balls and globe lights. From £9.99 for three metres (or 35 bulbs).

Habitat
121-123 Regent Street, W1B 4HS (0844 499 1134/www.habitat.co.uk). Oxford Circus or Piccadilly Circus tube. **Open** *10am-7pm Mon-Wed, Fri, Sat; 10am-8pm Thur; noon-6pm Sun.*

Just because the budget is tight and the venue is small, it doesn't mean you won't be able to create some special effects. Habitat offers a range of lovely outdoor lighting options, including a row of upright 'Zumi' stake lights (just stick 'em in the lawn or flower beds, £18); 'Folie', a string of multicoloured garland lights (£29); and 'Lanterne', outdoor lantern lights which could be threaded through a tree (£49). There is also a large range of candles to pick from.

Invisible Blue
7733 1144/www.invisibleblue.com
Invisible Blue can transform your venue for the evening, whether charged with creating an impressive interior or enchanting exterior lighting scheme (the company also specialises in looking after the entire event). Alternatively, you can hire from their extensive collection of gear, such as basic uplighters, which will wash colours over interior walls. You'll need six to eight of these for a great effect; each one is between £10-£20 to hire. Lighting a small event, with technicians costs about £600-£800; an event for 800 people with AV and stage dressing – the whole shebang – will come in at over £30,000.

Lights 4 Fun
0800 061 2532/www.lights4fun.co.uk
This web-based company offers a vast selection of indoor and outdoor fairy lights – an easy and effective shortcut to a magical party atmosphere. Choose from twinkling ropes of lights to string across rooms or twist around tree branches, trailing light curtains for feature walls and windows or even a series of 25cm heart-

ESSENTIALS

shaped displays (perfect for a swanky engagement party or anniversary do). Colourful and white lights are both available and prices are competitive.

Mathmos

96 Kingsland Road, E2 8DB (7549 2700/ www.mathmos.com). Old Street tube/rail/55, 243 bus. **Open** 9.30am-5.30pm Mon-Fri; 10.30am-6pm Sat.
Mathmos should definitely be on the shopping list if you need a few fantastic light effects (rather than a full-on event organiser's scheme). The Space Projectors (£68) make an eye-catching feature wall in a darkened room, with extra oil wheels (which create different patterns) available to buy. There is also a great selection of LED lights in bright, juicy colours – including the rechargeable Bubble light (£39). Scatter a few in the garden for an extraterrestrial feel.

Party Lights

8892 3444/www.partylights.co.uk
With offices in Twickenham and Reading, Party Lights will undertake the lighting (as well as effects) for most events, parties and promotions. From home garden parties up to much larger-scale bashes, including large marquees and grounds, they promise to create a memorable, atmospheric effect both inside and out. A popular package, particularly for nuptials, costs £995 – which includes eight coloured up-lighters and a

NOTE

FESTIVE DECORATIONS
Try the big department stores' Christmas shops for decorations to be proud of – Selfridge's (0800 123400, www.selfridges.co.uk), Liberty (7734 1234, www.liberty.co.uk) and Fortnum + Mason (7734 8040, www.fortnum andmason.com) are our pick of the bunch. Better still, stock up just after the 25th for bargain prices.
London's museums and galleries are another prime browsing ground for unusual decs. Head for the V+A (7942 2000, www.vam.ac.uk), British Museum (7323 8000, www.britishmuseum.org) or the Courtauld Gallery (7872 0220, www.courtauld.ac.uk).
And if what you're really after is a one-stop shop packed with festive joy from ceiling to floor, look no further than the Christmas Shop (7378 1998, www.thechristmasshop.co.uk). It's open all year round.

twinkling LED light canopy draped from the ceiling. For this price they will deliver, install and collect all the gear afterwards too.

Redcat Event Lighting & Production

8579 6969/www.redcatlighting.co.uk
Redcat provides spectacular, wow-factor-heavy lighting and decorating packages for weddings, private parties and, bravely, even teenage bashes, as well as corporate do's for an impressive client list including Moët et Chandon and SriLankan Airlines. The cost obviously varies according to what you want but a realistic starting price is around £1,500 and they say 'you can get a lot for a couple of thousand'.

Something for the Wickend

0845 166 4051/www.somethingforthe wickend.co.uk
Like the funny punning name, love the great range of tea lights and other candles this company offers – perfect to transform a party room on a tight budget. Glamorous gold cup tea lights are just £10.99 for 100 and burn so slowly (over eight hours) that you won't have to worry about changing them. Clear cup multicoloured tea lights make a bright change and cost £4.99 for 20. Price's anti-tobacco versions (£1.99 for six) might prove useful, and if the party decamps outside, battery-operated tea lights with a flickering effect wick will do the job without blowing out (£1.25 each). They also do sweet 'bride and groom' candles (£10.99).

Surrey Sound & Light

8224 6499/www.sslgroup.net
As the name implies, you can hire sound as well as lighting equipment here, including systems that are iPod compatible. As for lighting, there is a good range of reasonably priced gadgetry for hire, such as a four foot UV light (from £7 a day, rising to £22.50 a week with a £50 deposit). Other goodies include LED moonflowers, flame lights, starballs (a kind of high-tech mirror ball) and even a 1960s-style psychedelic oil projector (from £29). Serial party-throwers can also buy new and used equipment.

Wise Productions

8993 3003/www.wiseproductions.co.uk
With 13 years' experience in the production business, this company can be counted on to make your event memorable, whether a star-studded concert, awards ceremony or a large sit-down dinner. Past events involving Wise's lighting design have taken place in wonderfully dramatic surroundings such as the Natural History Museum, the Design Museum and

Take a stand and create a perfectly girly party with **Utterly Sexy Café**. *See p195*.

Hampton Court Palace. 'Exceeding expectations' is the company mission statement and positive feedback on the website implies that it does.

Wishes in the Sky

0845 130 1879/www.wishesinthesky.com
Bringing a traditional Chinese custom to British shores, Wishes in the Sky sell authentic paper lanterns that make a cheaper alternative to fireworks. Flying lanterns were once used as a form of communication, but these days they are wished upon before release, with the lanterns that fly the highest being the most likely to have the wish granted in heaven. Practical as well as magical when released en masse, the paper is treated with both flame retardant and 'accelerated biodegradability'. A box of ten costs £40 plus VAT.

FINISHING TOUCHES

Caravan

3 Redchurch Street, E2 7DJ (7033 3532/ www.caravanstyle.com). Liverpool Street tube/ rail. **Open** 11am-6pm Tue-Fri; 1pm-5pm Sat; 11am-5pm Sun.
Relocated from its original Spitalfields Market location, Caravan continues to attract a steady stream of East End fashionistas, style queens and magpies looking for quirky decor touches. Owner Emily Chalmers – a stylist who's worked

on interiors tomes *Flea Market Style* and *Table Inspirations* – has a real eye for the unusual, the unique and the beautiful. Party-perking items on offer include delicate teacups, singing birds and wings with which to accessorise your candles. A fine browsing ground for inspiration.

Cotton Bunting Company

01376 329845/www.cottonbunting.co.uk
CBC produces beautiful cotton bunting for bohemian garden soirées, weddings, birthdays and children's parties. Choose from punchy nautical shades, rainbow brights and cute pastels in plain, patterned and mix and match designs (£11 for five metres). The quality is fantastic. A range of polyester flag bunting and large flags is available for sporting celebrations or moments of spontaneous national pride.

Cox & Cox

0870 442 4787/www.coxandcox.co.uk
For stylish fripperies to finish off your party look, Cox & Cox have plenty of ideas that work particularly well for an intimate garden party or wedding. Heart-shaped sugar lumps, grosgrain ribbon, cardboard favours boxes (ready to be customised) and delicate name place holders which double up as vases are just some of what's on offer. Larger scale offerings are no less chic: paper fiesta ribbon and cute signs directing traffic to the party are all as useful as they are eye-catching.

Cybermarket

01799 533480/www.cybermarket.co.uk
For that authentic disco feel, Cybermarket sells mirror balls and the motors to go with them. You can get a half decent one for £34 (the cheapest useable mirror ball is £16) but prices go up to a whacking £700. Free-standing mirror balls, perfect for those who don't want to mount theirs on the ceiling, cost from £11.95. Other effects goodies available to buy include LCD projectors and screens, disco lighting and smoke and bubble machines (from £24). There are disco lights available from £15).

Graham & Green

4 Elgin Crescent, W11 2HX (7243 8908/ www.grahamandgreen.co.uk). Ladbroke Grove tube. **Open** 10am-6pm Mon-Sat; 11.30am-5.30pm Sun.
This Notting Hill stalwart should be the first port of call for those finishing touches to get guests oohing and ahhing. Pretty tea lights in the shape of lotus flowers (£8.95), brightly-hued Aladdin lanterns (£5.95) or a mirrored table centrepiece (£49.50) will all set the mood for a classy soirée, while a wigwam (£43.50) will keep the nippers occupied. Buy online or put aside a couple of hours for browsing in one of Graham & Green's four London shops.

Ice Box

7498 0800/www.theicebox.com
If you want your ice to do a little bit more than just keep those cocktails chilled then the Ice Box's services are what you're after. Ice sculptures that have previously wowed party guests include Louis XV chairs, castles, a working lightbulb and a full-sized, eight-tonne car. Ice bars and logos also go with the territory but for the more down-to-earth gathering they also provide the lowly cube, as well as crushed ice, dry ice and fruit in ice. They can even rent you a freezer to put it all in, too. A 12kg bag is £5.50; ice cubes with fruit inside are 25p each.

Rockett St George

8350 5450/www.rockettstgeorge.co.uk
This online collection of gifts, accessories and homewares is a browser's paradise. Party planners should point their mouse at the quirky wall art, cool angel wing coat hooks (£8.25), champagne glasses, vinyl lace tablecloths (£27.50), pretty chopsticks and quirky 'Yum Brella' inverted umbrella-shaped bowls (£50). There are plenty of candles and holders on offer too, from colourful tea-light holders (four for £9.99) to metal garden lanterns (£5.95) and glam shell-shaped wall sconces (£45). Best of all, though, are the giant chinese spoons (£14)

– a novel way to serve the olives, nuts or pickled onion Monster Munch at your next cocktail party.

Story

4 Wilkes Street, E1 6QF (7377 0313/ 07949 827966). Liverpool Street tube/rail. **Open** 1-6pm Sun; by appointment daily.
Tucked away behind a curtain of ivy on a Spitalfields side street and only open on Sunday afternoons, Story is the ultimate secret hunting ground for stunning finishing touches. Among the expertly sourced vintage clothing, cool jewellery and reclaimed fabrics you'll find hanging glass tea light holders, candles and plenty of interesting decor ideas.

Talking Tables

8675 9811/www.talkingtables.co.uk
An online one-stop shop for your finishing touches, Talking Tables stocks everything from paper garlands in the shape of butterflies and flowers (from £4 for five metres) to champagne confetti poppers (£6) and glitzy table sprinkles (gold hearts, from £2.25). There's also a vast range of table trivia and ice-breaking games (Lessons in Love trivia, £4.50). We particularly like the cascarones (£1.50 for six) – coloured 'eggs' filled with jokes and confetti that you break over your friends' heads for good luck. Very entertaining.

VV Rouleaux

102 Marylebone Lane, W1U 2QD (7224 5179/www.vvrouleaux.com). Bond Street tube. **Open** 9.30am-6pm Mon, Tue, Fri, Sat; 10.30am-6pm Wed; 9.30am-6.30pm Thur.

NOTE

CHRISTMAS TREES
Need a Christmas tree to rival the Trafalgar Square spruce? For high-quality, sustainable firs look no further than the Christmas Forest (0870 758 6862, www.christmasforest.co.uk). Visit one of seven farm sites across London (delivery also available) to choose from six fabulous tree varieties. And with a donation made to Tree Aid for every tree bought your conscience can remain clear too.
Pine and Needles (0845 458 2788, www.pinesandneedles.com) has two sites in London and can also deliver to your door. Best of all for lazy types, they can deliver you (in certain London postcodes) a fully decorated tree.

ESSENTIALS

Idyllic Days. *See p195.*

Surely London's finest passementerie (that's the making of elaborate trimmings, boys and girls), VV Rouleaux is packed to the rafters with wonderful ribbons, curtain tassels, silk flowers, bead garlands, shells and feathers – all of them available in a kaleidoscope of colours. Beloved of fashionistas into customising their clothes, a hostess with a pinch of creative flair can also pick up all kinds of treasures with which to embellish her table, festoon her party room or even adorn her guests.

Zigzag Bunting

01264 720806/www.zigzagbunting.co.uk
For that VE Day street party look, what could be more retro cool than some brightly coloured cotton bunting? From the traditional Union Jack for the patriotic partygoer to the bespoke bunting service, where it can be made up in your choice of size, colour and fabric (past commissions have included camouflage for a Land Rover and the family tartan), the price tag is £12.99 for two-and-a-half metres of mini-bunting, while standard swags are £24.99 for five metres.

FURNITURE, CATERING & ACCESSORIES HIRE

For barbecue and hog roast hire *see p131*.
For sound system hire *see p162*.

Funky Floors

01702 556878/www.funkyfloors.com
Hire the retro dancefloor of your '70s technicolour dreams here. Everything on the website is available for hire for London events, including *Big Brother*-style diary room chairs (from £900), flashing dance podiums (from £150) and mobile bars (from £400 including delivery). Party packages are also available such as the 'Barry White' which includes a dancefloor, DJs, a DJ booth, mirror ball, smoke machine, lighting and sound from £1,200. Children's party hire packages are also available starting at £600.

Gorgeous Hire

8944 7771/www.gorgeousgourmets.co.uk
This reliable Wimbledon-based firm has been around since 1982 to provide everything needed for a swanky bash, with white French porcelain or English bone china with gold edging costing from 20p for a dinner plate. The selection of glassware is above average, from conical red goblets to cut crystal. Furniture is also available for hire: round tables seating three to five people are just £4.95 each; a gilt banqueting chair is £2.60. Garden furniture and gas-fired cooking equipment is also available. Delivery and

ESSENTIALS

collection is not included in the price, but it's worth remembering that they will do the washing up for an extra 20 per cent charge.

Idyllic Days

01483 203455/www.idyllicdays.com
If plain white crockery is just too dull for your event, or you covet that effortlessly chic boho look at your wedding, party or afternoon tea, Idyllic Days' collection of exquisite mix-and-match china, accessories and props (including glass cake stands and vintage birdcages) will absolutely fit the bill. A styling service is also available, where you will not only be helped with your selection but will have them set up and arranged to perfection on the day. A cup and saucer is £2; a teapot £5.

Jones Hire

24 Creekside, SE8 3DZ (8320 0600/ www.joneshire.co.uk). Deptford Bridge DLR/ rail/Deptford rail. **Open** 8.30am-5.30pm Mon-Fri; 8.30am-noon Sat. **No credit cards**.
This eminent firm has provided catering equipment to no less distinguished party throwers than the Queen and Prince Charles so you can be assured you're in the hands of professionals. Tasteful cutlery, china, glassware and linen is available, all of it suitably classy (though you wonder if the HRHs avoided the gold-edged 'Spencer' line). A wide assortment of kitchen equipment, chairs, tables and foyer furniture (including cheval mirrors and coat rails) is also for hire.

Ratcliffs Catering & Event Hire

0845 017 0776/www.ratcliffhire.co.uk
All your catering hire needs can be met here straightforwardly and not prohibitively expensively, with chairs, tables, garden furniture, linen, marquees, glass and chinaware all available. As a guideline, plastic garden chairs are a mere £1.30 each, while a cheltenham banqueting chair will set you back £3.25. Meanwhile, dinner plates are £1.95 for a box of ten.

Utterly Sexy Café

01747 870812/www.utterlysexycafe.co.uk
Based in Wiltshire, this friendly company is happy to work in London and the south-east generally. Party venue styling (including flower arranging) is a big strength and Amanda Baird and her team are adept at creating an old-fashioned girlish ambience for any wedding or bridal shower, which are the mainstays of the business. You can just hire the lovely vintage china, however, along with a host of suitable props, including embroidered or lace napkins, tablecloths and fantastic antique glass cake stands.

Kim Neville
CO-DIRECTOR OF IDYLLIC DAYS

Decorations are crucial because as soon as you walk into a room, they tell you what kind of party you're at – whether it's a formal affair or a relaxed one, and how you are expected to act. They reflect the overall style of the event, and, of course, the personality of the host.

People often forget about the lighting, but it can totally transform a room. Whether it's turning down a dimmer switch, or not having all the lights on at once, it can make a massive difference to the atmosphere. Sometimes you find people have got candles but they forgot to light them.

The most stunning party I've done was a London wedding in a wood panelled room at Chandos House in winter – all deep pinks, roses, pearls and vintage candlesticks, with Victorian cake stands displaying the cheeses and petit fours.

This weekend, I'm going to an old-fashioned English summer fête-style wedding with coconut shies, stalls and vintage teacups.

If you want something weird and wonderful, I've got a massive ten-candle iron candelabra you can hang from the ceiling, and lots of old cream wire birdcages which are great for filling with flowers and using as centrepieces.

My best decorating tip is to stick flowers in teapots – they're much more interesting than vases. Or even teacups filled with rose heads look very pretty.

When I get married I'll have a winter wonderland affair with lots of glass and crystal, old tarnished mirrors and tea lights – it'll be very rich and sumptuous.

Idyllic Days is a one-stop shop for vintage china hire and event styling. See left.

Organisation & Planning

You've spent weeks contemplating the venue, hours deciding on the menu and several nights holed up with your CD collection creating a playlist to end all playlists, so don't mess up on things like toilet facilities, printing, cleaners and waiting staff. You'll find a host of potential suppliers below. And if you'd rather leave the whole shebang to the professionals, we've also listed party planners (for adults and children). Check out the caterers in Food & Drink (*see p122*) as many of them can also provide event management services.

(*see p122*)

Confetti

INVITATIONS

STATIONERY

Chartula
Chartula Studio, South Bank House, Black Prince Road, SE1 7SJ (7138 4055/ www.chartula.co.uk). Vauxhall tube/rail. **Open** by appointment.
This bespoke stationer prides itself on quality and service. Designs span classic and contemporary styles and the company's bespoke creations, such as a lovely 'Thistle and Rose' invitation created for a marriage between a Scottish bride and English groom, are stunning. An online boutique makes for interesting browsing – you can

choose a design, view prices and colours, check out typefaces and look at coordinating items.

Confetti
80-81 Tottenham Court Road, W1T 4TE (0870 774 7177/0870 840 6060/ www.confetti.co.uk). Goodge Street or Warren Street tube. **Open** 10am-6pm Mon-Wed, Fri, Sat; 10am-8pm Thur; 11am-5pm Sun.
If you can't make it to the Tottenham Court Road shop, Confetti's website offers reams of advice on buying wedding stationery, including tips on how to word invitations and what to do if you need to postpone the day. Prices are good value (20 invitations start at around £80) with the cost of each invitation decreasing as the order increases. The online service allows you to

choose your typeface, colours, wording and insert personal details with minimal fuss. Place cards, table planners and guests books are also available. It's also a great place to buy invites for engagement parties, landmark birthdays, anniversaries and kids' parties, wedding favours and confetti, and stuff for making invites by hand.

Hello! Lucky

Unit 1.6, The Leathermarket, 11/13 Weston Street, SE1 3ER (07771 931101/www.hello lucky.com). London Bridge tube/rail. **Open** by appointment.

A quick look at Hello! Lucky's well-designed website reveals a huge range of wedding stationery covering all style bases. A set of 50 invites in the 'Butterfly & Bouquet' range will cost

£356 and there are menu, seating and thank you cards to match. Fifty 'Enchanted Garden' save-the-date cards cost £250. There's a useful 'etiquette' section taking you step-by-step through the whole shebang, from 'how to word your invitation' to 'thank you cards' and 'gift registry etiquette'. There's also a custom design service, a great range of personalised stationery (for thank yous, informal invitations and notes) and lots of cool greetings cards.

Imagine Wedding

0845 500 3400/www.imaginewedding.co.uk. **Open** 9am-5pm Mon-Thur.

Whether handmade or printed, Imagine promises to meet all your wedding stationery needs with finesse. Prices are reasonable: popular design

HOW TO BE THE HOSTESS WITH THE MOSTEST

The key to a good party is a good host. **Nuala Calvi** works the room for charm pointers from those in the know.

ESSENTIALS

The Beginning
• 'The host is crucial to getting any party started, and it's up to them to stop things flagging,' says Johnny Roxburgh, director of the Admirable Crichton (see p203), party planners to the rich and famous.
• Approach entertaining as a job that starts as soon as the doorbell rings. 'There's nothing worse than walking into a house full of people and having no one greet you,' says Roxburgh.
• If you can't make it to the door yourself, send a partner or close friend. Make sure everyone has their coat taken and a glass put into their hand. 'If you've spent money on a vintage bottle of champagne, you want to give it to your host personally, not just see it stuck on the side,' adds Roxburgh.

Conversation Starters
• Next, it's time to get people talking. 'It's fine to bring different social groups together, but you've got to make sure they're mixing,' says Carole Stone, MD of market researchers YouGovStone and author of *Networking: the Art of Making More Friends*.
• 'There's nothing wrong with saying, "Come on you two, I'm going to split you up – I'd like you to meet so-and-so", before whisking them away,' says Stone.
• If you want people to continue talking once they've been introduced, give them something on which to hang their conversation. 'Come up with an amusing or quirky one-liner, so they don't have to fall back on "how do you know the host?" – always the kiss of death,' says Roxburgh. 'And steer clear of jobs.'
• If someone is particularly shy, get him or her to hand out nibbles. And ask friends to keep an eye out for anyone on their own.

Mingling
• Even if you've employed caterers, taking a bottle around yourself is a good way of doing a quick circuit of the room to check everyone is having a good time.
• Just don't spend too long with any one person. 'A minute or two each – that's enough,' advises Stone. 'If you're taking your hosting role seriously, this isn't the time to have a good old chinwag with someone you haven't seen for ages.'

Boozing
• Drink by all means – it's a party after all – but don't get so drunk you forget people's names (or start thinking an impromptu conga is exactly what everyone's waiting for).

Fun
• 'Towards the end of the evening you can relax a bit more, but you should never enjoy your party too much, because what really matters is how much your guests enjoy it,' says Roxburgh. 'Your time to have fun is when you're invited back.'

Planning Essentials
Guest list – 'Choose your invitees with care, not purely because you have to return hospitality,' advises Liz Brewer, author of *The Party Bible*. But don't be afraid to mix friendship groups: 'People are generally fascinated with others from a different world.'
Venue – 'The best parties are the one's where people are jammed into a space that's cosy and intimate,' says Roxburgh.
Food – 'If you're not providing dinner, start the party with cocktails at 10pm and offer finger foods or 'breakfast' around midnight,' suggests Brewer.
Drink – Always offer soft drinks, white wine, champagne, vodka and a few cocktails. Never scrimp on quantities. And ignore anyone who tells you a good guide is 'half a bottle of wine per head'. You'll always need more.
Lighting – Lighting is key to creating atmosphere. 'But if you're using candles, think about where you put them,' warns Roxburgh. A guest on fire can really take the edge off a good bash.
Smell – 'The fragrance of a room has as much impact as the way it looks,' says Roxburgh. Invest in a non-sickly room fragrance or fabulous scented candles.
Invitations – 'The invitation needs to be creative, titillating and enticing,' says Brewer. Think imaginative and interactive.
Music – If you can afford it, hire a professional DJ. 'You don't have the flexibility to judge the mood of the evening with a pre-made playlist,' says Roxburgh.
USP – If you want to go down in party folklore, you'll need one.

'Blush' – bright pink with a collection of flowers in the centre, finished with a contrasting insert and ribbon tie – starts at £1 for a place card, rising to £75 for a table plan. Funkier designs such as 'Coco Spots' cost £60 for 20 evening invitation menus. The website has examples of wording to use, and extras include photograph albums, guest books, keepsake boxes and journals. Turnaround time during the busy summer period is approximately six weeks.

Impresos

01273 832142/www.impresos.co.uk. **Open** 10am-6pm Mon-Fri; by appointment Sat.
Using eco-friendly printing methods and materials, Impresos offers unusual and personalised designs for party invitations. Take a look at the website for examples of their wedding, anniversary, birthday and christening invitations – all original and memorable – then send for the catalogue. Contact them for bespoke designs, which cost around 20 per cent extra.

Les Enfants

90 Long Acre, WC2E 9RZ (8502 9988/ www.lesenfants.co.uk). Covent Garden tube. **Open** 9am-5.30pm Mon-Fri.
Founded by a working mum with over ten years' experience of organising events, Les Enfants is best-known for its personalised children's party planning service. But the company also offers a beautiful range of bespoke children's party invitations, as well as other stationery. Choose from existing designs for inspiration or create something completely unique with the help of the in-house team. The invitations are postcard size and printed full colour on 300gsm card, with envelopes supplied. Les Enfants can also offer more specific printing services such as lamination and unusually shaped cards. An RSVP service is available to process replies for your event.

Notting Hill Notes

7419 1340/www.nottinghillnotes.com
Notting Hill Notes, founded by New Yorker Hazel Betinck, offers stylish customised stationery. Whether you are organising a Christmas bash, christening party, wedding, birthday or a small private dinner, NHN offers one of the best selections of personalised invitations (we like the 'Orange Dots' design) you'll find online. Wedding invitations range from £1.50-£2.50 per card, with a minimum order of 20 cards.

Oh So Cherished

01983 853629/www.ohsocherished.co.uk. **Open** 10am-5pm Mon-Thur; 9am-noon Fri.
Oh So Cherished are specialists in sourcing beautiful guest and visitor books for weddings or other big events. A handmade white leather wedding guest book (£47.99) comes with a black presentation box and a small plate that can be engraved for you (£9.99). Special designs for civil partnership ceremonies are also offered. If you are getting married abroad, choose from their range of exotically inspired leather guest books, starting at £17.85. They also offer a selection of fair trade/recycled books, and all can be personalised. There are album and guest book ranges for hen nights, anniversaries, christenings and birthday parties too, and all orders are processed online.

Piccolo Press

01667 454508/www.piccolopress.co.uk. **Open** 8.30am-5pm Mon-Thur; 8.30am-2pm Fri.
Although this prestigious stationery company is based in Scotland, the bulk of its business comes from London. This is one of few remaining stationers still using traditional engraving, die-stamping and letter-pressing techniques. Nearly all of the stationery is bespoke. Make an enquiry and they'll send you a sample pack (costing £7.50, deducted from your final order) and devote lots of time to discussing your ideas. Great for traditional, slightly conservative designs, you'll need to give two to three weeks' notice for an order to be fulfilled (slightly longer in peak wedding season). The best-selling invite is a duplex, letterpress square wedding invite on thick 700gsm card – few stationers can print on such thick card nowadays. Place cards, order of service documents, menus and reply cards are also offered.

Pink & Blue Stationery Designs

07790 594173/www.pinkandbluewedding.com
Pink & Blue produces handmade, contemporary wedding stationery, including save-the-date cards, wedding and evening invitations, RSVP cards, order of the day and order of service sheets, place cards, menus, camera cards, table plans and thank you cards. Popular designs include the signature 'Wedding Windows' range (featuring Swarovski crystal hearts, butterflies and flowers, starting at £2.40 per invite) and a 'Mix, Match & Mount' range of pocket-fold and flat invitations (starting at £1.50 per invite). All invitations come with handmade pearlescent envelopes. Wedding wallets that combine an invite, guest information and an RSVP card are another best-seller.

Ruth Kaye Design

48 Chalcot Road, NW1 8LS (7722 7227/ www.ruthkayedesign.com). Chalk Farm tube. **Open** 9am-5.30pm Mon-Fri; by appointment Sat.

Ruth Kaye Design offers bespoke wedding stationery, party invitations and guest books. The wedding range is especially popular, covering everything from invites to place cards and order of service sheets. Corporate invitations are also a big seller. If you are lacking in inspiration, they can provide advice and samples. The average turnaround for design and printing is four weeks. Costs can be adapted to suit any budget, starting from just £3 per invite up to very elaborate and more expensive options.

Smythson

40 New Bond Street, W1S 2DE (7629 8558/7318 1515/www.smythson.com). Bond Street tube. **Open** *9.30am-6pm Mon-Wed, Fri; 10am-7pm Thur; 10am-6pm Sat.*
Luxury stationer Smythson is the place to head for all high-end event stationery. Popular ranges include the 'At Home' cards, available with a gilt edge (£40 for 25 cards and envelopes). Pewter place card holders, in the shape of pigs, apples or grapes, are £120 for eight. As well as an impressive pre-designed stationery range, including high-quality invites, envelopes and correspondence cards, Smythson also offers a personalised stationery service at stationery salons in Bond Street and Sloane Square. Invitations and 'At Home' correspondence cards can be personalised with different lettering styles, card and ink colours, starting from £390 for 50 cards. A selection of guest books is also available: a wedding guest book with gilded leaves, bound in new off-white pigskin, costs £155.

Walton Street Stationery Company

97 Walton Street, SW3 2HP (7589 0000/www.ckpress.com). South Kensington tube. **Open** *1-6pm Mon; 10am-6pm Tue-Fri.*
This is the London boutique for CKPress, which recently acquired luxury stationer Alastair Lockhart. The company is popular for wedding stationery (no guest books, though), invitations and personal stationery, both designed and bespoke. If you are after something specific and want it designed from scratch, visit the shop and talk through your ideas with one of the designers, who will help turn your vision into reality. A set of newly designed invitations can be produced in just five hours if necessary; however, the normal turnaround time is seven days. Prices are all by quotation. As everything is produced in-house, the company is able to process any number of invites efficiently, whether 25 or 2,500.

Wren Press

1 Chelsea Wharf, 15 Lots Road, SW10 0QJ (7351 5887/www.wrenpress.co.uk).
Sloane Square tube. **Open** *9am-5.30pm Mon-Fri.*
Family stationer the Wren Press has offices worldwide and is regarded by many as England's leading quality stationer. A range of diverse print services is offered, including high-quality bespoke invitations for weddings, parties, christenings and bar mitzvahs, correspondence cards, headed writing paper and order of service sheets. All stationery is printed at their factory in south London, using a combination of traditional techniques and modern technology. There's also an in-house calligrapher for the design and addressing of wedding stationery. Save-the-date cards, table plans and leather-bound books are also available.

CALLIGRAPHY

Christopher Austin Cheirographics

8785 2780/www.cheirographics.com
London-based calligrapher Christopher Austin has over 20 years of experience providing high-quality calligraphy services for weddings and parties. He specialises in fluid, elegant handwriting and his extensive experience means he is able to reproduce any style. You can either have invitations printed and ask him to add the names, or he can design a handwritten invitation.

Euan MacGregor Calligraphy

01323 641008/www.designcalligraphy.com
Calligrapher Euan MacGregor offers handwritten calligraphy services for envelopes, invites, menus, place/table cards and certificates. He also offers lettering design for more personalised stationery. Samples of his work are available on his website.

Fluid Calligraphy

07769 895147/www.fluidcalligraphy.co.uk
Fluid Calligraphy offers personalised hand calligraphy services for invitations, place cards, invitations and wedding vows, each designed to your own specifications. A wide choice of calligraphic styles and ink colours (including gold and silver) is available. Writing styles include italic, flourished italic, foundational, gothic and traditional hands. Prices start at 80p per invitation, and £95 for table plans.

Paul Antonio Scribe

7720 8883/www.paulantonioscribe.com
Calligrapher Paul Antonio runs his own London studio and currently works for clients such as Gucci, Yves Saint Laurent, Jo Malone and Burberry. He recommends traditional, formal, historical calligraphic scripts for citations, wedding

The party people with a real sense of fun. **Kasimira**. *See p204.*

ESSENTIALS

invitations, illuminated addresses and place cards, and more modern scripts to give invitations a contemporary feel. There are examples of each on his website; call for a consultation on what would work best for your event – scripts can be specifically tailored to your needs.

Rosella Garavaglia

7274 7516/www.calligraphyserviceslondon.com London calligrapher and lettering artist Rosella Garavaglia can provide calligraphy and lettering design for wedding stationery and other events. As well as commissioned work, she also creates her own designs for exhibitions and sales.

PRINTING

Brightside Print & Design

G7 Linton House, 164-180 Union Street, SE1 OLH (7960 5111/www.brightsideonline.com). Southwark tube/London Bridge tube/rail. **Open** 9am-5.30pm Mon-Fri.
Brightside provides high-quality printing services for brochures, posters, leaflets and stationery. Graphic design services can be offered too should you need them. Prices are decent value for money and the service is reliable. There's a digital press on-site, which is ideally suited to short-run, fast-turnaround printing work.

Double Image

0141 954 2307/0141 954 5555/www. doubleimage.co.uk. **Open** 9am-5.30pm Mon-Fri.

Double Image offers professional quality printing of leaflets, posters, personal stationery, invites and menus. The company's services are best for larger print runs. Printing your own invitations starts at £216 for 500 invites – far cheaper than high-street printing services. Full colour glossy A4 posters start at £190 for 500.

Impress Print

10 Thornsett Road, SW18 4EN (8871 9950/ www.impressprint.net). Earlsfield rail. **Open** 9am-6pm Mon-Fri.
This well-respected digital and lithographic printer can print to tight schedules and even print different versions of the same project within a single print run (adding names, addresses and other relevant information, for example). The digital printing servic is a more cost-effective, fast turnaround than traditional lithographic methods. The team can work 24-hours a day, six days a week, and can offer same day printing.

Solo Image

01702 460047/www.solopress.com. **Open** 9am-6pm Mon-Fri; 9am-1pm Sat.
Solo Image can print brochures for events, flyers, leaflets, posters, stickers and stationery. A 24-hour turnaround is offered for London-based customers. Flyers on 350gsm gloss art board start at £70 for 250, while A3 posters start at £70 for 100. Various colours/sizes are available.

10th Way

0845 388 3863/www.10thway.co.uk. **Open** 9.30am-5pm Mon-Fri.

The best guides to enjoying London life

(but don't just take our word for it)

'A treasure trove of treats that lists the best the capital has to offer'

The People

'Armed with a tube map and this guide there is no excuse to find yourself in a duff bar again'

Evening Standard

'I'm always asked how I keep up to date with shopping and services in a city as big as London. This guide is the answer'

Red Magazine

'Get the inside track on the capital's neighbourhoods'

Independent on Sunday

'You will never again be stuck for interesting things to do and places to visit in the capital'

Independent on Sunday

Rated 'Best Restaurant Guide'

Sunday Times

10th Way offers a variety of flexible printing services, including flyers, leaflets, menus, event tickets and posters. They can design specific items or print your own designs to the highest quality in a cost-effective manner. Advice is offered on fonts, colours and the type of paper that should be used to really maximise the impact of your chosen design.

PARTY ORGANISERS

Also take a look at the caterers listed in Food & Drink (*see p122*); many of those featured can organise events and parties too.

Admirable Crichton
5 Camberwell Trading Estate, Denmark Road, SE5 9LB (7326 3800/www.admirable-crichton.co.uk). Oval tube. **Cost** from £5,000.
Admirable Crichton can arrange anything from a dinner party for 20 to a film première for 2,000. With corporate clients such as Louis Vuitton and De Beers on the books, it's no surprise that AC bashes lean towards the extravagant – a shindig in your local community centre this ain't; think costumes, elaborately designed cinematic sets and vast quantities of champagne. The company's catering arm offers top-notch inventive food and service is always first-rate. Tons of ideas and access to some of London's most interesting venues add another string to the company's party-planning bow. Events can also be arranged abroad, so if you simply must get hitched in a French château or just have to have your birthday bash in Marrakech, they can certainly oblige. Of course, parties like this always come at a price.

Admirable Crichton

Bentley's
7 Square Rigger Row, Plantation Wharf, York Road, SW11 3TZ (7223 7900/ www.bentleys.net). Clapham Junction rail. **Cost** call for details.
Bespoke party planner Bentley's is best known for organising weddings for the likes of the Beckhams, Liz Hurley and Arun Nayer, and Elton John and David Furnish. High-rolling clients mean high prices but if you've recently come into a small fortune or have found a millionaire to marry, these guys will sort you out with a stupendous celebration. Bentley's can organise all aspects of a party from the stationery, set design, flowers and catering to entertainment and lighting. The company is happy to help with organising any aspect of an event, however large or small, but comes into its own for fabulously extravagant, big budget dos. Recent events in Bentley's portfolio

include a Moulin Rouge-themed birthday party, a 'Bond Mission Weekend' in Gstaad and a ruby wedding anniversary in Herefordshire. Unusual events abroad are another speciality – a high fashion wedding in Mauritius, a *Pirates of the Caribbean* weekend in Barbados and a Russian wedding in the south of France were all recently given the Bentley's treatment. We can but dream.

Blonde Productions
Unit 1.4C, Barley Mow Centre, 10 Barley Mow Passage, W4 4PH (8996 1614/www.blonde productions.co.uk). Turnham Green tube. **Cost** from £20,000.
Blonde is a cutting-edge event design and production agency that organises parties with edge. Its multi-skilled team can create bespoke celebrations for any occasion – ranging from intimate soirées to big celeb bashes – across the UK, Europe and USA (though they specialise in party planning in London). They work with some of London's hottest venues (Studio Valbonne, Fabric and the like) and use innovative catering company Last Supper (*see p126*) as in-house caterers. They can offer dry hire of some venues (check the website or call for details) or can produce an event in full, from entertainment, production and lighting and event design to management of proceedings on the day.

Heathcote Bailey
The Gallery, 8-10 Conlan Street, W10 5AR (07939 573198/www.heathcotebailey.co.uk). Westbourne Park tube. **Cost** from £10,000.

Heathcote Bailey offers a creative events service specialising in bespoke party production, cutting-edge DJs, bands and lighting, and distinctive 'one-off' vibes. The company is pretty flexible about the types of events it'll take on, though tends not to favour excessively 'corporate' bashes. HB also puts on its own events and, as a result, boasts a huge database of contacts that comes in handy when the team is planning product launches and promotional events. Key to the success of all their events is, they say, a reasonable budget to expectation ratio. You could easily blow £30,000 on one of their parties but they are also happy to just help clients source things like DJs or bartenders for much smaller outlays. See also Tailor-made Madness on page eight of this guide.

Kasimira
29 South Terrace, SW7 2TB (7581 8313/ www.kasimira.com). South Kensington tube.
Cost from £20,000.
Set up five years ago by three friends who decided London needed a party organiser with 'an unprecedented sense of fun', Kasimira has put together an enthusiastic team of party managers willing to take on any event – weddings, christenings, bar mitzvahs, special birthdays, product launches, garden parties or corporate functions. On offer is good quality catering, a great selection of props, impressive decorations and even a full-time illustrator to design bespoke invitations. They can also deal with RSVPs from your guests. For entertainment,

Kasimira can source an array of artists, from musicians and fire-eaters to magicians. A Narnia-themed bash at Kensington's art deco Debenham House, complete with igloos and falling snowflakes, was one of Kasimira's highlight events in 2007.

Lettice
18 Stannary Street, SE11 4AA (7820 1161/ www.letticeparty.com). Kennington tube.
Cost from £30/person.
Lettice offers a complete party planning and design service, as well as catering services, for a wide range of events; the website features separate sections for private events, weddings and business events. Best known for innovative design and presentation, the company designs all their own service equipment (their Perspex stacks and stacks of bowls have been widely imitated) and creates a new range each year. Service methods work brilliantly with the equipment – the 'stacks of bowls' method, for instance, can feed large numbers of people very quickly and was used to serve 2,500 people at the opening of the Royal Festival Hall. Prices start from around £30 per head for a canapé party and the company is happy to work on anything from a small dinner for 20 to a huge celebration for over 2,000. Lettice works extensively in the art and fashion world and is on the preferred caterer list at many of London's leading arts venues, including the Serpentine, Design Museum, Hayward, New Saatchi and Whitechapel Art Gallery.

Lettice

91 Events and Weddings

G39 Waterfront Studios, 1 Dock Road,
E16 1AG (7474 9391/www.ninetyone.co.uk).
West Silvertown DLR. **Cost** from £3,000
(for weddings).
Bespoke wedding and event-planning company
91 specialises in Indian-themed parties and
weddings. Ideally, they like to work with budgets
of £15,000 upwards; an Indian-themed wedding
with 200-300 guests would cost on average
between £25,000 and £30,000. They offer a
flexible, fluid service and can source or arrange
every aspect of your event, including catering,
decor, entertainment, a venue, accommodation
for your guests, concierge services and event-
day management. They can also organise the
stag and hen dos, and even honeymoons, as
part of their wedding planning service. The
company prides itself on offering a transparent
service to clients and party-planning staff are
contactable 24/7. They also offer a free, no
obligation initial consultation.

Pink Pumpkin

01483 203450/www.thepinkpumpkin.co.uk.
Cost from £700.
Award-winning bespoke wedding planner Pink
Pumpkin offers a service tailored to the needs
of every couple they work for. Depending on how
involved the bride and groom wish them to be,
PP can do anything from arranging the whole
shebang to just turning up on the day to make
sure everything runs smoothly. As part of the
service they can recommend leading suppliers
in the industry and source the perfect venue
for the big day too. They also have exclusive
access to two magnificent countryside locations:
Chiddingstone Castle in Kent and Greyfriars
House in Surrey.

Pure Events

35 Harwood Road, SW6 4QP (7736 8103/
www.pureevents.net). Fulham Broadway tube.
Cost call for details.
Pure Events specialises in the corporate side
of the events market, particularly Christmas
and summer parties, team-building events,
conferences, client entertainment and annual
parties. They can also plan weddings, birthdays
or dinner parties and offer a full event production
service, providing speakers, microphones,
projectors, screens, staging, amps, lecterns, set
design, furniture, themed equipment and rigging
materials for events anywhere in the UK. Strict
budgets and deadlines are no problem and the
company's venue-finding service has extensive
reach. They have access to thousands of venues
across the UK and overseas, from castles,
private houses and hotels to private members'
clubs, nightclubs, restaurants, bars, villas, boats,
lodges and chalets. The service is free.

Quintessentially Events

10 Carlise Street, W1D 3BR (0845 475
8400/www.quintessentiallyevents.com).
Oxford Circus or Tottenham Court Road
tube. **Cost** from £25,000 (£75,000
for weddings).

ESSENTIALS

Quintessentially Events (part of the 'members' club' and concierge service of the same name) organises high-end, high-budget corporate and private events. The team is used to dealing with demanding clients (they were once asked to source a herd of zebras for an African-themed party in Surrey) and demonstrates impressive attention to detail (going the extra mile to source perfect welcome gifts, for example). Clients include the V&A, David Tang and Keanu Reeves.

Strong & Co

Unit D, 19 Tewkesbury Road, N15 6SE (07980 827772/www.strongandco.net). Manor House tube. **Cost** *from £15,000.*
For parties and events with real wow factor, Deborah Armstrong's Strong & Co is the best in the business. She put together the fabulously offbeat and much-raved about Shangri La area (where Lost Vagueness once was) for Glastonbury 2008 and has had a creative hand in the making of endless unique underground parties and festivals. The company's more corporate clients tend to be music industry or media based and looking for a totally one-off landmark event. Strong & Co has exclusive ins to lots of wierd and wonderful London buildings and really has the edge when it comes to sourcing innovative entertainment and gob-smacking design. Armstrong has organised huge, bespoke events for the *Guardian*, Channel 4 and EMI, among others. See also Tailor-made Madness on page eight of this guide.

Theme Traders

The Stadium, Oaklands Road, NW2 6DL (8452 8518/www.themetraders.com). Willesden Green tube. **Cost** *call for details.*
Party and event management company Theme Traders offers clients the opportunity to 'be guests at their own parties', by taking the stress out of planning. A full event design service is offered, along with access to all manner of props, costumes, scenery, lighting and special effects. With vast Aladdin's cave showrooms and workshops in Cricklewood, Theme Traders has the largest theme hire stock in Europe (over 100,000 sq ft of it) and a fleet of vehicles to service parties across the globe. The company has worked on many high-profile projects ranging from a Great Ormond Street *Peter Pan* party in the park for 20,000 people, to production services for celebrities, rock bands and royalty. More unusual events planned by TT have included a romantic night for two involving 10,000 roses and a marquee. Anniversaries,

Strong & Co

21st birthday bashes and private celebrations for 50-500 are all also catered for. Theme Traders also organises children's parties, with costs starting from £3,500 for an event.

Zest Events

2 Swan Mews, Parsons Green Lane, SW6 4QT (7384 9336/www.zestevents.com). Parsons Green tube. **Cost** *from £20,000.*
Zest Events is expert at creating glamorous, gossiped-about parties thanks to meticulous planning and a friendly, dedicated team. Every event they organise is unique and budget-wise you'd be looking at a starting cost of £20,000 for them to organise an entire event for you. If that sounds too steep, Zest can also help source individual aspects of an event rather than plan the whole thing. The company prides itself on offering expert advice to ensure that clients get the best value for money and have access to every possible location. The team can recommend and manage all suppliers, including caterers, florists, marquees, set design and sound systems. They don't do 'packages' – each event receives a bespoke concept and quotation.

CHILDREN'S PARTY ORGANISERS

Action Station

0870 770 2705/www.theactionstation.co.uk
This friendly agency's books brim with magical storytellers, face-painters, clowns, dramatists, cheerleaders and magicians. Children of all ages are catered for. The discos and cheerleader parties go down particularly well with slightly older kids. Boys love the spy parties. Prices start at £176 per hour, £235 for two hours.

Adam Ants

8959 1045/www.adamantsparties.com
Entertainers and party accessories – including ball ponds and bouncy castles and kid-o-gram characters – can be hired from Ants. The company also does teddy bear, art and sports parties and can also hire out tables and chairs, as well as organise catering. Phone for a quotation.

Birthday Dreams

7700 2525/www.birthdaydreams.co.uk
Offering an integrated, bespoke party service, Birthday Dreams will 'take the mess and stress' out of party planning. It hosts events at its own venue, Islington's Kinloch Castle, where the 3D storybook interior, encompassing art murals, grass underfoot and a tree decorated with fibre-optics, is used to full effect for parties with special characters. Prices start from £450 (for

Deborah Armstrong
MANAGING DIRECTOR OF STRONG & CO

The maddest party I've ever organised was a Wild Things party in a big wood. I made lots of massive monsters, lit up all the ferns with green lights and gave the guests ears, tails and horns to wear.
I like using venues that are a bit unusual. I put a party on in a disused lead and glass factory with a huge atrium and had abseilers coming down the walls and trapeze artists swinging from the girders.
I often get inspiration from books and films – I have a whole file of future concepts in my head. I saw a documentary on Caravaggio recently, and now I've got a brilliant Caravaggio party in my head that I'm just waiting for an opportunity to use.
The most useful thing for planning parties is *The White Book* – it's like the *Yellow Pages* of events. It covers everything from toilet and stage hire to producers and performers.
The most bizarre request I've ever had from a client is 'Can we have naked snake ladies in a harem, please?' My bizarre-o-meter is set quite high, though, so not much seems weird to me.
The worst kinds of parties are really awful corporate dos where no one can let go or be themselves because they're worried what their boss might think and they feel like they should be networking.
My best party organising tip is not to try and do everything yourself. Get good people on board instead who really know what they're doing. I ruined my wedding trying to manage it all myself. The host's role is to look after the guests, not to worry about the logistics of the party.
Strong & Co is a bespoke event design and production company. www.strongandco.net

Let your imagination run wild with **Boo! Productions**.

the 'works' – entertainment, cake, party bags, invites, thank you notes etc). Birthday Dreams can also organise a party at your home or assist with elements including entertainers, invites, cakes and cleaning. There are packages with fairytale and film characters to arts and crafts, plus parties organised around a desired theme.

Boo! Productions
40 Frith Street, W1D 5LN (7287 9090/07825 310780/www.booparties.com).
Boo is a well-respected children's event specialist, with some 20 years of experience dealing with both corporate and private clients. Every service you could possible need for a kid's party is offered, including bespoke event design, entertainers, caterers, party bags, set building, script writing, and promotional ideas. Entertainers start at £170 plus VAT (for two hours), while the cost of one of Boo's themed parties would start at £680 plus VAT, all the way up to very elaborate, large scale bespoke parties for several thousand pounds. Entertainers will call the client ahead of the event to create a personalised programme suited to the child's imagination and personality. The team can also help organise any kind of event where children will be present, including birthday parties, corporate events, Christmas parties, bar mitzvahs, product launches, team building, film premières, promotions and road shows. If you're lacking inspiration, take a look at the website.

Nellie Shepherd Events
07710 479852/0114 263 0998/www.nellie shepherdevents.com
A dedicated, well-established company with many high-profile, returning clients extending across the corporate, entertainment and celebrity worlds, Nellie Shepherd Events brings real energy and expertise to children's parties. Favourite themes include Snow Princess, Animal Art, Space, and Pink Ballerina. With the emphasis on imagination and creativity, Nellie can organise anything and everything you can dream up, from Doctor Who and Underwater World to Cowboys and Circus, for children of any age. Prices from £1,000.

Puddleduck Parties
8893 8998/www.puddleduckparties.co.uk
Puddleduck puts together flexible packages that encompass all the party necessities such as catering (including tableware), decorations and entertainers. Teddy bears' picnics can be arranged for smaller children; otherwise, there's drama, sport or disco parties for all ages, starting from around £200 for two hours of fun.

Taylor-Made Entertainment
07974 901215/www.taylor-made entertainment.com. **No credit cards**.
Taylor-Made specialises in putting together bespoke two-hour party packages, particularly discos (with lights, scented smoke, bubbles and karaoke) as well as arranging makeover

artists, face-painters, musicians and party MCs. Supplying entertainment for young and easily bored guests at weddings is another speciality.

Twizzle Parties

8789 3232/www.twizzle.co.uk
Beloved of London's celebrity parents, Twizzle can organise anything from a glittering children's 'film première' or photo-shoot party to themed events such as singalong parties for toddlers and discos, make-over parties, stretch limos, close-up magicians and all sorts of other pop-starry, street-dancey shenanigans. Twizzle also runs a performing arts school during the holidays. Prices start at about £165 for one hour.

DETAILS, DETAILS

PARTY STAFF

Artista
01488 648763/www.artistaevents.com
Artista provides charming and professional staff to help events run smoothly, including hosts and hostesses for receptions or promotional activities, cloakroom staff and guest liaison staff. Experienced staff can be provided for anything from a private or corporate dinner to a large-scale ball or product launch.

At Your Service
7610 8610/www.ays.co.uk

At Your Service can provide a huge variety of different staff for parties and events. You could just hire one person to help out at a small private dinner at home or some 150 assistants to make sure a big weddings or awards do runs like clockwork. The company specialises in waiting and bar staff, while sister company Bamboo (www.eventmixology.com) can provide more experienced bartenders and 'mixologists' to prepare the drinks at your event. Another division of the company, Sherpa (www.eventsherpa. co.uk), provides staff for loading and unloading vehicles, kitchen porters and drivers, while Rebel (www.rebelpromotions.co.uk) provides hosts and hostesses, often used for promotional events. Prices are by quotation.

Aubergine Events
0845 257 8731/www.aubergine recruitment.co.uk
Aubergine supplies everything from corporate hosts and waiters to event managers, cloakroom attendants and chefs. The company has a roster of well-known clients and has run events for the likes of the Natural History Museum and Madame Tussauds. Aubergine provided crew catering for ITV's *Hell's Kitchen* too.

Esprit Group
7384 4100/www.esprit-group.com
Esprit can supply wait staff, butlers and hosts and hostesses for any type or size of event, whether it is in your home or at a venue. The company is particularly popular for weddings, private dinner

ESSENTIALS

The journey could be as much fun as the arrival with **Karma Kabs**. *See p212.*

parties and corporate events. Waiting staff cost just £11.50 an hour (£13 for more senior staff). There is a minimum hire of four hours, plus you'll need to cover the cost of a taxi for staff if the event finishes after 11.30pm. Butlers and hostesses cost from £18.50 per hour.

High Society
7228 0333/www.high-society.co.uk
High Society offers professional, reliable and efficient staff for parties and events. A client manager will source the staff for your event and provide full details about them before it. In addition to their numerous satisfied private clients, High Society has worked with the likes of Burberry, the BBC and Virgin (and helped out Gordon Ramsay for two weeks in *Hell's Kitchen*).

Randolphs
7801 6300/www.randolphs.uk.com
Randolphs specialises in hiring out butlers for private parties and events, such as weddings, corporate lunches and dinner parties. They can also provide chefs, hostesses, cocktail bartenders and all other service staff. A wide range of equipment, such as china, silver, glassware, crystal, linen, tables and chairs, is available for hire too.

CLEANING

When it's all over you might just want to take yourself off to a darkened room

and leave the 'clearing up' bit to the professionals. The following companies all offer after-party services and will come to your home or a venue. It's important to check whether or not the company has a minimum number of hours that they expect to work.

Absolutely Spotless
8932 7360/7839 8222/www.absolutely spotless.co.uk. **Cost** from £90 + VAT (for a studio apartment).

Any Clean
0845 230 6111/www.anyclean.co.uk/ party_help.html. **Cost** £9 + VAT/hr.

Domestic Clean
7247 5555/www.domestic-clean.co.uk. **Cost** from £9.50/hr (min 2hrs 30mins).

Fast Klean
0870 228 3165/www.fastklean.co.uk. **Cost** from £8.50/hr.

My Maid
0845 838 5980/www.mymaid.co.uk. **Cost** from £9.95/hr.

Sara-Int Ltd London Cleaning Services
0870 041 4672/www.prl24.net/ sara_cleaning/after_party_cleaning.htm. **Cost** from £13/hr (min 3hrs).

Routemasters. *See p212.*

PORTALOOS

If you're planning an outside event, a party in a space that's lacking in facilities or are preparing to let your mates run amok in your parents' garden at your wedding, you'll need loos. The below should be able to meet your requirements.

Acorn Event Hire

07730 897636/www.acorneventhire.com
Bottle-green loos for outdoor use start at £350.

Igloos

0800 112 3205/www.igloos.co.uk
Igloo has the rather dubious honour of being considered the best in the business by many leading events planners. The company offers 'beautiful toilets for beautiful events' and some designs are so impressive guests might not even realise they're portaloos. Prices by quotation.

Just Loos

01962 876808/www.justloos.com
Just Loos offer luxury mobile toilets for corporate events, weddings (they provided the loos for Liz Hurley's) and parties. Ranges span basic to serious luxury.

Loos for Do's

0845 123 2901/www.loos.co.uk

Sweet Pea Toilet Hire

01306 631804/www.sweetpeatoilets.co.uk

TRANSPORT

A & F Executive Chauffeur Service

8861 4466/www.afchauffeurs.co.uk.
Cost from £20/hr.
This executive service (offering chauffeur-driven Mercedes S Class or Viano) starts at £20/hr.

Cabair

8953 4411/www.cabairhelicopters.com.
Cost from £3,450 + landing fees/3hr flight (seats 5).
Cabair is one of the largest helicopter charter companies in the UK. It provides an extensive fleet of helicopters for private hire from a base in North London's Elstree Aerodrome.

Duck Bus

7928 3132/www.londonducktours.co.uk.
Cost from £570/1hr 15 mins (seats 30).
Duck Bus offers a pick-up and drop-off service for corporate and private events.

ESC Events

01252 795507/www.esc-events.co.uk.
Cost £30-£50/hr.
As part of its event organisation service, ESC can hire out transport such as chauffeur-driven cars, coaches, aircraft or a fleet of cars for your guests.

Executive London Group Cars

7450 0050/www.londonexec.com. **Cost** call for prices.

Executive London offers passenger cars, VIP and chauffeur cars, luxury vans and coaches – even motorcycle chauffeurs – for any occasion.

Gallagher's Travels Ltd

7384 9711/07949 674970/ www.gallaghertravelltd.com. **Cost** £80 minimum spend.

Chauffeur-driven coach hire operator with a range of luxury air-conditioned vehicles seating from 13 up to 74 passengers.

Horse Drawn Carriage Hire

01992 419293/www.horse-drawn-carriage-hire.co.uk. **Cost** from £350.

HDCH offers a selection of quality horse-drawn carriages. For weddings they offer a glass-fronted landau with leather hood, pulled by a pair of black friesian horses.

Hot Hire

07947 028899/www.hot-hire.co.uk. **Cost** from £99/hr. **No credit cards**.

This fully converted fire engine limo serving London and beyond lends itself perfectly to hen nights and novelty weddings. You can book it for just an hour or book a full day or night's hire.

Karma Kabs

8964 0700/07770 693979/www.karmakabs. com. **Cost** from £60-£80/hr (central London).

Popular for weddings, Karma Kabs are strewn with flowers and boast wonderfully glitzy interiors. Perfect for a dramatic departure after the ceremony.

Limo in London

8965 1724/0800 599940/www.limoin london.co.uk. **Cost** from £295/return trip.

Limo in London provides cars for hire 24/7. On offer are stretch, Hummer H2, Excalibur and Bentley cars, a limo party bus and a new pink limo especially for weddings.

Maxwell Car Services

8748 3000/www.chauffeurdrive.com. **Cost** from £34/hr.

Limousines and luxury saloons for hire, including the BMW 7 Series, the Mercedes 'E' class, 'S' class and 7-seat stretch. You can hire people-carriers too, such as the Chrysler Grand Voyager.

Morgan Motors

01684 573104/www.morgan-motor.co.uk. **Cost** from £110/day.

Morgan Motors has a fabulous range of classic cars for private hire. Perfect for weddings and special days out. Prices start from a reasonable £110 per day.

Routemasters

01707 276066/www.routemasterhire.com. **Cost** from £575/event.

Hire out an original Routemaster double-decker bus to transport your guests to your event. Popular for weddings, corporate events and Christmas parties.

Thames Clippers

0870 781 5049/www.thamesclippers.com. **Cost** from £550 (for first hr).

The fleet includes catamarans with seat capacities of 62, 138 or 220. Speak to the private charter manager to discuss your booking and catering requirements.

VP Coaches

0800 980 0482/www.vpcoaches.co.uk. **Cost** £400/evening (seats 50).

As well as offering a 'to' and 'from' pick-up service, VP coaches can be hired to take you further afield to, say, the coast, or even France.

INSURANCE

If you're even contemplating the possibility that your event might need insurance, it probably does. It's always worth checking what insurance your venue offers too. The below offers a starting point for research – always seek professional advice on insurance requirements.

Clarity Event Insurance

01883 734999/www.clarityevent insurance.com

Event Insurance Services

0800 515980/www.events-insurance.co.uk

Events Insurance

www.eventsinsurance.co.uk

Hiscox

0845 213 8448/www.hiscox.co.uk/events

Insured Risks

0844 582 1413/www.insuredrisks.co.uk

RESOURCES

White Book

7657 1176/www.whitebook.co.uk

The White Book costs £90 but for anyone involved in the events industry, it's an essential and indispensable A-Z of venues, suppliers and artists. Also available on-line.

Weddings

weddings

There's no bigger excuse for a huge bash than tying the knot. And whether you fancy blowing a stack of cash on the party of a lifetime or prefer something more intimate, the venues below (many of which are licensed for civil ceremonies) should offer inspiration. There are, of course, many other venues in this guide that could also fit the bill. Below you'll also find great places to kit yourself out for the big day, recommended beauty treatments, marquee hire and photographers. For lighting, flowers and finishing touches, turn to Party Shops & Decorations (*see p178*). For invitations, loos and transport, look at Organisation & Planning (*see p196*). And for entertainment, DJs, musicians and sound equipment, see Music & Entertainment (*see p148*).

Jacqueline Byrne. *See p233.*

VENUES

CENTRAL

Arts Club
40 Dover Street, W1S 4NP (7499 8581/ www.theartsclub.co.uk). Green Park tube. **Available for hire** *8am-2am daily.* **Capacity** *Venue 160 seated/250 standing. Private rooms 6: 14-120 seated; 60-200 standing.* **Hire charge** *Private rooms from £250. 1st floor £3,500. 1st & ground floor £6,000. Venue £8,000 (all + VAT).*
Founded in 1863 by a group of artists (including Millais and Whistler) as a meeting place for like-minded, thinking folk, the Arts Club fills an elegant 18th-century townhouse and has nine different spaces for hire. The overall impression is one of quiet exclusivity, with dark leather furniture, heavy drapes and an ornate staircase. The main dining room has changing art exhibitions and looks out on to an orderly courtyard garden, making it ideal for a smart wedding reception. The boardroom is often used for private meetings and the first floor drawing room is a fine spot for a cocktail party. Food, from sit-down three coursers to canapés, is provided by the in-house catering team – hosts are offered a complimentary tasting session to help them decide on the perfect menu. There's a range of AV equipment to hire and the club has a list of florists, photographers and entertainers. *Catering: in-house. Civil ceremony licence. Outside space: courtyard (for hire).*

Century Club

*61-63 Shaftesbury Avenue, W1D 6LQ
(7534 3080/www.centuryclub.co.uk).
Leicester Square or Piccadilly Circus tube.*
Available for hire 10am-1am daily. **Capacity**
Venue 80 seated/250 standing. **Hire charge**
Venue £1,000 (£500 members). **Minimum
spend** £2,000 + VAT.

This is a venue that takes pride in its hidden
location. It's on Shaftesbury Avenue so should
be a breeze to locate, but it's just as easy to find
yourself walking into a two-bob pizzeria by
mistake (make sure you give guests good
directions). Once you've found the right place,
however, it's immediately obvious why
membership is so sought after here. Not only
does the members' bar have an enormous drinks
list (17 kinds of vodka), but stroll upstairs and
you'll find yourself faced with two enormous and
fantastically lavish function rooms. Joined
together these can host nigh-on 300 people, and
with plasma screens, a piano, mic facilities and
even a fireplace in the smaller room, they make
a spectacular setting for a glam wedding
reception. The management is extremely flexible,
and can divide the main room into different areas
or set up a bar in a suitable spot.
*Big screen. Catering: in-house. Civil ceremony
licence. Projector.*

Claridge's

*Brook Street, W1K 4HR (7629 8860/
www.claridges.co.uk). Bond Street tube.*
Available for hire 10am-midnight daily.

WEDDINGS

Claridge's

Blakes

A little sigh escapes at every turn, such is the beautiful attention to detail at Anouska Hempel's luxurious boutique hotel. A favourite hideaway for globe-trotting, pap-weary VIPs, the hushed, discreet exclusivity of its suites are the scene for many small, intimate weddings. The opulent 007 suite is decorated with cream and gold banded wallpaper, and features a Victorian fireplace and mother of pearl tallboys. Bespoke after-ceremony celebrations take place in the Chinese room, a secluded, exotic nook clad in heavy black and ginger fabrics, with handpainted oriental murals, excellent acoustics and polished glass and china. French/Asian delicacies (sashimi, beluga caviar, truffles) or sit-down meals are served on two long tables and screened off from the adjacent restaurant; alternatively the entire floor can be hired for larger parties.
Best for Couples wanting to treat the people who really matter to them.
Must do Blow the budget on Hempel wedding couture and flowers.
Inside Tip Bag the pure white honeymoon suite – it's the envy of the affianced.
For listings, see p230.

Claridge's

If you're after art deco opulence and the very best of pedigrees, this formidable Mayfair gem is hard to beat. The 1930s ballroom is spot on for a wedding celebration reeking of old-school glamour; it's unbelievably grand, with its own private entrance and a marble rotunda. For something smaller but just as elegant, opt for the salon and drawing room – both have stunning original decor and grand paintings. Staff are happy to work with you to get your menu just right: canapés can be themed, for example. The fish is excellent here, as is the hotel's dedication to artisan wines.
Best for Those with grand tastes.
Must do Use the piano – someone tinkling on the ivories is perfect for this setting.
Inside tip For something a bit different, serve afternoon tea.
For listings, see p215.

Dorchester

Possibly central London's most impressive banqueting venue, and the hotel choice of many an A-lister, the Dorchester is a prestigious luxury venue for any event. The ballroom can hold up to 1,000 guests for drinks and seats 500 for dinner, making it perfect for larger wedding dos. Guests will be awestruck by the sheer grandeur of the room, with its dramatic blue ceiling lights that resemble upside-down pools. The smaller rooms make more private and intimate venues for ceremonies and receptions. The Orchid has an air of serenity, with white plasterwork highlighting stylish mirrors and lights. The Pavilion is another attractive room, with pear-green walls and gold detailing.

Best for Splash-out weddings with style.
Must do Pick the penthouse (private terrace).
Inside tip Pick a day from the venue's 'Value Dates' to benefit from a discount.
For listings, see right.

Mandarin Oriental

'Opulent' doesn't begin to describe this internationally renowned hotel, complete with Michelin-starred restaurant. The Loggia boasts lovely French windows, a central round table (seating approximately ten guests) as well as other, smaller, tables. Subtle touches of green complete the look of the minimally adorned space. For a more traditional look, the Rosebery rooms seat larger parties, with comfortable chairs and artwork from the National Maritime Museum adorning the walls. There's a ballroom for extravagant weddings, with a private entrance, a terrace and a fabulous air of exclusivity; think high ceilings, chandeliers and statuesque plants. The Oriental is also big on complementary services, such as its Wedding Belles (*see p239*) beauty fest for brides-to-be.
Best for High society gatherings.
Must do Use the spa before/after the big day.
Inside tip The events managers are open to suggestions so get theme-creative.
For listings, see p220.

Zetter

Covering the whole of the ground floor, with impressive floor-to-ceiling windows, the restaurant at this modern Clerkenwell hotel is great for a glitzy wedding bash. And if your party is likely to carry on into the evening, part of the space can be converted to a dancefloor. The newly furnished River room works well for smaller wedding parties, especially evening dos (it's on the lower ground floor), as well as decadent cocktail parties, club nights or private dining. It can cater for 80 revellers and has a stage, two comfy sofas, a projector and a full PA system with CD decks. Wedding packages include 'breakfast for the boys' and 'pampering for the girls', and a dedicated events manager will ensure your day goes according to plan.
Best for Great weddings in London's heart.
Must do Check out the massive cocktail list and Mediterranean menus.
Inside tip The basement rooms have air-conditioning – great for summer parties.
For listings, see p225.

Capacity *Ballroom* 192 seated/400 standing. *Salon & drawing room* 96 seated/200 standing. **Hire charge** *Ballroom* from £3,700. *Salon & drawing room* from £2,800.
For review, *see left*
Catering: in-house. Civil ceremony licence. Disabled: lift, toilet. Licence extension possible.

Conway Hall

25 Red Lion Square, WC1R 4RL (7242 8032/www.conwayhall.org.uk). Holborn tube. **Available for hire** 9am-midnight daily.
Capacity *Main hall* 500 seated/standing. *Private rooms* 12-80 seated. **Hire charge** *Venue* from £750. *Private rooms* from £50.
No credit cards.
Opened in 1929 by the left-leaning South Place Ethical Society as a centre where 'men and women of advanced thought could meet and enjoy the amenities of social discourse, with facilities for writing, rest and refreshment', Conway Hall continues to host rehearsals, exhibitions and talks by political and cultural figures. The building is a fine example of 20th-century architecture. The main hall has a large stage, wooden floors and ornate panelled walls and fits 500, including 175 seated on the upper balcony. It can be hired with an adjacent bar and another two smaller rooms if needed – as cloakrooms or storage rooms, for example. The hall has become popular for wedding receptions and parties of all kinds, particularly civil partnership parties. The weekend curfew of midnight can be extended by application and guests can also make use of a PA system and even a grand piano.
Catering: kitchen facilities. Disabled: toilet.

Dorchester

Park Lane, W1K 1QA (7629 8888/ www.thedorchester.com). Hyde Park Corner tube. **Available for hire** 11am-1am daily.
Capacity *Ballroom* 500 seated/1,000 standing. *Orchid room* 140 seated/250 standing. *Holford room* 40 seated/140 standing. *Penthouse* 16 seated/40 standing. *Pavilion* 34 seated/60 standing. *Park suite (left)* 60 seated/100 standing. *Park suite (right)* 30 seated/60 standing. *Crystal suite* 60 seated/120 standing. **Hire charge** *Ballroom* from £3,500. *Orchid & Holford room* from £2,000. *Penthouse & pavilion* from £1,000. *Park suites* from £1,000. *Crystal room* from £1,250.
For review, *see left.*
Catering: in-house. Civil ceremony licence. Disabled: lift, toilet. Licence extension possible. Outside space: terrace (for hire).

House of St Barnabas

1 Greek Street, W1D 4NQ (7437 1894/ www.atthehouse.org.uk). Tottenham Court Road tube. **Available for hire** noon-midnight daily. **Capacity** *Venue* 350. *Private rooms* 7: 20-50 seated/50-100 standing. *Chapel* 80 seated/120 standing. *Garden* 120 standing. **Hire charge** from £150/hr. **No credit cards**.

Behind this Grade I-listed building's heavy black door lie the offices of the House of St Barnabas in Soho charity, as well as a series of spectacularly ornate Georgian 'historical rooms' available for private hire. The florid plasterwork you'll see here is one of the finest surviving examples of English rococo style of the 1750s. The house's continuing survival depends on the fund-raising work of the charity, raising commercial income through room hire in order to refurbish the whole of the crumbly-in-parts building. The charity plans to work in partnership with Beyond Boyle (*see p64*) to further these changes. Meanwhile, wedding receptions (as well as drink and canapé receptions, dinner parties, recitals and so on) can be held in one or all of the eight diverse spaces, which include a real charmer of a shady garden (Charles Dickens once wrote under the mulberry tree) and a bijou Victorian chapel. At the time of writing the house had applied for a civil ceremony licence.

CEREMONY BASICS

Church of England Ceremonies

Anglicans will need to contact their local priest to arrange a C of E ceremony. Couples can marry in their local parish church and a recent tweak in the law has made it easier to marry in a different parish. If one of you was baptised in the church you wish to wed in, has (at any point) lived in the parish for more than six months, has attended services in the parish for six months (or your parents or grandparents have), or if your parents/ grandparents were married in the church, you should qualify. Once your date is confirmed, the 'banns' (notice of intended nuptials) will be read out for three Sundays prior to the wedding. Contact the Church of England Faculty Office (7222 5381, www.facultyoffice. co.uk) for more information.

Civil Ceremonies

To get hitched without the religious stuff, you'll need to choose a register office (for our faves, *see p224*) or licensed premises in which to do the deed. Marriages can take place on any day between 8am and 6pm. Civil ceremonies must not contain any religious references, so make sure the celebrant is happy with your readings and music. You will need two witnesses and must give notice of your intentions at your local register office at least 15 days before you intend to wed. The General Register Office for England and Wales (0151 471 4200, www.gro. gov.uk) can supply a list of potential venues.

Civil Partnerships

The Civil Partnership Act came into being on 5th December 2005, allowing same-sex couples to register their partnership. Working in much the same way as civil marriages (*see above*), they afford couples the same rights in relation to next of kin and inheritance as any other couple. The General Register Office (*see above*) can supply lists of licensed venues. Stonewall (www.stonewall.org.uk) has a handy guide to the process which is worth checking out too.

Humanist Ceremonies

Humanist ceremonies are not recognised in England (though they are in Scotland), so Londoners wanting to marry this way will have to arrange to have a civil marriage prior to a humanist ceremony. As they are not legally binding, humanist marriages can take place almost anywhere. Contact the British Humanist Association (7079 3580, www.humanism.org.uk) for more information.

Other Religious Ceremonies

Ministers of other religions can be authorised to register a marriage as long as they have a licence from the local superintendent registrar. Jewish and Quaker weddings are automatically recognised in this way. For other faiths, if the ceremony official is not licensed couples may need to have both a religious and a civil marriage (or the marriage could be attended by a registrar). At least one of you must be baptised Catholic to marry in the Catholic church. It is generally necessary to attend some sort of marriage preparation class prior to a Catholic wedding. Always check the exact requirements with the official at the place you wish to marry and be sure everything is arranged for your chosen date before booking other services such as photographers and reception venues.

WEDDINGS

Catering: preferred caterer list; kitchen facilities. Licence extension possible. Outside space: garden (for hire).

Mandarin Oriental Hyde Park

66 Knightsbridge, SW1X 7LA (7235 2000/ www.mandarinoriental.com). Knightsbridge tube. **Available for hire** *11am-1am daily.*
Capacity *Ballroom 250 seated/400 standing. Suites & private rooms 40-150 seated/70-250 standing.* **Hire charge** *Ballroom from £1,500 + VAT. Suites & private rooms from £750 + VAT.*
For review, *see p217.*
Catering: in-house. Civil ceremony licence. Disabled: lift, toilet. Licence extension possible. Outside space: terrace (for hire).

National Liberal Club

Whitehall Place, SW1A 2HE (7930 9871/ www.nlc.org.uk). Embankment tube/ Charing Cross tube/rail. **Available for hire**

Smoking & dining room 9am-1am Sat, Sun. Other rooms 9am-1am daily.
Capacity *Smoking room 100 ceremony. Dining room 120 seated. Other rooms 12-120 seated/70-200 standing.*
Hire charge *Smoking & dining room £2,500. Other rooms from £85.*
This hotel, private club and Grade I-listed building on the banks of the River Thames had its foundation stone laid by William Gladstone in 1884 and is every bit as momentous and mighty as that might imply. Inside, high ceilings and ornate decor lend a stately feel, and the club boasts the largest free-standing marble staircase in Europe (a perfect backdrop for wedding pictures). There are 13 rooms for hire of varying sizes, some better suited to business and corporate events, with state-of-the-art facilities including audio/visual technology. But several larger rooms are perfect for wedding receptions, and a couple are licensed to perform the ceremony too. The River room, accommodating

Stylish, sophisticated and a bit of a statement. **Mandarin Oriental Hyde Park**.

up to 70 guests and looking over the London Eye, has particularly majestic views. Impressive. *Catering: in-house. Civil ceremony licence (Smoking & dining room). Disabled: toilet.*

Royal Institution

21 Albemarle Street, W1S 4BS (7670 2905/ www.rigb.org). Green Park tube. **Available for hire** 8am-11pm daily. **Capacity** *Theatre* 440 seated. *Library* 70 seated/100 standing. *Other rooms* 10-70 seated/10-100 standing. **Hire charge** £280-£3,000 + VAT.

Home to various scientific artefacts, including the first electrical transformer, the Royal Institution is as much a museum as it is a public forum for science-related discussion. Seven function rooms can host a variety of events, from performances (Faraday Theatre), to an intimate dinner for ten. Crystal chandeliers hang from the first floor's grand Ante room, which can hold large receptions, while the library, with books all along its walls, can do dinners, buffets and drinks receptions. The Institution recently underwent a £22-million redevelopment, adding a new chapter to a history that spans two centuries. It was granted a licence to perform wedding ceremonies in 2008 and is set to become one of London's more unusual wedding venues. *Catering: in-house. Civil ceremony licence (theatre; library). Disabled: toilet.*

NORTH

Burgh House

New End Square, NW3 1LT (7431 0144/ www.burghhouse.org.uk). Hampstead tube. **Available for hire** 10-11am, 5-10pm Wed-Fri, Sun; 10am-10pm Sat. **Capacity** 55 seated/60 ceremony/100 standing. **Hire charge** *Ceremony* £295 1hr. *Reception* £395 2hrs, £145/extra hr. **No credit cards.**

This Queen Anne Grade I-listed house and museum makes a smart and traditional venue, perfect for the wedding (and reception) of a couple who want something comfortable yet stylish. The large and airy oak-panelled music room is a good-sized space which, together with the annexed library and hall, provides plenty of room for a wedding party. If you want a bit more space, you can also requisition the chicly modern Peggy Jay gallery. A baby grand piano is available for hire, if you're after some light musical accompaniment for your festivities. Award-winning gardens ensure that your summer wedding pictures will do full justice to the day. The Burgh House buttery, a garden café connected to the house, deals with the catering. *Catering: in-house. Civil ceremony licence. Disabled: toilet. No amplified music. Outside space: gardens.*

Kenwood House

Hampstead Lane, NW3 7JR (8341 5384/ www.english-heritage.org.uk). Archway or Golders Green tube, then 210 bus. **Available for hire** *Old kitchen* 11am-11.30pm daily. *Brew House* (summer) 5-11.30pm daily, (winter) 7-11.30pm daily. *Orangery* 3.30-5.30pm daily. **Capacity** *Venue* 120 seated/180 standing. **Hire charge** *Old kitchen/Brew House* £1,500 + VAT. *Orangery* £1,000 + VAT.

The pale stuccoed exterior of Hampstead Heath's romantic country house makes a photogenic backdrop for refined, unmistakably English wedding celebrations (although Kenwood is only licensed to perform Jewish weddings ceremonies). You'll have to share the daytime views of the heath and Kenwood's own lake with visitors, but two rooms are available for exclusive use – the Orangery and the nostalgic Old Kitchen, with its Wedgwood displays and intriguing original features crowned by a huge Victorian range. Just sitting here works up an appetite for hearty, simple fare, and fortunately this is what in-house caterers Company of Cooks do best (salmon fillets with chunky tartare sauce, groaning cheeseboards and so on). In the evening the Brew House café is cleared to make a flagstone dancefloor. The little terrace is delightful, and the isolated location provides a rare opportunity to turn up the trad jazz. Ask permission in advance to use the private tree-lined driveway for stylish arrivals. *Catering: in-house. Disabled: toilet. Outside space: garden (for hire).*

London Irish Centre

50-52 Camden Square, NW1 9XB (7916 7272/www.londonirishcentre.net). Camden Town tube/Camden Road rail. **Available for hire** 9am-11pm daily (presidential suite until midnight Fri-Sun). **Capacity** *McNamara hall* 300 seated/standing. *Presidential suite* 100 seated. **Hire charge** call for details.

The London Irish Centre is on leafy Camden Square, a nice spot for wedding photos. The main

McNamara hall has space for 300 people, with a licensed bar, a large stage and a sprung wooden dancefloor. The room can also be rented in conjunction with the Presidential suite (100 capacity) and with the Centre's smaller meeting rooms (with a capacity of around 40), which can also be used as reception rooms or cloakrooms. There's a lift for disabled access and the venue is well equipped, with a PA system, air-conditioning and a 52-inch plasma TV. Another practical boon: the venue is outside the congestion charge zone.
Catering: in-house; kitchen facilities. Civil ceremony licence. Disabled: lift; toilet.

The Vine
86 Highgate Road, NW5 1PB (7209 9001/ www.thevinelondon.co.uk). Kentish Town tube/rail/Gospel Oak rail. **Available for hire** noon-midnight daily. **Capacity** *Garden* 80 seated/100 standing. *Fireplace* 50 standing. *Dining rooms* 14-22 seated. **Minimum spend** *Garden* (summer) £2,500; (winter) call for details. *Fireplace* £500. *Dining rooms* £250.
The Vine was just a humble gastropub until designer Christopher Woods transformed it with theatrical themed private rooms. A newly flamboyant Vine then stepped onto the party stage, ideal for special birthdays with close friends, and, of course, wedding celebrations. Two private dining rooms crank up the camp with Moroccan and Parisian themes (for the latter, think red walls, theatrical candelabras, bowls of fake fruit and Sapphic scenography). The real boon, though, is the garden – a cool, leafy, canopied patio (with outside heaters for winter) – which is spot-on for local, celeb-flecked weddings. Food is Italian and comes in a range of set menus, while buffets and finger food are available for smaller budgets. Florists, photographers and cakes can all be arranged.
Catering: in-house. Licence extension possible. Outside space: garden (for hire).

06 St Chad's Place
6 St Chad's Place, WC1X 9HH (7278 3355/ www.6stchadsplace.com). King's Cross tube/rail. **Available for hire** noon-1am Sat. **Capacity** *Venue* 50 seated/120 standing. **Hire charge** *Venue* £400 (including DJ; minimum spend applies).
Once a derelict mechanics' workshop, 06 St Chad's is now an elegant warehouse space with floor-to-ceiling windows and exposed brickwork, which has become a popular venue for fashionable wedding receptions. It's a laid-back kind of venue; the space looks spectacular set up for formal dining, but there are also comfy leather sofas, and you can opt for cafeteria-style

dining too. Staff are happy to provide a buffet service or a full sit-down meal. The location, hidden away behind the old King's Cross Thameslink station, is unlikely and discreet to the point of secrecy. A mic and TV screen are available, as well as DJ equipment.
Catering: in-house. Disabled: toilet. Licence extension possible. Music: DJ equipment; MP3 port.

EAST

Barbican Garden & Conservatory
Silk Street, EC2Y 8DS (7382 7246/ www.barbican.org.uk). Barbican tube or Moorgate tube/rail. **Available for hire** 6-11.30pm Mon-Fri; noon-11.30pm Sat, Sun. **Capacity** *Garden* 280 seated/300 standing. *Conservatory* 72 seated/150 standing. *Conservatory terrace* 164 seated/200 standing. **Hire charge** *Garden & conservatory* £1,500-£2,000 + VAT. *Conservatory terrace* £950 + VAT.
The brick and woodwork of the Barbican's upper floors is long overdue a refurbishment (scheduled for 2010) but the conservatory at the City's cutting-edge arts centre gets top marks for creativity. Impressive tropical greenery bursts and sprawls upon red brick beds and concrete balconies, and kids will love exploring its maze, although the 'exotic' fish and aviary might disappoint. The space comes to life at night with colourful, dramatic uplighting. For larger banquets and parties, the adjacent Garden room offers a plain, flexible space overlooking St Giles Cripplegate – one half can be sumptuously dressed for dinner while the second half has the facility for DJ decks and dancing. In-house caterer Searcy's chef boasts royal references; the modern British food uses locally sourced and seasonal ingredients.
Catering: in-house. Civil ceremony licence. Disabled: lift, toilet. Outside space: garden, terrace.

Bleeding Heart Tavern
Bleeding Heart Yard, 19 Greville Street, EC1N 8SJ (7404 0333/www.bleeding heart.co.uk). Farringdon tube/rail. **Available for hire** noon-4.30pm, 6pm-midnight daily. **Capacity** *Private rooms* 4: 16-44 seated. **Hire charge** *Restaurant & other rooms* free. *Crypt* £750. **Minimum spend** *Restaurant & other rooms* £360. *Crypt* £38.50/person.
Centred around a cobbled courtyard, the Bleeding Heart bistro, tavern and restaurant cater for work parties and private dining, in spaces ranging from

WEDDINGS

Royal Institution. *See p221.*

WEDDINGS

discreet back rooms to converted wine cellars. The Bleeding Heart's restaurant is available for wedding parties at weekends; it's an elegantly decorated formal space, with mahogany panelling, gilt-framed 18th-century paintings and a mirrored wine bar. However, the jewel in the Bleeding Heart crown is the 600-year-old crypt, where Henry VIII and Catherine of Aragon hosted a five-day celebration in 1531 (putting Kate Moss's recent birthday all-nighter to shame). The ecclesiastical interior seems a fitting setting for a wedding reception, and the exposed beams, rustic pews and candlelit oval tables are pleasingly romantic. Expect the food to be first class; chef Peter Reffell has conjured up a fine three-course French menu with lamb, venison and guinea fowl as specialities. Staff are happy to recommend wine and champagne to complement the menu from their 450-odd bottle list.
Catering: in-house. No amplified music.

Green

29 Clerkenwell Green, EC1R 0DU (7490 8010/www.thegreenEC1.co.uk). Farringdon tube/rail. **Available for hire** *Venue* noon-midnight Sat. *Private room* noon-midnight daily. **Capacity** *Venue* 100 seated/150 standing. *Private room* 55 seated/70 standing. **Minimum spend** *Venue* £2,800. *Private room* £250.
The Green has a lot going for it. Set in the heart of Clerkenwell Green, the simple but stylish venue includes an upstairs bar and light, airy restaurant suitable for parties and relaxed wedding receptions for anything between 30 and 150 guests. Staff pride themselves on their hospitality and flexibility. The chef and general manager will be happy to sit down and adapt a menu for you from their selection. Cooking is sophisticated and modern European-oriented and menus cover finger buffet, buffet, small plate, lunch and dinner options, with canapés also available.
Catering: in-house. Music: DJ equipment (venue); MP3 port.

St Germain

89-90 Turnmill Street, EC1M 5QU (7336 0949/www.stgermain.info). Farringdon tube/rail. **Available for hire** noon-midnight daily. **Capacity** *Venue* 160 standing. *Restaurant* 90 seated/100 standing. *Bar* 50 seated/60 standing. **Minimum spend** call for details.
A play on the classic Parisian brasserie, but with more than a touch of New York about it, St Germain is located in a converted 19th-century print house between Smithfield and Farringdon. It has lovely tall windows, a stylish black-and-white palette mixed with dark woodwork, and serves good brasserie fare along with classy cocktails. It works well for wedding receptions and there's not even a charge for hire, though a minimum spend that varies according to the day of the week (for example, hiring the entire venue on a Saturday might entail a minimum spend of £3,000) applies. Staff will be happy to provide whatever kind of catering you choose, from a sit-down dinner with a classic French menu to canapés and party nibbles. An in-house stereo system plays discreetly in the bar, but you can also arrange to bring in your own decks and they'll even clear away some tables to create an area for dancing.
Catering: in-house. Disabled: toilet.

WE'RE GOING TO THE TOWN HALL & WE'RE...

So, you've decided to tie the knot registry office style? Below are some of our London favourites (old and new).

Chelsea Old Town Hall

King's Road, SW3 5EE (7361 4100/ www.rbkc.gov.uk). Sloane Square tube. **Open** 9am-12.30pm, 2-4pm Mon-Wed, Fri; 9am-12.30pm, 2-7pm (by appointment) Thur; 9am-5pm (by appointment) Sat. **Capacity** 4-40.
Probably one of the hippest and most famous wedding venues of all, Chelsea Old Town Hall is a graceful Victorian building where celebs and even royalty have tied the knot: Patrick Vieira, Judy Garland, Mick Jagger and Prince Pavlos of Greece to name but a few. There are several beautifully appointed suites available, including the Rossetti room and the Brydon room, catering for parties of four to 40. Rooms are decorated with floral arrangements – or you can bring your own. Hire a Routemaster bus (*see p212*) to pick you up after the service to complete the whole swinging Sixties vibe.

Hackney Town Hall

Mare Street, E8 1EA (8356 3000/ www.hackney.gov.uk). Hackney Central rail. **Open** 9am-5pm Mon-Fri; 9am-1pm Sat. **Capacity** up to 120.
Christopher Biggins and Neil Sinclair tied the knot at Hackney's lovely art deco town hall. It's available for civil ceremonies, all the rooms have sound systems, and photographs can be taken throughout the ceremony. The Gold suite (with glam chandeliers) accommodates up to 120 (50 seated and 70 standing) people and the waiting room has a 'bride's corner' with full-length mirror and chaise longue.

Old Finsbury Town Hall

Urdang Academy, Rosebery Avenue, EC1R 4RP (7713 7710/www.theurdangacademy. com/fthmain.html). **Open** 8.30am-5pm Mon-Fri. **Capacity** 25-300.
Now the Urdang Academy (a dance school), the former Old Finsbury Town Hall – a lovingly restored art nouveau treasure – is once again available to hire as a venue for tying the knot (as well as for magazine shoots, receptions and corporate entertaining). There are many rooms that can be hired, housing up to 300 people, and the Great Hall is particularly good to hire for a shindig later on. There are no gardens, but there is a lovely green space close to the hall where photos can be taken.

Richmond Register Office

1 Spring Terrace (corner of Mount Ararat/ Paradise Roads), Surrey TW9 1LW (8940 2853/2651/www.richmond.gov.uk). Richmond tube/rail. **Open** 9am-noon, 1.30pm-4pm Mon-Fri; 9am-noon Wed. **Capacity** up to 40.
Whether you want a low-key private ceremony or a more elaborate affair, Richmond has plenty of licensed venues as well as its own Register Office, where Jean Shrimpton and baseball player Michael Whitney were married. The Grade II-listed building is set within a quarter of an acre of gardens and can accommodate up to 40 guests. Richmond Park is a ten-minute walk from the office.

Waltham Forest Register Office

The Old Vicarage, 106 Grove Road, E17 9BY (8496 2716/www.walthamforest.gov.uk). Walthamstow Central tube/rail. **Open** 9am-4pm Mon-Fri; (by appointment) Sat. **Capacity** up to 40.
Despite looking a little like something Albert Speer might have designed, Waltham Forest Register Office is wonderfully imposing and has its own grounds (including a fountain) for photo ops. The newly decorated Forest suite marriage room can hold a maximum of 40 people, although 30 is a more comfortable number and allows the majority of guests to be seated. Fresh flowers and music are provided, but you can personalise things by bringing your own floral arrangements.

Westminster Council House

97-113 Marylebone Road, NW1 5PT (7641 1161/www.westminster.gov.uk/registrar). Baker Street tube. **Open** 9am-4pm Mon-Fri; 9am-noon (by appointment only) Sat. **Capacity** 20-100.
You don't have to be a rock star to get married at this popular wedding venue, but the steps of the former Marylebone Town Hall have seen a few: Paul and Linda McCartney, Ringo Starr and Barbara Bach, and Liam Gallagher and Patsy Kensit (and in true rock star style, Liam again with Nicole Appleton on Valentine's Day 2008). Choose from one of four splendid, elegant panelled rooms housing up to 100 guests and costing from £70 to £700, depending on room. There is no garden – but with Regent's Park close by, who needs one?

WEDDINGS

Shoreditch Town Hall

380 Old Street, EC1V 9LT (7739 6176/ www.shoreditchtownhall.org.uk). Old Street tube/rail. **Available for hire** *7.30am-midnight Mon-Fri; 7.30am-1am Sat, Sun.* **Capacity** *Private rooms 6: 12-400 seated/20-800 standing.* **Hire charge** *from £300/day (hrly rates available).* **No credit cards.**
This spectacularly restored East End venue has seen some serious debauchery in its time, including Elton John's 60th birthday celebrations back in 2007. With its fabulously ornate spaces – think balconies, high ceilings, stained glass and a wonderfully olde worlde vibe – it offers plenty to fire the imagination while retaining enough of a blank canvas feel to ensure your own creative ideas really shine through. The council chamber makes a picturesque spot for a cool wedding, while smaller spaces such as the Mayor's parlour fit the bill for intimate dos. Hourly hire rates are available but with a venue this versatile we'd recommend holding the reception bash here too. Great for generating a real London vibe and plenty of edge.
Catering: kitchen facilities. Civil ceremony licence. Disabled: toilet.

Stationers' Hall

Ave Maria Lane, EC4M 7DD (7246 0999/ www.stationers.org). St Paul's tube/ Blackfriars tube/rail. **Available for hire** *9am-midnight.* **Capacity** *Hall 150 seated/ 200 ceremony/400 standing. Court 90 seated/120 ceremony/160 standing. Stock room 100 standing. Garden 250 standing.* **Hire charge** *£2,200/day + £250-£400/extra hr.* **No credit cards.**
Your guests can dine at 340-year-old tables, surrounded by polished wood panelling, huge stained-glass windows, oil paintings of distinguished aldermen and the banners and shields of the Stationers' and Newspaper Makers' Company if you have your wedding at this Grade I-listed building, which has been the guild's home since 1673. There are three imposing function spaces (and let's face it – who wouldn't want to be able to say they'd smooched the night away in the stock room?), all equipped with mod cons such as vast LCD screens; disco set-ups can also be brought in. There's no in-house catering, but Stationers has a long list of approved caterers that clients have to choose from. The glorious courtyard garden, dominated by a 250-year-old plane tree, recently underwent a £120,000 makeover and is an irresistible draw for a summer wedding.
Catering: preferred caterer list. Civil ceremony licence. Disabled: toilet. Outside space: garden (for hire).

Zetter

St John's Square, 86-88 Clerkenwell Road, EC1M 5RJ (7324 4401/www.thezetter.com). Farringdon tube/rail. **Available for hire** *Restaurant 11am-10.45pm daily. River room 11am-2am daily.* **Capacity** *Restaurant 100 seated/150 standing. River Room 46 seated/80 standing.* **Minimum spend** *£70/person.*
For review, see p217.
Catering: in-house. Disabled: lift, toilet. Music: DJ equipment.

SOUTH

Beauberry House

Gallery Road, SE21 7AB (8299 9788/ www.beauberryhouse.co.uk). West Dulwich rail. **Available for hire** *11am-midnight daily.* **Capacity** *White room 60 seated/80 ceremony/150 standing. Ground floor restaurant 80 seated. Marquee 400 seated.* **Hire charge** *Venue £3,500 (£10,000 minimum spend). White room & 1st floor £650-£1,300. Other rooms call for details.*
Beauberry House is just five minutes from the station in leafy West Dulwich so transport links into town are excellent. There are several rooms available for your ceremony and celebrations. On the first floor is the private White room, with an adjacent bar and a private balcony (fantastic for wedding photos). The ground floor has a restaurant area and a bar. And if your event is really large, a marquee can be put up in the grounds. A full DJ set-up is available and, unusually, this venue has a late, late licence, allowing your guests to live it up until 2am.
Catering: in-house. Civil ceremony licence. Disabled: toilet. Licence extension possible. Music: DJ equipment; MP3 port. Outside space: balcony (for hire).

Cambridge Cottage

Royal Botanic Gardens, Surrey TW9 3AB (8332 5641/www.kew.org). Kew Gardens tube/rail. **Available for hire** *9am-11pm daily.* **Capacity** *Gallery 80 seated/120 standing. Drawing room 80 seated; both 150 standing.* **Hire charge** *from £3,500 + VAT.* **No credit cards.**
Kew Garden's former royal residence is spot-on for a wedding reception with an English, country garden feel. The Grade II-listed building is wonderfully genteel and will suit English Rose brides and their grooms down to the ground; think string quartet accompaniments, Pimm's and old-fashioned glamour. For the hire fee you get the run of the gallery, with walls adorned with

botanical themed art, and the drawing room. Both open on to the private Duke's Garden, where your guests can smell the roses as they tuck into their canapés. The only encroachment on this idyll is the occasional roar of a 747 as Kew is on the Heathrow flight path.

Catering: preferred caterer list. Civil ceremony licence. Disabled: toilet. Outside space: garden (for hire).

Cannizaro House

West Side, Wimbledon Common, SW19 4UE (8970 2773/www.cannizarohouse. com). Wimbledon tube/rail. **Available for hire** *7am-midnight daily.* **Capacity** *Private rooms 5: 20-100 ceremony/30-120 standing.* **Minimum spend** £120/person (wedding package).

Hotels often make ideal wedding venues, so it is little surprise that Cannizaro House – Wimbledon's only four-star affair – is a popular booking for local nuptials. Set in the middle of the Common, the house certainly makes a distinguished setting. The biggest room available, the Viscount Melville suite, has a grand piano and can accommodate 120 guests for an evening reception. It is also licensed for the ceremony, as is the Queen Elizabeth suite. The drawing room, with its large terrace and sweeping staircase, makes a fabulous backdrop for memorable wedding pictures. The hotel's events staff are happy to work together with brides and grooms, using the hotel as a blank canvas to create the event of their dreams.

Catering: in-house. Civil ceremony licence. Disabled: toilet. Outside space: terrace (for hire).

Dulwich Picture Gallery

Gallery Road, SE21 7AD (8299 8713/ www.dulwichpicturegallery.org.uk). North Dulwich or West Dulwich rail. **Available for hire** *Venue 8am-midnight Mon; 5pm-midnight Tue-Sun. Conference room & café 8am-midnight daily.* **Capacity** *Venue 120 seated/350 standing. Conference room 50 seated/80 standing. Café 50 seated/100 standing. Marquee 220 seated.* **Hire charge** *Venue £6,000. Conference room £125/hr; café £400. Marquee call for details.*

It's hard to think of a more magnificent setting for a wedding than this gorgeous early 19th-century building, designed by Sir John Soane. Now that the gallery has acquired a ceremony licence, it's possible for your whole day to take place on the impressive premises too. The main

PEMBROKE LODGE

Rustic Pembroke Lodge offers a fabulous solution to the search for an outdoor wedding space in London. Its setting, high in Richmond Park, in 11 acres of private grounds, makes it ideal for summery celebrations. On the ground floor of the listed house is the Belvedere, where you get a private entrance and a terrace that's perfect for champagne or sun-kissed cocktails. Inside, part of the space can be given over to a dancefloor. The PA system allows you to plug in your iPod and control your tunes, and the twinkling ceiling lighting lends a bit of magic to the evening. Essentially it's a blank canvas – a bit rough around the edges in places – but staff will let your creative vision take hold. Fancy something a bit more intimate and formal? Upstairs is the Georgian three-room Russell suite, with grand windows showcasing the majesty of the park, and smaller spaces for dancing and drinking. The venue sometimes host two weddings simultaneously – so do check when booking – and part of the Lodge is a public café open until about 5pm, but all areas are self-contained. In-house caterers offer a wide choice and the chef is open to suggestions.
For listings, see p228.

gallery, which houses a stunning permanent collection including Rembrandt's *Girl at a Window*, can accommodate up to 120 for a sit-down banquet (the gallery has a list of approved caterers). If you don't trust your guests not to throw wine on the paintings, then you may prefer to use Rick Mather's brick-and-glass 1997 extension, including café, conference room (which makes a great ballroom) and a terrace, overlooking the beautifully manicured grounds. *Catering: in-house; preferred caterer list. Civil ceremony licence. Disabled: toilet. Music: MP3 port (Conference room). Projector (Conference room). Outside space: garden (for hire).*

Eltham Palace

Court Yard, off Court Road, SE9 5QE (8294 2577/www.elthampalace.org.uk). Eltham or Mottingham rail. **Available for hire** *Feb-Dec* 6.30pm-midnight Mon-Thur, Sun; 3pm-midnight Fri, Sat. **Capacity** *Venue* 200 seated/300 standing. **Hire charge** from £2,000 + VAT.

Once home to the textile magnates, Stephen and Virginia Courtauld, Eltham Palace is drenched in history. The art deco masterpiece was built alongside the medieval remains of Henry VIII's childhood home and there are four breathtaking spaces to choose from or combine for your ceremony and/or reception. The sky-high ceilings will certainly add some grandeur to the occasion, while the minimal but chic 'ocean liner' decor adds a certain elegance. Within the 19 acres of surrounding gardens are a sunken rose garden and a medieval bridge. It's hardly surprising that the place is popular; it'd be best to book at least a year in advance. *Catering: preferred caterer list. Civil ceremony licence. Disabled: toilet. Outside space: garden (for hire).*

Garden Museum

Lambeth Palace Road, SE1 7LB (7401 8865/ www.museumgardenhistory.org). Lambeth North tube, then 3, 344 bus. **Available for hire** 5pm-1am Mon-Sat. **Capacity** *Venue* 100 seated/200 standing. **Hire charge** £1,750-£2,200 + VAT.

Nestled between the Thames and Lambeth Palace, the Garden Museum (formerly the Museum of Garden History) is housed in the former church of St Mary-at-Lambeth. Its decor is an intriguing mix: the current building is medieval with Victorian embellishments, and stained glass windows were installed post-war to add some colour after bomb damage. Understandably, the garden is a huge selling point in such a central location – great for drinks or a

barbecue. However, due to its day job you can only gain access after 5pm. Exhibitions can be used as a backdrop or moved to make more room for a sit-down dinner or more guests. The 17th-century-inspired knot garden is a romantic setting for photos. *Catering: preferred caterer list. Disabled: toilet. Outside space: garden (for hire).*

Le Gothique

The Royal Victoria Patriotic Building, John Archer Way, off Windmill Road, SW18 3SX (8870 6567/www.legothique.co.uk). Wandsworth Common rail. **Available for hire** noon-midnight daily. **Capacity** *Venue* 90-120 seated/150 standing. **Hire charge** free (minimum 50).

This fabulous venue is free to hire – refreshingly, you just fork out for the food and drink (expect to pay around £50 per head). Le Gothique is a French restaurant located within Wandsworth's spectacular Royal Victoria Patriotic Building. Originally an asylum, it's been home to a scandal-ravaged orphanage (source of the current ghost), a school and a wartime base for MI5 and MI6, where Rudolph Hess was interrogated. The upstairs dining room is slightly cramped, so for space make use of the courtyard too. The bar is also used as a dancefloor, under the watchful eye of a massive gargoyle. *Catering: in-house. Disabled: toilet. Music: DJ equipment. Outside space: courtyard (for hire).*

Marble Hill House

Richmond Road, Twickenham, Middx TW1 2NL (7973 3494/www.english-heritage. org.uk). St Margarets rail. **Available for hire** *Mar-Dec* 3-6pm Mon-Sat. **Capacity** *Venue* 50 ceremony/standing. **Hire charge** *Apr-Sept* £1,000 Mon-Fri; £1,250 Sat. *Oct-Dec, Mar* £800 Mon-Sat.

If you fancy some fresh air and a rural feel, but need to stay close to the Big Smoke, head to the former home of King George II's mistress. Perfect for wedding ceremonies with a small guest list, the Great Hall is easy on the eye with soothing, cream-coloured walls hung with imposing Georgian paintings. The Tetrastyle hall is ideal for a casual drinks reception, with ionic columns standing tall in a very reasonably sized mingling space. A view of endless green from the windows adds to the illusion you're in the middle of nowhere; you can add to the faraway feel by hiring a local riverboat to pick up and drop off guests too.

Catering: preferred caterer list. Civil ceremony licence. Disabled: toilet (ground floor). No amplified music (list of recommended musicians available). Outside space: gardens (for hire).

Pembroke Lodge

Richmond Park, TW10 5HX (8940 8207/ www.pembroke-lodge.co.uk). Richmond tube/rail. **Available for hire** *Belvedere room* noon-midnight daily. *Russell suite* noon-11pm daily. **Capacity** *Belvedere room* 140 seated. *Russell suite* 70 seated. **Hire charge** *Belvedere room* £375-£3,950. *Russell suite* £350-£1,500.
For review, *see p226.*
Catering: in-house. Civil ceremony licence. Disabled: toilet (Belvedere Room). Music: DJ equipment. Outside space: garden; park.

Ranger's House

Chesterfield Walk, SE10 8QX (8294 2577/ www.english-heritage.org.uk). Cutty Sark DLR. **Available for hire** noon-11pm Thur-Sat. **Capacity** *Venue* 60 seated/80 standing. **Hire charge** from £1,700 + VAT.
Greenwich is home to a number of urban sanctuaries and this Georgian villa effortlessly fits the bill. The building's greatest asset is its homey yet aristocratic look, shaped by a fireplace, wooden antiques, Renaissance paintings, an imposing angel statue and finally, Sir Julius Wernher's rare jewellery collection. As is usually the case with using historic houses for parties, limitations apply: food and music must come to an end 30 minutes before the party winds down and Ranger's House is only available for hire three days a week. Guest can take full advantage of the walled garden during the summer, while the cosy vibe of the gallery is spot-on for a chilly winter night.
Catering: preferred caterer list. Civil ceremony licence. Disabled: toilet. No amplified music. Outside space: garden (for hire).

Syon Park

London Road, Brentford, Middx TW8 8JF (8758 1888/www.syonpark.co.uk). Gunnersbury tube/rail/Kew Bridge rail, then 237, 267 bus. **Available for hire** 6.30pm-midnight Mon-Thur, Sun; 11am-midnight Fri, Sat. **Capacity** *Great hall* 120 seated. *Conservatory* 150 seated/200 standing. **Hire charge** from £2,800.
If stately gardens, freshly manicured lawns and huge glass conservatories match your idea of the perfect wedding, then Syon Park will be just the ticket. At the heart of the grounds is Syon House, dating from the 16th century, with a civil marriage licence and a sumptuous interior as grand as its long history might suggest. The mighty conservatory, the building that inspired the Crystal Palace, is not too far across the lawns, and can easily fit up to 200 people for the night time rave-up; the management even allow a marquee to be used on the lawns for really big parties. Outside of the nuptials, both the house and conservatory convert well for evening dos, dinners, musical evenings or company promotions.
Catering: preferred caterer list. Civil ceremony licence. Outside space: courtyard, garden (for hire).

Trafalgar Tavern

Park Row, SE10 9NW (8305 3091/ www.trafalgartavern.co.uk). Cutty Sark DLR/Maze Hill rail. **Available for hire** 9am-midnight daily. **Capacity** *Venue* 200 seated/ 350 standing. **Hire charge** from £650 + VAT.
A Greenwich institution, the Trafalgar Tavern is one of the Thames's quintessential drinking dens – and while the pub itself is very much of the oak bench and pint of ale school, the spaces upstairs for private functions ooze opulent splendour. The Admiral's Gallery bar is decorated with the sort of gilt-framed paintings that will have you reaching for your pipe and sextants, and the Nelson room, all high white stucco and chandeliers, reached via regal red-carpeted stairs (and now equipped with a civil marriage licence), is the sort of space where Horatio himself might have tied the knot. Catering and entertainment can be arranged in-house and will always include an epic view of the river and Canary Wharf beyond.
Catering: in-house. Civil ceremony licence (Nelson Room). Licence extension possible.

Winchester House

10 Lower Richmond Road, SW15 1JN (8789 4447/www.winchesterhouse.co.uk). Putney Bridge tube. **Available for hire** 8am-11pm Mon-Thur; 8am-1am Fri, Sat; 8am-midnight Sun. **Capacity** *River room* 124

WEDDINGS

DO ME A FAVOUR

Step away from the sugared almonds with these alternative favour ideas.

Seed favour packets, 50 for £32.40; Love origami, £10 for 30; name place baubles, 10 for £11.90. **Cox & Cox** (www.cox andcox.co.uk). *See p192.*

Fortune cookies, 300 for £80. **Unique Wedding Favours** (0845 370 7262, www.unique weddingfavours.co.uk).

Hunt car-boot sales for vintage cups & saucers. Pictured set £2 (to hire). **Idyllic Days** (www.idyllic days.com). S*ee p195.*

Wedding Bells tin with biscuits, £38.50; biscuits, from £2.75. **Biscuiteers** (09704 588358, www.biscuiteers.com).

Lucky Lotto envelopes, 20 for £3.50; whimsical wonderball, 10 for £22.50. **Talking Tables** (8675 9811, www.talking tables.co.uk).

Chocolates, from £1.80. **Charbonnel & Walker** (7491 0939, www.charbonnel.co.uk).

seated/160 ceremony/180 standing. *Library* 20 seated/40 ceremony/50 standing. **Hire charge** from £500 + VAT. **No credit cards**.

This Putney private club is a rather grand affair, with a well-maintained garden overlooking the river. The period decor is atmospheric, especially in the library and the main first-floor River room, which can later be adapted into a dancefloor and stage for a band or DJ. Both these spaces are licensed to host civil ceremonies. The downside is that you'll have to share the club with the members. Although they can't access any of the rooms you've hired, they do have a bar and a section of the garden, and it might be a good idea to find out in advance whether staff expect a lot of members to be around on your chosen day. A wet weather tent is available for hire if you're worried about showers.

Catering: in-house. Civil ceremony licence. Licence extension possible (Mon-Thur). Outside space: garden.

Amadeus Centre
50 Shirland Road, W9 2JA (7286 1686/ www.amadeuscentre.co.uk). Warwick Avenue tube. **Available for hire** 9am-2am Sat, Sun. **Capacity** *Venue* 250 standing. *Upper hall* 180 seated. *Lower hall* 70 seated. **Hire charge** *Venue* from £1,550.

This duck-egg blue 19th-century former Welsh Presbyterian chapel may look oddly placed next to a west London housing estate, but once inside guests will be open-mouthed as they set foot in the wood-panelled gallery of the Upper Hall, complete with its very own pipe organ. It's a dramatic setting for a sit-down wedding meal or simple buffet, and also one that can be dressed up and themed – Caribbean, gothic and sci-fi have all been done here. You also get the Lower Hall for your money – the former church crypt has a low ceiling and solid soundproofing to give it a really intimate feel. Live bands sound amazing here, so let guests kick off their shoes and kick up their heels.

Catering: preferred caterer list. Disabled: toilet (access upper hall only).

Blakes
33 Roland Gardens, SW7 3PF (7370 6701/ www.blakeshotels.com). Gloucester Road or South Kensington tube. **Available for hire** 10am-11pm (until 2am for hotel guests) daily. **Capacity** *007 suite* 40 ceremony. *003 suite* 20 ceremony. *Chinese room* 36 seated/ 40 standing. **Hire charge** *007 & 003 suites* £1,900 + VAT. *Chinese room* £1,000 + VAT. For review, *see p216*.

Catering: in-house. Civil ceremony licence. Music: MP3 port.

Chelsea Gardener
125 Sydney Street, SW3 6NR (07788 580961/www.chelseagardener.com). South Kensington tube, then 49 bus. **Available for hire** 6.30pm-midnight daily. **Capacity** *Venue* 500 standing. *Showroom* 150 seated/ 300 standing. *Canopy area* 150 seated/ 350 standing. *Decked area* 30 standing. **Hire charge** call for details. **No credit cards**. Available for hire for evening receptions, the Chelsea Gardener provides half an acre of greenery in SW3. The venue is actually a popular garden centre and nursery, boasting landscaping services and Barbour clothing. As you might expect, it offers the service of in-house florists so your flowers can match the well-cultivated surroundings to perfection. The space is split into three areas: the large showroom (capacity 300) is indoors and useful when the outside is cold

GIFT LISTS

Alternative Wedding List
www.thealternativeweddinglist.co.uk
Ethically minded types can use this online service to ask guests to make charity donations in their honour.

Berry Bros & Rudd
www.bbr.com
Start married life as you mean to go on – with a well-stocked wine cellar courtesy of BBR, Britain's venerable wine merchant.

Grays Antique Market
www.graysantiques.com
Lists here can include specific items from individual dealers (as well as those at sister market Alfie's) or guests can make contributions towards a larger gift.

John Lewis
www.johnlewis.com
It's a classic choice and not without good reason. A professional service, free delivery and an endless array of great items for the home make this a winner every single time.

Trailfinders
www.trailfinders.com/giftlist
They have devoured your pricey canapés and heckled throughout your speech – now let them pay for your honeymoon.

Chelsea Gardener

and wet; the decked area is a good choice for serving cocktails or champagne when guests arrive, but has no cover; and the canopy is generous (enough room for 150) and an excellent spot to seat guests for dinner. You'll feel a million miles away from the buzz of the city and surrounded by tropical colour. You also have the option to bring in your own caterer.
Catering: preferred caterer list. Licence extension possible. Outside space: garden (for hire).

Chelsea Physic Garden

66 Royal Hospital Road, SW3 4HS (7352 5646/www.chelseaphysicgarden.co.uk). Sloane Square tube. **Available for hire** 5.30-10.30pm daily. **Capacity** *Reception room 70 seated/120 standing. Marquee 325 seated/ 400 standing.* **Hire charge** *Reception room £1,000. Reception room & garden £3,000-£6,000. Marquee call for details.*
The Chelsea Physic Garden is a wonderful historic green space, established in 1673 as the Apothecaries Garden to teach the identification of medicinal plants. The garden is open to the public on Wednesday, Thursday, Friday and Sunday; have your wedding reception or party on other days and you'll have the whole place to yourself. There is a 120-person reception room, but this venue is all about the spectacular garden: you'll miss out on a lot if it rains. Music and any drinks service must be over by 10pm and amplified music is banned in the garden – opt for a string quartet or something similarly

refined. Do also bear in mind that hire prices go sky high during the annual Chelsea Flower Show.
Catering: in-house; preferred caterer list. Disabled: toilet. Licence extension possible. No amplified music. Outside space: garden (for hire).

Chiswick House

Burlington Lane, W4 2RP (7973 3292/ www.chgt.org.uk). Chiswick rail, then E3, 190 bus. **Available for hire** *May-Sept* 4pm-midnight Fri, Sat. **Capacity** *Venue 96 seated/100 ceremony/150 standing. Marquee 150 seated.* **Hire charge** *Ceremony & reception from £3,250 Fri; from £4,000 Sat. Marquee call for details.*
Every corner of this Palladian villa has been festooned with classical ornamentation. The building's neo-classical architecture will impress your guests from the outset, while the interior – with white couches, gold touches to the furniture and splashes of royal blue wallpaper – continues the theme. Chiswick House takes great pride in its Italianate gardens, which are said to have provided the jumpstart to the English Landscape Movement; your guests will have the freedom to stroll around during your reception. Civil ceremonies can be held on either Fridays or Saturdays, but book early as this is an understandably popular venue.
Catering: preferred caterer list. Civil ceremony licence (Fri, Sat). Disabled: toilet. Licence extension possible. Outside space: courtyard; gardens.

Hurlingham Club

Ranelagh Gardens, SW6 3PR (7471 8220/ www.hurlinghamclub.org.uk). Putney Bridge tube. **Available for hire** 9am-1am Mon-Thur; 9am-2am Fri; 4.30pm-2am Sat; 6.30pm-midnight Sun. **Capacity** *Private rooms* 10: 30-1,200 standing/30-1,000 seated. **Hire charge** £750-£6,106 + VAT.

Set in 42 acres of rolling countryside, the Hurlingham Club is perhaps the most idyllic spot for a summer wedding in London. The *pièce de résistance*, the glass-domed Palm Court and Orangerie, is flanked by six fantastically flexible function rooms, ranging from the conservatory-style terrace to the Musgrove room, which has a stage, making it perfect for bands. There are also two fully sprung dancefloors. Each function room has a corresponding outdoor area, romantically illuminated by floodlit trees. The services of a wedding planner (on hand to help with requests about anything from food to flowers) are included in the hire cost. To ensure the ultimate fairytale entrance to your nuptials, take a boat along the Thames (which runs through the grounds) and alight at the club's pontoon, gliding up to the house to greet awaiting guests.
Catering: in-house. Civil ceremony licence. Disabled: toilet. Licence extension possible. Outside space: garden (for hire).

MARQUEES & TENTS

Bedouin Tents

01865 200634/www.bedouintents.com/ weddings. **Open** 24 hr. **No credit cards.**
Bedouin specialises in high-quality Moroccan tents with unique linings (woven, hand-block printed, patchwork and embroidered) and designs. The company can also provide tents for more classic English country garden weddings too. The structures can offer a variety of 'areas' for entertaining, such as reception, dining and chill-out spaces as well as dance tents. Bedouin also offer advice on entertainers, caterers, PA equipment and conveniences.

Marquee Hire Company

7351 1990/01483 200716/www.marquee hire.co.uk. **Open** 9am-5pm Mon-Fri.
Claiming to be the largest marquee hire company in the south east of England, Guy Charlesworth's service boasts a huge range of accessories, including chairs, tables and lighting, as well as catering (local, organic and free range where possible) and waitress service if required. There is a handy online calculator where you plug in your numbers and requirements and the cost is worked out for you.

Stunning Tents

01256 882114/www.stunningtents.co.uk. **Open** 9am-5.30pm Mon-Fri.
Catering from six to 2,000, Stunning Tents have a range of unusual tents – Nordic tipis to nomadic yurts – and furnishings for every event. The giant 'hats' or single/duo span tents are best for weddings and can be fitted out with anything from Swedish long tables and benches (optional reindeer skin covering) or bean bags, pouffes and cubes. Lighting can be arranged, as can heating, flooring, dancefloors and walkways, even a central fire. Prices from £1,925.

Sunset Marquees

Unit 5, Glenville Mews, Kimber Road, SW18 4NJ (8741 2777/www.sunsetmarquees.com). Southfields tube. **Open** 8am-6pm daily. **No credit cards.**
As well as large marquees for weddings and events, Sunset can also provide you with a mini tent (from £190) – perfect for filling with boisterous children at a party. For an extra charge, lighting, furniture, candy-floss machines, heating and carpeting can be provided.

World Tents

01296 714555/www.worldtents.co.uk. **Open** 9am-5pm Mon-Fri.
Proprietor David Field runs World Tents from the environmentally aware Buckinghamshire community he and his family are part of. The tents, marquees, domes, yurts and tipis available to buy are gorgeous and range from ornate octagon-shaped medieval-style erections to easily-transportable geodesic domes (from £800). Tents can be delivered or you can collect yourself, and get a tour of the community chucked in. In line with the owner's beliefs, all materials are natural, made from recycled materials or sourced from sustainable forests.

LOOKING THE PART

WEDDING DRESSES

Annie's Vintage

12 Camden Passage, N1 8ED (7359 0796). Angel tube. **Open** 11am-6pm Mon, Tue, Thur, Fri; 9am-6pm Wed, Sat; 11am-3pm Sun.
The perfect browsing ground for a one-off frock, Annie's is one of London's best-loved vintage emporiums. Bridal stock is constantly changing, but on any given visit you're likely to find beautifully wispy 1920s frocks, intricate lace and plenty of accessories. A perfectly lovely place to find The Dress.

Browns Bride

11-12 Hind Street, W1U 3BE (7514 0056/
www.brownsbride.com). Bond Street tube.
Open by appointment 11am-6pm Mon-Sat.
The fashionista's choice – a bride sporting a
Browns' gown can't help but become the object
of intense envy. Among big-name designers are
fashion royalty such as Alberta Ferretti,
Alexander McQueen, Alice Temperley, Collette
Dinnigan (*see below*) and Carolina Herrera. Many
of the ranges on offer are exclusive to Browns,
including über-popular Monique Lhuillier and
Oscar de la Renta. Make an appointment (it's
always busy) for the ultimate dress-up session
and be prepared to splurge. Prices start at the
£2,000 mark and go up to around £15,000.
Accessories are also available.

Collette Dinnigan

26 Cale Street, SW3 3QU (7589 8897/
www.collettedinnigan.com). South Kensington
tube. **Open** 10am-6pm Mon-Sat.
Popular with brides down under, Australian
designer Collette Dinnigan's bridal designs are
beautifully sophisticated. Ideal for urban brides
who can't bear the idea of flouncing around in a
meringue on the big day, you'll find wonderful
silks, intricate detailing and lots of sparkly crystal
and quartz features. Best of all, staff are cheerful
and totally relaxed, so there's no pressure when
trying on frocks here. Appointments are not
always necessary but it's best to call ahead just
to make sure. Prices start at £300.

Expectant Bride

9 Worcester Drive, W4 1AB (07930 329690/
www.expectantbride.com). Turnham Green
tube. **Open** by appointment.
Brides in the family way will love maternity
wedding dress specialist Expectant Bride. Each
bride-to-be is given a two-hour consultation in
order to help identify the perfect bump-flattering
frock. The team here are experts at predicting
what will fit and at what stage of pregnancy – as
many happy clients will happily attest. Designers
stocked include Tiffany Rose, Sarah Houston
Maternity and Nicole Mitchell. And whether you
want to show off the bump in all its glory or keep
things somewhat under wraps, there's a dress
to suit your needs here somewhere. Gowns range
in price from £175 to £950.

Jacqueline Byrne

19 Arlington Way, EC1R 1UY (7833 0381/
www.jacquelinebyrne.co.uk). Angel tube.
Open by appointment 10am-7pm Mon-Sat.
No credit cards.
Having a wedding dress made by the lovely
Jacqueline Byrne is a real experience. Since

opening her peaceful studio off St John Street
in 2007, Byrne has built up a loyal following. The
fact that this has been through word-of-mouth
alone speaks volumes. The design process
starts with discussion, ideas, sketches and
experimentation with toile mock-ups, and ends
with a totally bespoke, hand-finished dress like
nothing you've ever worn before. Byrne uses fine
silks, vintage lace and beading, and a well-honed
sense of attention to detail (the bride's name
embroidered into the finished article, for
example). For 2009, Byrne intends to expand
into the shop next door where she will display a
range of basic dress shapes for brides-to-be to
try on. They will then be able to personalise the
style they like with trimmings, beautiful lace and
detailing – a great idea for girls who want a one-
off dress but feel they must try something on in
order to commit. Prices start at £1,500.

Jenny Packham

75 Elizabeth Street, SW1W 9PJ (7730
2264/www.jennypackhambride.com).
Sloane Square tube/Victoria tube/rail.
Open by appointment 10am-6pm daily.
This white, bright and airy shop (chandeliers,
grey velvet pouffes for bridesmaids to sit on,
cabinets full of twinkly things and a fairytale
garden out back) is a great place to get in touch
with your inner bride. Frocks are fantastically
glam (lots of sequins and glitz; fabulous trains)
and helpful, hands-on staff make whittling down
the options a breeze. Prices start at £1,200 and
all fittings are done in-house (the first session
is two months before the big day). A lovely space
to spend an hour of indulgence.

Mirror Mirror

37 Park Road, N8 8TE (8348 2113/
www.mirrormirror.uk.com). Finsbury Park
tube/rail. **Open** 8am-5.30pm Mon-Thur;
10am-6pm Fri, Sat.

NOTE

TRASH THE DRESS
Forget packing it away neatly
for posterity, the latest wedding
photography trend involves one last
fling with the frock. The 'Trash the
Dress' concept involves shooting high-
fashion images of the dress with none
of the constraints of cleanliness the
bride has to deal with on the big day.
Think fairground rides, frolicking on
beaches, even tramping among sheep
in a muddy field. Check out www.
trashthedress.com for more info.

Whether you're looking for a classic bridal number or something low-key and chic, Maria Yiannikaris and Jane Freshwater know the wedding dress business inside out. They started Mirror Mirror some 19 years ago and have a roster of satisfied customers (many of them celebrities) to show for it. In addition to their own Mirror Mirror Couture range, the Crouch End and Angel (56 Penton Street, N1; 7713 9022) shops stock stunning designer gowns in modern and classic styles (the vintage-inspired dresses are particularly lovely). Dresses start from £800 (£3,000 for couture).

Temperley London Bridal Room

2-10 Colville Mews, Lonsdale Road, W11 2DA (7229 7957/www.temperleylondon. com). Notting Hill Gate tube. **Open** by appointment 10am-6pm Mon-Wed, Fri; 10am-7pm Thur; 11am-6pm Sat.
A fabulous place to soak up some bohemian bridal spirit, the wedding room at Alice Temperley's ever-expanding boutique has a relaxing, boudoir feel and appointments start with a glass of champagne. Assistants are helpful and relaxed, and there's no hard sell – probably because the clothes sell themselves. The gowns are beautifully unique, featuring lots of intricate embroidery, lace and sequins. There are also shorter dresses (ideal for bridesmaids) and the quality is very high. Prices start at £1,000 and go up to £5,000. A fitting service ensures a perfect silhouette on the big day.

Wedding Shop

171 Fulham Road, SW3 6JW (7838 1188/www.weddingshop.com). Sloane

Square or South Kensington tube. **Open** by appointment 10am-6pm Mon-Sat.
A more personal Vera Wang experience than the one available at mega-busy Selfridges (www.selfridges.com). Prices start at £2,775 and climb upwards of £30,000 for those with cash to flash on a bespoke gown. For a more affordable touch of VW magic, check out the Vera Wang Maids collection, which offers spectacular full-length and cocktail-style bridesmaids' dresses (the kind that won't have your friends retaliating with wet-look peach the minute the boot is on the other foot). Many can even be ordered in white/ivory (a popular maid look in the US), though they do request that you order three. Still, with prices at just £250 to £350, girls determined to marry in Wang might want to consider banding together.

SHOES & ACCESSORIES

Agent Provocateur

6 Broadwick Street, W1V 1FH (7439 0229/www.agentprovocateur.com). Oxford Circus or Tottenham Court Road tube. **Open** 11am-7pm Mon-Wed, Fri, Sat; 11am-8pm Thur; noon-5pm Sun.
For big day lingerie to be proud of, nothing quite beats a spot of Agent Provocateur. The 2008 bridal range – modelled by Kate Moss – included classic shape-sculpting corsets (£210), seductively innocent babydolls (£125) and racy open-cup bras (£75) and nipple pasties. Fabrics are luxuriously glamorous and feel great against the skin. The classic pink and black packaging is a winner too. For starter-level wedding AP, try the cute tie-sides knickers (£35), with 'something blue' bows and wedding bells on the bum. Perfect for under the gown on the day.

Basia Zarzycka

52 Sloane Square, SW1W 8AX (7730 1660/ www.basia-zarzycka.com). Knightsbridge or Sloane Square tube. **Open** 10am-6pm Mon-Sat.
Basia Zarzycka's shop is a treasure chest full of hair grips, tiaras and extravagant costume jewellery. The exquisite pieces, which start at around the £50 mark and go beyond £5,000, are made in her basement workshop and include delicate wreaths and garlands, brooches, combs, bags and shoes. She also makes stunning bridal gowns (prices start at £10,000) and offers a costume jewellery repair service. Make an appointment (or just drop in) to sit in front of the shop mirror while she transforms you with crystals. Basia's online shop will give you a taste of what's in store.

Emmy

Christian Louboutin

23 Motcomb Street, SW1X 8LB (7245 6510/ www.christianlouboutin.com). Knightsbridge tube. **Open** *10am-6pm Mon-Fri; 11am-6pm Sat.*

If there's ever an excuse to get your feet into a pair of fabulous Louboutins, a wedding is surely it? Best known for his Parisian sensibility, expressed in skyscraper heels, peep toes and Hepburn-esque ballet pumps, celeb-favourite Louboutin certainly isn't afraid to experiment. Classic designs in ivory, white and metallics should suit fashion-conscious brides down to the ground. Brides wearing full-length gowns might want to check out the brighter shades too (something blue, perhaps?). Flash those signature red soles with pride.

Coco de Mer

23 Monmouth Street, WC2H 9DD (7836 8882/www.coco-de-mer.com). Covent Garden tube. **Open** *11am-7pm Mon-Wed, Fri, Sat; 11am-8pm Thur; noon-6pm Sun.*

Every bride needs a few tricks up her sleeve for the honeymoon – she'll find enough here to last the rest of the marriage too. The shop's relaxed, boudoir feel makes browsing a pleasure, while friendly staff somehow manage to make asking questions about designer sex toys seem almost mundane. Think 'the five senses' as you shop for a trousseau: beautiful lingerie, blindfolds, lickable massage oils, feather ticklers and erotic fiction to read aloud. Coco de Mer also runs glamorous salons, covering subjects such as bondage (great for couples or groups of girls),

and offers personal shopping services too; and if you're looking for a bit of inspiration, check out the online Honeymoon guide.

Emmy

65 Cross Street, N1 2BB (7704 0012/ www.emmyshoes.co.uk). Highbury & Islington tube/rail. **Open** *by appointment 10.30am-5.30pm Tue, Thur-Sat; 11.30am-6.30pm Wed.*

For beautiful, bespoke bridal shoes this is definitely the place to come. Emmy's wonderfully flexible approach enables brides to choose from an array of designs (round toe, pointed toe, peep toe, sandals and even boots are covered), materials and heel heights to create shoes that are unique and totally personal. We love the vintage-style 'Bella' sandals and the classic 'Emmy' Mary Janes. Shoes can also be bought 'off-the-rack'; prices start at £260. Lovely accessories, such as crystal pins (five for £35) and pearl and crystal drop combs (£130), are also sold here.

Luella's Boudoir

33 Church Road, SW19 5DQ (8879 7744/ www.luellasboudoir.co.uk). Wimbledon tube/ rail. **Open** *11am-7pm Tue, Wed; 11am-8pm Thur; 11am-6pm Fri; 10am-6pm Sat; noon-5pm Sun.*

The pressure's off – you've found the dress, but there's still a world of bridal accessories for you to deliberate over. At Luella's, you'll find bridesmaids' dresses (made to order in a huge range of colours), stylish shoes (by Olivia Morris,

Cyrus Shahrad searches the capital for stag-friendly entertainment – so you can concentrate on lamp posts and handcuffs.

Missing rings, boring speeches – the burden upon a best man can inspire nerves comparable with those racking the happy couple in the run-up to a wedding, but organise a decent stag party and you're halfway to victory.

Those determined not to break with stag activity tradition, will find a sprawling outdoor paintball centre at Paintzone in Croydon (8688 1118, www.paintzone.co.uk), and kart action galore at Go Karting London (7005 0318, www.gokartinglondon.co.uk) in both Mile End and King's Cross. Bowling, however, would be a much more original option: All Star Lanes (*see p36*) is a leather-upholstered haven of retro '50s chic, while the slightly rough-around-the-edges Bloomsbury Lanes (7183 1979, www.bloomsburybowling.com) boasts private karaoke rooms for stags who take their 'Bohemian Rhapsody' as seriously as their beer consumption.

For a different kind of swing, high-tech computer simulations at Urban Golf (7434 4300, www.urbangolf.co.uk) allow backseat drivers to play 40 of the world's most famous golf courses without leaving Soho, while Namco Station (*see p90*) offers a selection of games arcades for stags with fond memories of thumb-blistering Tekken tournaments. Equally nostalgic, although decidedly more outdoorsy, is to descend on one of London's parks for a self-organised school sports day – scratchy sacks, eggs, spoons and all – followed by a picnic; plump for Highbury Fields and you can legally throw a barbecue into the mix.

More traditional is an hour or two ogling anonymous ladies in the nude. Far cheaper and more surreally exciting than Stringfellows (7758 0670, www.stringfellows.co.uk) is to start the day with a pint and a pocket full of pound coins at noon-time opener the Griffin (7405 3855, www.browns-griffin.co.uk), where a quid goes in the glass for every girl who takes the stage (roughly every ten minutes), and where private dances cost just £10. For a classier start to the afternoon, gangs of boys already married to their mirrors can partake in an old-fashioned shave and a manicure at Truefitt & Hill (7493 2961, www.truefittandhill.co.uk) or Geo F Trumper (7499 1850, www.trumpers.com). Looking thus buffed and acting appropriately civilised, partake in a Men's Afternoon Tea at the Mandeville Hotel (7935 5599, www.mandeville.co.uk; 3-5.30pm Mon-Sat), where you'll find swanky sandwiches and classy cakes combined with the finest teas, whiskies and champagnes – and, true to the treehouse code, no girls allowed.

One logical progression from such plushness may be a Bond-themed casino blowout – the Park Tower Casino (7235 6161,

Tiroler Hut

www.parktowercasino.com) offers a degree of opulence without the financial ruination of the Ritz Club (7499 1818, www.theritz club.com) – but a more suitably seedy flutter can be had watching professional fighters beat ten bales out of each other at old-school Cockney bear pit York Hall in Bethnal Green (8980 2243), or at Wimbledon Stadium (*see p84*), London's only greyhound racing track.

Dinner may be otherwise hard to come by for clamouring hordes of costume-clad, beer-soaked boys, but there are restaurants out there happy to take stags under their wing, including party-friendly Austrian joint Tiroler Hut (7727 3981, www.tirolerhut.co.uk) and boisterous Russian eatery Nikita's (7352 6326, www.nikitasrestaurant.com). Both offer a range of party menus (Tiroler from £25.50 per person; Nikita's from £22.50) and unadulterated fun. Think vodka served in hollow blocks of ice at Nikita's and manic singalongs and yodelling at Tiroler Hut.

Lastly, finding a decent club in which to round off a stag in style isn't easy – buying tickets in advance is the only way to ensure that bouncers don't baulk at the idea of letting in a gang of twenty blokes. Failing that, head for a notorious meat market like Infernos (7720 7633, www.infernos.co.uk) or Car Wash (0870 246 1966, www.carwash.co.uk) – just be sure to get there in good time, behave (or better still split up) in the queue and adhere to any dress code.

Beatrix Ong, Filippa Scott and Emmy, among others), jewellery, hairpieces, lingerie (Wolford, Damaris, Mimi Holliday, Alice & Astrid), shrugs and gifts – in short, everything but the gown. There are back issues of bridal magazines to browse through and Luella's also offers recommendations for great photographers, make-up artists, florists, wedding planners and stationers to take the stress out of planning.

SUITS

Anthony Formalwear

53 High Street, Billericay, Essex, CM12 9AX (01277 651140/www.anthonyformal wear.co.uk). Billericay rail. **Open** 9.30am-5.00pm Mon-Tue, Thur-Sat.

This Essex-based company does a fine line in wedding attire for hire (made-to-measure suits are also available). Choose from an array of jacket styles (lounge, frock, tail and nehru included), colours (lilac or sky blue, anyone?) and fabrics. Prices are extremely reasonable, right down to the fact that if you hire six outfits you only need pay for five. Evening suits start from £45, 'cruise packs' for one- or two-week hire start at £100 for an outfit for one week, while morning suits start at £60. You may need to trek out to Essex or Twickenham for stockists (though do give them a call for the most recent list) but the savings you'll make on hire costs should make it worth the trip.

Austin Reed

103 Regent Street, W1B 4HL (7534 7777/ www.austinreed.co.uk). Piccadilly Circus tube. **Open** 9.30am-7pm Mon, Wed, Fri-Sat; 10am-7pm Tue; 9.30am-8pm Thur; noon-6pm Sun.

Whether you plan to buy or hire your wedding suit, Austin Reed is a great place to start the hunt. The Regent Street store has a personal tailoring department for made to measure suits and stocks Hugo Boss, Gant, Hilfiger and more as well as own-brand clothes. Styling is reassuringly classic with a decent amount of contemporary oomph. The range of colourful shirts (from £40) and ties (from £35) is particularly pleasing. On the hire side, morning, evening, children's and Highland wear (Prince Charlie outfit from £70) are stocked, as are outfits for Asian weddings. Prices start at £50 for a tailcoat package.

Moss Bros Hire

27-29 King Street, WC2E 8JD (7632 9700/ www.moss.co.uk). Covent Garden tube. **Open** 9am-6pm Mon-Wed, Fri, Sat; 9am-7pm Thur; 11am-4.30pm Sun.

WEDDINGS

The go-to guys for student balls and black-tie emergencies, Moss Bros are used to dealing with befuddled grooms, disorganised best men and ushers of all shapes and sizes. All the basics are covered (morning wear, evening suits, Highland gear and stuff for kids), stock is huge and prices are reasonable (£79 for a 'Classic' package: suit, waistcoat, shirt, tie and handkerchief). Bridal colour-scheme whims are catered for with plenty of pretty pastel shades for ties – including pink.

Paul Smith
40-44 Floral Street, WC2E 9DG (7379 7133/www.paulsmith.co.uk). Covent Garden

tube. **Open** 10.30am-6.30pm Mon-Wed; 10.30am-7pm Thur, Fri; 10am-7pm Sat; 12.30-5.30pm Sun.
If you've decided to buy rather than hire your wedding suit (and, seriously, why should the bride get the monopoly on cash-flashing fun?), then Paul Smith is your man. Styles are contemporary and supremely stylish (one of his midnight blue numbers would see you right at all manner of social occasions for years to come) and fabrics run the gamut from cool linens to lightweight but sturdy wools. Prices start at £450. Fabulous print shirts add the perfect finishing touch. Best of all, the Covent Garden store has a fabulously laid-back feel that makes shopping a pleasure. Great hats, scarves and cufflinks too.

BRIDAL BOOTCAMP

You meant to start a 'cleanse, tone, moisturise' routine the minute the date was set. You meant to start going to gym instead of just paying for it. You meant to have regular facials, waxings and great nails by now. You meant to do a lot of things... but you haven't, have you? Thankfully it's never too late to make a few choice improvements – get the below booked up pronto.

BEAUTY BLITZ

Blink Eyebrow Bar
Fenwick, 63 New Bond Street, W1A 3BS (7408 0689/www.blinkbrowbar.com). Bond Street tube. **Open** 10am-6.30pm Mon-Wed, Fri, Sat; 10am-8pm Thur.
Also at Harvey Nichols and Selfridges, Blink's innovative threading bars offer a speedy walk-in service for brows in need of some TLC. Appointments can also be booked in advance and the face-framing results are impressive – most people won't notice what you've had 'done' but they will spot the subtle improvement. Eyebrows take 15 minutes and cost £17 (threading for other parts of the face is also offered, as is lash and eyebrow tinting); the majority of therapists here were trained in India.

Bliss
60 Sloane Avenue, SW3 3DD (7590 6146/ www.blisslondon.co.uk). Sloane Square or South Kensington tube. **Open** 9.30am-8pm Mon-Fri; 9.30am-6.30pm Sat; noon-6pm Sun.
When time is not on your side, there's no point faffing around with facials that don't deliver

WEDDINGS

results. Bliss Spa's Triple Oxygen Treatment (£145) combines serious pampering (lots of massage while various creams and sprays do their jobs) with complexion-perfecting extractions to fine effect. You'll notice the difference instantly and the glowy results last a week or more. And what's not to like about a spa that offers cheese, chocolate brownies and even wine as pre-treatment snacks? The ground-floor Quickbliss salon offers great mani- and pedicures too.

Eve Lom

2 Spanish Place, W1U 3HU (7935 9988/ www.evelom.co.uk). Bond Street tube.
Open 9am-5pm Tue-Sat. **No credit cards.**
Eve Lom's signature facial (£140/90mins) involves thorough cleansing, a pore-opening paraffin wax mask, necessary extractions, lymphatic drainage and an acupressure massage. As well as being fabulously relaxing and indulgent, the results are impressive; afterwards, even spa cynics have admitted to seeing a visible difference. To maintain results after your treatment, check out Lom's skincare range, which has an almost cultish following among her many fans. To see the woman herself (£245), book a couple of months ahead.

Leighton Denny

Urban Retreat, 5th Floor, Harrods, 87-135 Brompton Road, SW1X 7XL (7893 8333/ www.harrods.com). Knightsbridge tube.
Open 10am-8pm Mon-Sat; noon-6pm Sun.
Even if you forgo every other beauty treatment in the run up to your wedding, all that 'oohing' and 'ahhing' over the ring means that great nails are an absolute must. An expert when it comes to the perfectly shaped nail, the ebullient Leighton Denny and his crack team of manicurists can be found at Harrods' Urban Retreat. Using his long-lasting polishes a mani costs £35, a pedi £45. Well worth it.

Otylia Roberts

Greenhouse, 142 Wigmore Street, W1U 3SH (7486 5537/www.otyliaroberts.co.uk). Bond Street tube. **Open** 10am-6pm Mon; 10am-7pm Tue-Thur; 10am-5.30pm Fri; 9.30am-4.30pm Sat.
Prepare to bare all on your honeymoon with a trip to the Queen of the Brazilian Otylia Roberts. Polish-born Roberts has been whipping hair off the intimate areas of London's most fashionable girls for years and the results speak for themselves. The team here use beeswax-based hot wax instead of strips, which is less painful and more effective. It is pricier too, though: from £34 for a half leg (the Brazilian is £49, while a Hollywood is £51).

Strip

112 Talbot Road, W11 1JR (7727 2754/ www.2strip.com). Westbourne Park tube.
Open 10am-8pm Mon-Fri; 10am-6pm Fri, Sat; noon-6pm Sun.
Strip attempts to make waxing a more pleasurable experience with distracting plasma screen TVs in its treatment rooms and an array of lingerie to purchase once the deed is done. The therapists here use Lycon wax, which promises – and, say our sources, delivers – a less painful treatment. Prices aren't too steep, with a bikini costing from £22. The lengthy menu also has plenty of options for men, from back waxes to 'Male Brazilians'.

BRIDAL PACKAGES

Mandarin Oriental

66 Knightsbridge, SW1X 7LA (7838 9888/ www.mandarinoriental.com). Knightsbridge tube. **Open** 7am-10pm daily.
If you've cash to flash and a taste for the high life, this is the place to come for pre-wedding pampering. The Wedding Belles packages (£1,000) starts with a day-long Purifying Programme two months before the wedding, moving on to a half-day Nourishing Ritual two weeks before and a stress-reducing Oriental Harmony massage a couple of days before. A more pleasurable way to get in shape for your nuptials we can't imagine. Brides are also given a bath-and- body oil so that they can recreate the spa vibe on honeymoon.

Parlour

3 Ravey Street, EC2A 4QP (7729 6969/ www.theparlouruk.com). Liverpool Street or Old Street tube/rail. **Open** 11.30am-8pm Mon-Thur; 10.30am-7pm; 10am-5pm Sat.

NOTE

SOMETHING BLUE
Tougher than old, new and borrowed put together. We suggest you try:
• A fabulous pair of blue shoes
• A small heart tattoo
• Agent Provocateur's £35 wedding knickers with blue tie-sides
• A piece of blue ribbon sewn into the seam of your dress
• Blue flowers in your bouquet
• Blue/black mascara
• Pale blue toenail polish
• Sapphire earrings

GIRLS ALLOWED

Emma Howarth investigates hen nights with style.

The Berkeley

No matter how classy your friends or how civilised your intentions, there's something about a hen night that sends even the most restrained group of girls into a spontaneous smut spiral. Face facts, you won't make it through the night without at least one rendition of 'Girls Just Wanna Have Fun', and numerous references to the groom's private parts are a given, but the evening's activities can be lifted onto a higher plane with very little effort at all. Try one of these out for starters – all are certified L-plate free zones.

Art of Tease

Burlesque legend Jo King's London School of Striptease offers fabulous packages (from £25 per hen) for girls keen to combine champagne, gossip and general merriment with learning a valuable life skill. And what skill could be more crucial to the soon-to-be married than the 'Art of Tease'? Either Jo herself (a dynamo of positivity with some 30 years' experience in the world of exotic artistry) or one of her inspiring and energetic team will turn up at the venue of your choice ready to distribute feather boas and take you through the essentials of exotic dance or burlesque. No clothes are removed and even girls who start the evening insisting they'd rather sit it out end up shaking their booties with gusto before the session is over (at our tester's party, a pregnant woman two days past her due date joined in with particular gusto). A fabulous start to a night on the tiles.

London School of Striptease (07958 314107/ www.londonschoolofstriptease.co.uk).
Or why not try Time for Tease's (07971 130611, www.timefortease.co.uk) 'Afternoon Tea Burlesque Beauty' session. A champagne tea with make-up and manicure sessions starts from £80 per hen.

Girls' Night In

Perfect for small, intimate hen gatherings, the Berkeley's 'Girls' Night In' package is every bit as luxurious as would expect. We're talking full-on five-star glamour, access to the fabulous rooftop pool (complete with glass roof that rolls back on sunny days) and gym, and the whole of Knightsbridge on your doorstep. It doesn't come cheap (from £415), but when you consider how much a bog-standard London hotel room costs, all the extras (read on) you get thrown in and the restorative joy of a night of pure indulgence, we reckon it's a damned good deal. As well as a night in one of the hotel's wonderfully glamorous rooms, girls receive complimentary in-room mini manicures, cocktails sent up from the Blue Bar, Skinny Cow ice cream, a choice of chick flicks to watch and a huge hamper of goodies including a Diptyque candle, Bliss beauty products, popcorn, Green & Blacks chocolate, Hope & Greenwood sweets and more. Additional spa treatments can be booked and fabulous platters of snacks can be ordered too. You'll weep buckets as you leave it all behind the next day.

Lost in Beauty

WEDDINGS

The Berkeley, Wilton Place, SW1X 7RL (0808 238 0245/www.the-berkeley.co.uk). **Or why not try** The Metropolitan's (7447 1000, www.metropolitan.como.bz) Tote-to-Toe shopping experience. Prices start from £350 and include a one-night stay, complimentary pink champagne and a £50 voucher for Harvey Nichols, Selfridges, Browns or Dover Street Market.

Pampering Perfection

Primrose Hill's Lost in Beauty boutique is kitted out with vintage shop fittings and cool lit-up mirrors that give it a fabulous feeling of old world glamour. Bespoke parties (seriously, whatever you're after, ask and it can be arranged) for groups of girls are a speciality and make the perfect prelude to a classy night on the town. Prices start from around £80 per hen – you could decide to have your make-up professionally applied (including false eyelashes to flutter drunkenly later on) while sipping free champagne. A photographer can be provided to capture your transformations in action, as can a car to whisk you all away to the next part of the night. The shop stocks cool cult brands, including Becca, Chantecaille, Dr Hauschka, Jurlique and Rodial, and is a fine place to while away a few girly hours. *Lost in Beauty, 117 Regents Park Road, NW1 8UR (7586 4411/www.lostinbeauty.com).* **Or why not try** The Parlour (*see p239*) has fab packages (from £65 per hen, including free champagne and two mini treatments) for girls on a mission to unwind and glam up.

This compact, friendly and totally unpretentious salon is a fine place to get whipped into bridal beauty shape. Deliver yourself to their door a few months before the big day and the team will ensure you are buffed to perfection and ready to shine. Packages are flexible depending on each bride's needs but could include regular bespoke facials, mani- and pedicures, fake tan and make-up trials, hairdressing, waxing and finishing touches. Prices are based around a start price of £65 per hour. The Parlour also arranges fabulous pampering parties for groups of girls. Sip champagne, enjoy a selection of treatments and get stuck into some serious gossip.

MAKE-UP LESSONS

Pixi
22A Foubert's Place, W1F 7PW (7287 7211/ www.pixibeauty.com). Oxford Circus tube. **Open** 11am-7pm Mon-Sat; noon-5pm Sun.
Pixi's goodies range from candy-hued glosses and blushers to light, sheer foundations and credit-card slim eye-colour kits (£26), packed with subtle, deliciously easy-to-wear shades. Pop in for a browse and a quick 'little black dress' day-to-evening makeover (£20), or bring your make-up bag for the 90-minute masterclass (£60): staff will advise on what to clear out, as well as going through colours and techniques. After-hours parties are a bargain: for £15 a head, you get the shop to yourselves, a glass of bubbly and the services of two make-up artists.

Shu Uemera
24 Neal Street, WC2H 9QU (7240 7635). Covent Garden tube. **Open** 10.30am-7pm Mon-Sat; noon-5pm Sun.
Sophisticated make-up brand Shu Uemera offers all kinds of lessons that are suitable for nervous brides- and bridesmaids-to-be. There are one-to-one 90-minute classes (£40) and two-hour masterclasses; alternatively, staff will do your eye make-up for £10. Make time for a browse afterwards as the colour options are endless.

FIGURE FIXER

Good Vibes
14-16 Betterton Street, WC2H 9BU (7240 6111/www.goodvibesfitness.co.uk). Covent Garden tube. **Open** 7.30am-8pm Mon-Thur; 7.30am-6pm Fri; 10am-3pm Sat.
So, you kind of, umm, forgot to spend the last six months honing yourself into a vision of physical perfection? No problem. With six weeks to spare (and our tester saw definite results in

much less time), Good Vibes PowerPlate machines (like exercising on a washing-machine during spin cycle) will have you svelte and toned in no time. Three 25-minute sessions a week are the minimum you'll need and obviously the longer you can commit to the programme for (and the healthier your diet) the better. Off-peak sessions start at £10; packages such as the popular Bikini Bootcamp regime come in at around £300.

GROOMING THE GROOM

Jacks of London
15 Wimbledon Bridge, SW19 7NH (8971 5070/www.jacksoflondon.co.uk). Wimbledon tube/rail. **Open** 8am-8pm Mon-Fri; 8am-6pm Sat; 10am-5pm Sun.
With all the excitement it's sometimes forgotten that it's a big day for the groom too. To ensure he's groomed to perfection, this male-only salon has a range of packages that include a cut-throat shave, a style consultation and an ice-cold beer. PlayStation games and plasma screens will make sure the best man and ushers don't get bored while they wait their turn. Be warned – you'll need to book at least a week in advance.

Nickel Spa
27 Shorts Gardens, WC2H 9AP (7240 4048/ www.nickelspalondon.co.uk). Covent Garden tube. **Open** noon-6pm Mon; 10am-7pm Tue, Wed, Sat; 10am-8pm Thur, Fri; noon-5pm Sun.
With fantastic, male-specific grooming products upstairs, the treatments happen downstairs, where the decor is New York boxing gym meets submarine. Hour-long massages can be teeth-grittingly hard if you wish, but the aesthetic side is not overlooked – an eye-watering 'back, sack and crack' wax can be yours for £60.

Refinery
60 Brook Street, W1K 5DU (7409 2001/ www.the-refinery.com). Bond Street tube. **Open** 10am-7pm Mon, Tue; 10am-9pm Wed-Fri; 9am-6pm Sat; 11am-5pm Sun.
Gentlemen's club melds with contemporary spa at this reliable men-only venue closed off Bond Street. An hour-long sports therapy massage is suitably manly (£90), while traditional wet shaves are £40. For the office-bound chap, a (fake) sun-kissed face is £25.

BRIDAL HAIR

Burnett Forbes
15 Wells Street, W1T 3PE (7580 5006/ www.burnettforbes.co.uk). Oxford Circus or

Tottenham Court Road tube. **Open** 10am-6pm Mon, Wed, Thur, Sat; 10am-8pm Tue, Fri.
Specialising in Afro-Caribbean hair, this Marylebone favourite prides itself on bridal hair and staff are dab hands at extensions too. Its relaxed, chatty atmosphere will put brides at ease, and while it is central, the salon doesn't have quite the same eye-watering prices as some of its posh neighbours.

The Chapel
394 St John Street, EC1V 4NJ (7520 0460/ www.thechapel.co.uk). Angel tube. **Open** 11am-6pm Tue; 11am-9pm Wed; noon-9pm Thur; 10am-6pm Fri; 9am-5pm Sat.
This Angel salon is a stylish mix of quirky cool and modern elegance. Previously a butcher's shop, the Chapel now offers an intimate setting and a tailor-made service, with champagne at hand and prices by the hour. You can create your own 'mood board' of inspiration using pictures of styles you desire, with on-trend plaits and distressed buns replacing the clichéd barrel curl of yore. All together now: 'We're going to the Chapel and we're gon-na get maaaaaa-aarried…'

Gina Conway Aveda Lifestyle Salon
62 Westbourne Grove, W2 5SH (7229 6644/www.ginaconway.co.uk). Bayswater or Notting Hill Gate tube. **Open** 10am-5pm Mon; 9am-7pm Tue, Sat; 9am-9pm Wed-Fri; 10am-5pm Sun.
Brides concerned with all things green will adore this urban Westbourne Grove oasis. The aroma will hit you first – Aveda's plant and botanical-based range packs quite the pungent punch. It doesn't come cheap – the top of the range 'decadent' bridal experience is £650 – but this includes a trial day as well as the wedding itself, with hair and make-up consultation, a one-and-a-half hour facial, mani and pedicure, eyebrow wax and shaping, and hair 'spa', and all with either Gina or one of her creative directors. All-inclusive packages are also available for bridesmaids and mothers. There is also a Gina Conway Aveda Concept salon in Parson's Green (612 Fulham Road, SW6 5RP, 7731 7633).

Karine Jackson
24 Litchfield Street, WC2H 9NJ (7836 0300/ www.karinejackson.co.uk). Leicester Square tube. **Open** 10am-7pm Mon, Fri; 10am-9pm Tue, Thur; 10am-8pm Wed; 9am-6pm Sat.
Current London Hairdresser of the Year, Karine holds the prestigious L'Oreal Colour Specialist Degree – perfect if you're looking to overhaul your dishwater-hued locks ahead of the big day. She's also an expert on organic colour as a greener

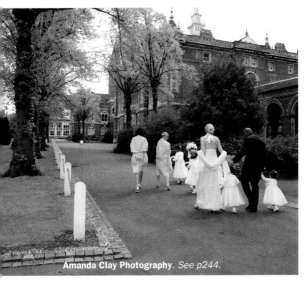

Amanda Clay Photography. *See p244.*

alternative to all those pongy chemicals. The salon is a real one-stop shop for brides-to-be, as hen party packages are on offer as well as beauty and make-up services. This includes the idBare Minerals range, apparently so natural 'you can sleep in it'.

Paul Edmonds London

166 Brompton Road, SW3 1HW (7584 7754/www.pauledmonds.com). Knightsbridge tube. **Open** *9am-7pm Mon-Wed, Fri, Sat; 9am-9pm Thur.*

This new Knightsbridge salon has the real wow factor; designed to feel very British, it's like stepping into a Georgian gentleman's club, although touches of '40s and '50s decor give it a glamorous edge. You can't help but feel completely cossetted in elegance and luxury – ideal for the Bridezilla who knows exactly what she wants and doesn't care about the cost. There are set packages, but to be honest this is the kind of setting where bespoke arrangements are common, so if you demand utter perfection, you'll be in safe (and well-manicured) hands.

Pimps and Pinups

14 Lamb Street, E1 6EA (7426 2121/ www.pimpsandpinups.com). Liverpool Street tube/rail. **Open** *10am-8pm Mon-Fri; 10am-6pm Sat, Sun.*

For the ultimate in retro style, this much-loved, unpretentious Spitalfields salon is bang on trend and excels in teasing tresses into stunning up-dos inspired by the '40s and '50s. The boutique salon's illuminated mirrors make you feel like a

Hollywood starlet in her dressing room too. A laid-back setting for the modern bride who wants something utterly original yet fabulously glam.

Taylor Taylor London

137 Commercial Street, E1 6BJ (7377 2737/ www.taylortaylorlondon.com). Aldgate East tube/Liverpool Street tube/rail. **Open** *10am-8pm Mon-Wed; 10am-9pm Thur; 10am-7pm Fri; 10am-6pm Sat, Sun.*

Want premium urban chic? Then try Taylor Taylor which, with its salons off Brick Lane and in Spitalfields, is the hip choice for brides getting married in the East End. The flagship Commercial Street salon has a distinctly '20s boudoir feel, with crystal and mother-of-pearl walls injecting a touch of glamour to proceedings. And rather than a glass of cheap plonk to calm the nerves on the big day, a tempting array of cocktails is hard to resist.

PHOTOGRAPHERS

It's probably taken a year to organise it, so you want the one of the most memorable days of your life to be recorded... but by who? As well as the selection below, the Society of Wedding and Portrait Photographers (www.swpp.co.uk) or the Master Photographers Association (www.thempa.com) have extensive lists of approved photographers on their websites. Many will travel beyond the M25 and even abroad. Always be sure you feel 100%

confident with your choice of photographer (ask to see lots of previous work) and package, as wedding photography is a very subjective business.

Amanda Clay Photography

07810 616104/www.clayphotography.co.uk.
Prices from £600.
Using an informal reportage style and picking up on lots of incidental details, Amanda Clay promises to come prepared, be professional and execute brilliant post-wedding editing. The testimonials on her website attest to the results.

Anne Brassier Wedding Photography

07946 354308/www.itakenicephotos.com.
Prices from £800.
Anne Brassier prefers an informal 'reportage' style of photograph and takes photos starting with the bridal party's preparations right through to the cake-cutting and first dance. Shooting colour and black & white film, Anne also provides digital files if required. London-based, she also travels all over the UK and abroad.

Big Day Weddings

8440 6144/www.bigday-weddings.co.uk.
Prices from £650.
David Pulsford (LSWPP) and Joanna Green (BPPA) work to the highest standards and are qualified members of professional trade bodies: the British Professional Photographers Association and the Society of Wedding and Portrait Photographers. Prices start very reasonably – the 'bronze' package (£650) includes photography of arrivals, the ceremony, group and formal shots, reportage shots, a preview DVD and 20 presentation prints.

Charlie's Weddings

07957 617857/www.charliesweddings.co.uk.
Prices from £650.
The website exhibits the variety of styles used, including portraits, groups, and 'behind the scenes'. Prices start at a very reasonable £650 (VAT inclusive) and services include albums, full sets of prints and proofs and hi-res images on disc. There are discounts for weddings booked a year in advance.

Chris Renton Wedding Photography

8767 5536/www.chrisrentonweddings.co.uk.
Prices from £695
SWPP member Chris Renton can provide contemporary, natural and stylish wedding photography. While based in London, Chris can cover most locations in the UK as well as abroad. Full and half-day packages are available.

Keith Appleby

7435 6882/www.applebyphotography.com.
Prices from £2,100.
Winner of (sadly now-defunct) WrapIt's 'Wedding Photographer of the Year', Keith Appleby and associates aim to bring a little magic to your wedding. The 'Just Prints' option includes a principal photographer for up to seven hours coverage, a full set of prints in a rosewood box, a password-protected web gallery, a disc with all the images in low-res (suitable for email or viewing online), and costs from £2,100.

Kevin Bird Contemporary Wedding Photography

7978 5472/www.kb-weddings.co.uk.
Prices from £900.
The company offers a range of wedding packages to suit any client, all of which can be discussed in a free pre-wedding consultation. All photography is undertaken from the beginning of the day including the bride's preparations, through to the end of the first dance, so every moment is captured.

Level Eleven

0845 071 1178/www.russpullen.com.
Prices from £1,495.
Russ Pullen cites among his influences Henri Cartier-Bresson, Jack Vettriano and Rankin. His website exhibits the range of his inspirations; his blog records his thoughts and the responses of his clients. Wedding books start at £1,495 and include a pre-wedding shoot and all-day coverage. Off-season and mid-week weddings are obviously cheaper.

Randolph Quan Wedding Photography

8343 3583/www.randolphquan.com.
Prices from £2,050.
Randolph Quan Wedding Photography offers its wedding photography service to clients throughout the UK. The company has almost ten years' experience in wedding photography. For £2,050 you would receive eight hours of photographic coverage, a pre-wedding creative consultation, a DVD with all images in their highest resolution and a private online web gallery.

Sixpence Wedding Photos

8670 1317/www.sixpenceweddingphotos. co.uk. **Prices** from £600.
A complete wedding photography service starting from a three-hour print-only package to an all-day package with CD and beautifully bound album. Paul has perfected a reportage style that captures a wedding as the exciting, romantic and memorable event that it is.

WEDDINGS

Indexes

Venues by Capacity

Venues featured in the guide are indexed below by maximum number of people. Always check the listings as many also have smaller areas available for hire.

UNDER 30

Central
Bea's of Bloomsbury, WC1	16
Coram's Fields, WC1	106, 108
Mildreds, W1	47
Oasis Sports Centre, WC2	107
Only Running Footman, W1	74
Planet of the Grapes, WC1	95, 142
Quo Vadis, W1	95
Zuma, SW7	47, 53

North
Clown Town, N12	108, 109
Engineer, NW1	49
Finchley Lido Leisure Centre, N12	108, 109
Gill's Cookery Workshop, NW11	109
Highbury Fields One & Two O'Clock Club, N5	110
Kentish Town City Farm, NW5	110, 112

East
Rookery, EC1	98
St George's Pools, E1	112
V&A Museum of Childhood, E2	112
Wenlock Arms, N1	34

South
All Fired Up Ceramics Café, SE22	113
Boot & Flogger, SE1	81
Centre for Wildlife Gardening, SE15	108, 113
Chez Bruce, SW17	51, 52
Crawley Studios, SE23	113
Garrison, SE1	82
Pavilion Café Dulwich, SE21	113

West
Gambado, SW6	115
Geales, W8	39
Pottery Café, SW6	115
Science Museum, SW7	117
Sutton Arena Leisure Centre, SM5	117
Warrington, W9	55

30-75

Central
Bam Bou, W1	71
Cellar Door, WC2	44
Covent Garden Hotel, WC2	47
5th View, W1	89

Green Man, W1	18
Mosimann's, SW1	47
Party Bus	20
St Giles, WC2	60

North
Albert & Pearl, N1	21
Barrio North, N1	21, 24
Island Queen, N1	76
Marquess Tavern, N1	49
Monkey Chews, NW5	23, 31
Pineapple, NW5	64
Prince, N16	49
William IV, N1	77

East
Bleeding Heart Tavern, EC1	222
Cat & Mutton, E8	79
Departure Art Centre, E14	110
Dollar Grills & Martinis, EC1	26, 30
Drunken Monkey, E1	26, 29
Exit, E1	24, 26
Golden Lane Leisure Centre, EC1	112
Karaoke Box Smithfield, EC1	28
Medcalf, EC1	28
Oasis, L', E1	80
Princess, EC2	50
Public Life, E1	28
Red Lion, N1	31
Waltham Forest Register Office, E17	224

South
Baltic, SE1	50
Dog House, SE11	34
Florence, SE24	37
Harrison's, SW12	51
Marble Hill House, TW1	227
Prince of Wales, SW15	82
Richmond Register Office, TW9	224
Tooting Tram and Social, SW17	38

West
Amuse Bouche, SW6 (birthdays)	39
Blakes, SW7	216, 230
Chelsea Old Town Hall, SW3	224
Cow, The, W2	52, 54
Crazy Homies, W2	39
Establishment, SW6	39
Grand Union, W9	68
Julie's, W11	54
Kiasu, W2	104
Number Sixteen, SW7	69
Pig's Ear, SW3	55
Puppet Theatre Barge, W9	108, 117
Westbourne House, W2	25, 41

INDEX

75-150

Central
Amuse Bouche, W1 (corporate)	87
Bentley's Oyster Bar & Grill, W1	43
Bourne & Hollingsworth, W1 16,	30
Crazy Bear, W1	24, 88
De Hems, W1	72
14 Henrietta Street, WC2	89
Gaucho, W1	89
Haymarket Hotel Pool & Bar, SW1	61, 90
Horse Hospital, WC1	90
Hub, The, NW1	58
Ivy, The, WC2	72
Lucky Voice, W1	18
October Gallery, WC1	60
Old Crown, WC1	73
Wellington Arch, W1	95

North
Burgh House, NW3	221
Camden Arms, NW1	21
Caxton House, N19	107
Dartmouth Arms, NW5	76
Harrison, WC1	23
Positively 4th Street, NW1	76
Roebuck, NW3	25
Vine, The, NW5	222
Westminster Council House, NW1	224
06 St Chad's Place, WC1	222

East
All Hallows by the Tower, EC3	64
Bar Kick, E1	77
dreambagsjaguarshoes, E2	26
Finsbury Leisure Centre, EC1	108, 111
FleaPit, E2	26
4 Princelet Street, E1	97
Green, EC1	223
Hackney Town Hall, E8	224
Old Cholmeley Boys' Club, N16	28
Old Gringo, EC1	80
Prenelle Gallery, E14	80
Royal Inn on the Park, E9	32
St Germain, EC1	223
Scolt Head, N1	32
Shoreditch House, E1	98
Space, The, E14	32
Three Kings of Clerkenwell, EC1	81
Whitechapel Art Gallery, E1	101
Zetter, EC1	217, 225

South
Cambridge Cottage, TW9	225
Cannizaro House, SW19	226
Cat's Back, SW18	34
Concrete, SE1	34
Conservatory, SW11	64, 66
Deck, The, SE1	66
East Dulwich Community Centre, SE22	113
Franklins, SE22	35
Gothique, Le, SW18	227
Hide, SE1	25, 37
Pembroke Lodge, TW10	226, 228
Ranger's House, SE10	228
Rosendale, SE21	51
Rye, The, SE15	38
Westbridge, SW11	67

West
Bowler, SW3	82
Chiswick House, W4	231
Cross Keys, SW3	83
Eddie Catz Wimbledon, SW19	115
Idlewild, W9	31, 41
London Rowing Club, SW15	69
Paradise By Way of Kensal Green, W10	69
Troubadour, SW5	41
White Horse, SW6	41

150-250

Central
Arts Club, W1	214
Boisdale, SW1	56
Carpenter's Arms, W1	17
Century Club, W1	215
Chiltern Street Studios, W1	57
Courthouse Hotel Bar, W1	17, 24
Dragon Hall, WC2	106
Hakkasan, W1	90
Momo/Mô Tearoom, W1	59
National Liberal Club, SW1	220
Serpentine Lido, W2	61, 62
Westminster Boating Base, SW1	63

North
Frederick's, N1	63
Kenwood House, NW3	221
Old Queen's Head, N1	25
St Aloysius Social Club, NW1	26

East
Dalston Jazz Bar, N16	26
Fox, EC2	49
Gramaphone, E1	28, 30
Gun, E14	97
Little Ship Club, EC4	65
Rosemary Branch, N1	32
St John, EC1	50, 53
Stationers' Hall, EC4	225

South
Bar du Musée, SE10	51
Design Museum, SE1	101
Garden Museum, SE1	227
North Pole, SE10	67
Princess of Wales, SE3	67
Royal Observatory, SE10	102
Syon Park, TW8	228
Winchester House, SW15	228

West
Amadeus Centre, W9	230

INDEX

INDEX

Venues by Type

Venues featured within the various chapters of the guide can be found indexed below by type.

INDEX

INDEX

INDEX

INDEX

A-Z Index

INDEX

INDEX

INDEX

Advertisers' Index

Please refer to relevant sections for addresses/telephone numbers